P9-DDK-902

Manhattan Project

WESTFIELD MEMORIAL LIBRARY
WESTFIELD, N. J.

Manhattan Project

THE UNTOLD STORY OF THE
MAKING OF THE ATOMIC BOMB

BY STEPHANE GROUEFF

with photographs

LITTLE, BROWN AND COMPANY · BOSTON · TORONTO

623.451
Gro

92469

COPYRIGHT © 1967 BY STEPHANE GROUEFF

ALL RIGHTS RESERVED. NO PART OF THIS BOOK MAY BE REPRO-
DUCED IN ANY FORM WITHOUT PERMISSION IN WRITING FROM THE
PUBLISHER, EXCEPT BY A REVIEWER WHO MAY QUOTE BRIEF PAS-
SAGES IN A REVIEW TO BE PRINTED IN A MAGAZINE OR NEWSPAPER.

LIBRARY OF CONGRESS CATALOG CARD NO. 67-11231

FIRST EDITION

Published simultaneously in Canada
by Little, Brown & Company (Canada) Limited

PRINTED IN THE UNITED STATES OF AMERICA

For my wife, Lil

WESTFIELD MEMORIAL LIBRARY
WESTFIELD, N. J.

Acknowledgments

I FIND, as I look back over the history of the writing of this book, that there were so many people who gave me aid and advice that it is now virtually impossible to give proper credit to each individual. However, I feel especially indebted to some for their help and participation.

Among the editors of *The Reader's Digest,* which generously sponsored my book project, I would like to thank Maurice T. Ragsdale, who was a constant source of inspiration; John D. Panitza, who, during the preliminary stages of my work, recognized the potentialities of this book and encouraged me to write it; Robert F. Rigby, who spent endless hours working over the original draft of my manuscript; and Shirley W. Tawse, who helped me so much with the research.

My gratitude goes to Lieutenant General Leslie R. Groves, not only for generously giving entire weeks of his time for my exhaustive tape-recorded interviews, but also for the confidence he has shown in me.

I would also like to thank the United States Atomic Energy Commission for facilitating my task by declassifying certain documents and for showing great consideration in reviewing the passages containing classified information. I am indebted particularly to the AEC's Chief Historian, Richard G. Hewlett, for the competent and efficient help he offered with such readiness. Without his aid, and without the superb history of the AEC, *The New World,* that he wrote with Oscar E. Anderson, Jr., my undertaking would have been imcomparably more difficult.

I want to express my gratitude to my own organization, *Paris-Match Magazine,* for relieving me, with much understanding, of some of my regular duties during the writing of this book.

Special credit must be given to my publishers, Little, Brown and Company, and particularly to Stanley Hart, for the remarkable care taken in editing and presenting this book.

Below I have attempted to list the people of the Manhattan Project who were interviewed by me or by Shirley Tawse; I have named them in relation to their organization at that time, which should prove helpful to the reader. To the following individuals I am deeply indebted:

ACKNOWLEDGMENTS

MANHATTAN DISTRICT

Brigadier General Leslie R. Groves, Colonel James C. Marshall, Colonel Kenneth D. Nichols, Lieutenant Colonel Franklin T. Matthias, Lieutenant Colonel James C. Stowers, Captain Samuel S. Baxter, Captain Wilbur E. Kelley, Mrs. Jean O'Leary.

PRODUCTION OF FISSIONABLE URANIUM BY ELECTROMAGNETIC PROCESS

University of California, Berkeley: Donald Cooksey, Harold A. Fidler, Elmer L. Kelly, Clarence E. Larson, Edward J. Lofgren, Wallace P. Reynolds, Duane C. Sewell, Robert L. Thornton, James Vale, Eleanor Davisson.

Allis-Chalmers, Milwaukee: Joseph L. Singleton, Gordon W. Clothier, Howard Brem, Fred Bush, Karl Wiederkehr.

Eastman Kodak, Rochester: Albert K. Chapman, William Arnold, Wyatt Bummitt, John C. Hecker, James Sterner, John Veal, Julian H. Webb.

General Electric, Schenectady: C. Guy Suits, Frank Kaestle, Kenneth H. Kingdon, Robert W. Larson, Herbert C. Pollock, Richard Rhea, Henry H. Zielinski.

Stone and Webster, Boston: Russell Branch, Fred W. Argue, James R. Chapman, Charles Chaves, Frank C. Creedon, Thomas A. Fearnside, Ray L. Geddes, Robert Jacobs, Leslie Waite, Rex Wisner.

Tennessee Eastman, Kingsport: James C. White, George Banic, Edward Bettis, Frederick R. Conklin, Thomas M. Divine, James Ellis, Leon Love, Charles Normand, Elwood D. Shipley, Wiley Thomas, Helen Hall Brown, Marjorie Cabbage, Francie Gee, Edna Patterson Hansard, Ruth H. Henderson, Meredith Hill, Nell Oder, Marjorie Shipley.

Westinghouse, Pittsburgh: A. W. Robertson, E. Bruce Ashcraft, Charles O. Beltz, Royal C. Bergvall, John A. Hutcheson, Rudolph E. Peterson, Walter G. Roman.

PRODUCTION OF FISSIONABLE URANIUM BY GASEOUS DIFFUSION

Columbia University: Harold C. Urey, John R. Dunning, Edward Adler, Henry A. Boorse, Elliott Charney, Arthur C. Hagg, Edward Norris, Leonard Shazkin.

Princeton University: Hugh S. Taylor.

University of Minnesota: Alfred O. Nier.

Bell Telephone Laboratories, New York: Foster C. Nix.

Kellex, New York: Percival C. Keith, John A. Arnold, Manson Benedict, Howard Elsey, P. Ben Gordon, J. C. Hobbs, Clarence A. Johnson, Evan A. Johnson, Otto W. Manz, Ludwig Skog, Arthur Squires, Judson Swearingen, George Watts.

Allis-Chalmers, Milwaukee: Charles C. Codrington, Oscar A. Haas, Charles W. Bloedorn.

American Chicle, New York: Thorwald H. Smith, Douglas M. Brown, Reginald E. Charles.

Bart Manufacturing, Belleville, New Jersey: Siegfried Bart.

Chrysler, Detroit: K. T. Keller, Alan G. Loofbourrow.

Houdaille-Hershey, Decatur, Illinois: Walter L. Pinner.

) *viii*

ACKNOWLEDGMENTS

J. A. Jones Construction, Charlotte, North Carolina: Edwin L. Jones, J. J. Haynie.

Union Carbide, New York: Lyman A. Bliss, Lauchlin M. Currie, Clark E. Center, Hartselle D. Kinsey, Augustus B. Kinzel, Leon K. Merrill, Peter Riede, Alvan H. Tenney, Mrs. Frazier Groff.

PRODUCTION OF PLUTONIUM

University of Chicago: Samuel K. Allison, Norman Hilberry, Glenn T. Seaborg, Eugene P. Wigner, Herbert L. Anderson, Frank G. Foote, Joseph J. Katz, Alexander S. Langsdorf, Jr., Robert Nobles, David Rudolph, James F. Schumar, William J. Sturm, John A. Wheeler, Volney C. Wilson.

College of Fisheries, University of Washington: Lauren R. Donaldson.

Du Pont, Wilmington: Walter S. Carpenter, Crawford H. Greenewalt, Tom C. Gary, Dale F. Babcock, Gilbert P. Church, Raymond Genereaux, Daniel D. Friel, Philip Gardner, Raymond Grills, Samuel McNeight, Walter O. Simon, Lombard Squires, Newton Stapleton.

Westinghouse, Bloomfield, New Jersey: John W. Marden, Norman C. Beese, Stanley Frankel, Rudolf Nagy.

PRODUCTION OF FISSIONABLE URANIUM BY THERMAL DIFFUSION

Naval Research Laboratory, Washington, D.C.: Philip H. Abelson.

H. K. Ferguson, Cleveland: Frank W. Buck, Ben T. Cherry, Francis W. Daniels, Wells N. Thompson.

DESIGN, ASSEMBLY AND TESTING OF THE BOMB

Los Alamos Laboratory: J. Robert Oppenheimer, Robert F. Bacher, Hans A. Bethe, George Kistiakowsky, John H. Manley, Cyril S. Smith. Harry S. Allen, Richard Baker, Berlyn Brixner, Charles Critchfield, Richard P. Feynman, Robert van Gemert, Henry Hurwitz, Jr., Percy King, Charles A. Thomas, Stanislaw Ulam, John C. Warner.

ARCHITECTS FOR THE TOWN OF OAK RIDGE

Skidmore, Owings and Merrill: John O. Merrill, William S. Brown.

UNITED STATES TREASURY DEPARTMENT

Under Secretary Daniel W. Bell, F. Leland Howard, Theodore Schreiker.

My special thanks for their cooperation go to James B. Conant, Alexander Sachs, Lew Kowarski and Mrs. Leslie R. Groves.

WESTFIELD MEMORIAL LIBRARY. WESTFIELD. N. J.

Preface

THE VENTURE of which I write in this book represents, in the opinion of most engineers, scientists and industrialists interviewed by me, the greatest single achievement of organized human effort in history. Though such superlatives are usually exaggerated, a detailed study of the Manhattan Project convinced me that the scope of the performance was indeed without precedent.

The history of the atomic bomb is so vast that the subject of this book had to be limited. The magnificent scientific discoveries leading to the first nuclear chain reaction are by now relatively well known. Enough had also been said about Hiroshima and Nagasaki, and about the moral and strategic aspects of the atomic weapon. But as a journalist I realized that, on the contrary, the public still did not know *how* the first bomb was built, by whom and under what circumstances. It was surprising to me that the Americans themselves were still unaware of the prodigious adventure into which their country's industrial power was launched, secretly and boldly, at a colossal cost and with an unprecedented effort, in order to produce the bomb.

This is the story of the men who, in the summer of 1942, received the order to go ahead and build, with extreme urgency, the first nuclear weapon: determined men who could not suspect the incredible difficulties of the task and who could not know how immensely different the problems of the laboratory would be from those related to the actual manufacturing of the bomb.

Many parts of this story were till recently strictly classified; others have never before been told publicly by the people who participated in the Manhattan Project. From several scores of personal interviews all over the country I tried to reconstruct this fabulous tale of human ingenuity and determination. I was allowed to disclose many details after clearing them with the United States Atomic Energy Commission. Other details will remain rigorously secret for many years to come.

Besides being a history of the actual building of the bomb, this story is, in my opinion, a superb illustration of the way the American system operated in the early 1940s. What I attempted to describe was the manner in which America reacted to a concrete danger, to a precise task. The majority of the people involved did not know what the final product of their efforts would be. For them, there was a gigantic challenge to be met, an apparently impossible job to be done, and they carried it to an end splendidly.

Most men who appear in this book sincerely wish that the Manhattan Project's efforts had been employed for other, nobler goals. Unfortunately, the choice was not theirs. Here is the story of how history involved them in the mechanism of the system, and how they responded, individually, to the task.

S.G.

Manhattan Project

I

THE BURLY, impatient-looking brigadier general strode down the platform in Washington's Union Station and, at exactly five minutes before departure time, hurried through the gate where the night train for Chicago was waiting. At his heels, and half running to keep up with him, was a young blue-eyed woman carrying a briefcase. On boarding the train, the general reluctantly surrendered his suitcase to the car porter but kept a tight grip on a thick manila envelope in his hand as he was shown to his compartment.

He entered, followed by the young woman, closed the door and motioned her to sit down. She opened her briefcase, took out a stenographic pad and immediately began to take the general's rapid-fire dictation. Fifty minutes later, as the train pulled into Baltimore, the secretary closed her notebook and, with a slight nod to the unsmiling general, left the compartment and got off the train. She crossed the platform, then boarded the waiting train going back to Washington, as she had done so many times before. It had become routine; she had a boss who never wasted a second, even when traveling.

As soon as his secretary had left, the general locked the compartment door and examined the lock carefully. It was none too secure, he thought, but it would be enough: if an intruder tried to force it, the noise would certainly waken him. He sat down and waited impatiently for the train to leave. A massive man in his mid-forties, with a good crop of dark-brown hair and a neat mustache, he had an oversized waistline that gave a bulging look to his uniform. The face was jowly, but his blue eyes were penetrating and gave his face an impression of energy and decisiveness.

After the train pulled out of the station, he opened his suitcase and quickly changed from his Army uniform into a dark civilian suit; then he slipped a small Colt automatic pistol — a .32 caliber model on a .25 caliber frame — into his trouser pocket. Taking the manila envelope along with him, he left the compartment and headed for the dining car.

The dining car steward showed him to the only seat still vacant, next to an Army colonel in uniform. The newcomer sat down on his manila envelope and pretended to be absorbed in reading the menu. When he looked up, he saw that the colonel was staring at his West Point class ring.

"I see you're a West Pointer, too," the colonel remarked.

"Yes, that's right."

The colonel looked curiously at the general's civilian suit. "You've left the Army, I suppose?" he asked. In time of war — and this was the fall of 1942, when the United States was fighting on two far-flung fronts — special authorization was required before an officer could wear "civvies"; it was rarely granted.

The heavyset man hesitated, then said, "No, I'm still in the Army. But just forget you've seen an officer in civilian clothes — it's been authorized."

The colonel got the point. Throughout dinner he discreetly avoided asking any further personal questions; their conversation was strictly limited to nonprofessional topics.

As soon as the general in civvies had paid his check, he excused himself, gathered up the manila envelope and returned to his compartment, locking the door behind him. Fifteen minutes later there was a knock at the door. The general rose and eased the pistol from his pocket.

"Who is it?"

"Colonel Nichols, sir."

He unlocked the door and admitted a slender, bespectacled man in his thirties who was also wearing civilian clothes. The manila envelope was opened, and the two men proceeded to discuss far into the night the complicated drawings and formulae the reports in it contained.

It was well after midnight when the younger officer was finally allowed to return to his own compartment and go to bed. The general sat up a little longer, studying the reports and jotting down notes. Then, reluctantly, he stuffed the papers carefully back into the envelope and prepared for bed. Before turning out the light, he checked the door lock again, then placed the manila envelope under his mattress and the Colt pistol within easy reach.

Brigadier General Leslie R. Groves, the newly named chief of the nation's most secret military project, was not a man to take any chances.

Only a few weeks earlier, on the morning of September 17, Groves, then a colonel and concerned with military construction, was in a particularly good mood as he entered the committee room of Congress. As the Army's Deputy Chief of Constructions, he was to give his testimony on the new military housing bill. Politely but without being overly deferential, he analyzed for the committee the Army's expenditures for construction — an average of $600 million monthly. No one in the room could have guessed that the colonel's real thoughts were far from the business at hand, and that he was impatiently waiting for the hearing to end.

Since the day before, Groves had had the feeling that his career was about to take a new, stimulating direction. As a military engineer he had never commanded troops in action, and for a regular officer this was a sore point. He had graduated from West Point (fourth in his class) too late in 1918 to take part in the fighting in France. Ever since, during twenty-four years of slow postwar promotions, he had been sent from company duty to construction work to military schools to general-staff duties. Now, at last, he had been offered an overseas combat assignment. All he had to do was go through the formality of getting the consent of his top superior, Major General Brehon Somervell, Commanding General of the Army Services of Supply.

As soon as Groves left the committee room, he ran into Somervell in the hall. "I've just been offered an overseas assignment, General," he announced happily. "I hope you have no objection to my being relieved of my present duties."

Somervell, an urbane and energetic Southerner, shook his head firmly. "Sorry, Groves, but you can't leave. You can't leave Washington."

Much surprised, the colonel made an effort to control his disappointment. He felt the refusal was unfair; he did not deserve it after his long years of humdrum construction service.

Somervell took Groves to a quieter part of the hall. Lowering his voice, he said, "The Secretary of War has selected you for a very important assignment. The President himself has approved the assignment."

"Where?"

"Here in Washington."

"But I don't want to stay in Washington, General!"

"Listen, Groves. If you do this job right, it will win the war. You can do it if anyone can. General Styer will brief you."

Groves rushed to Styer's office immediately. Major General Wilhelm D. Styer, Somervell's popular and efficient Chief of Staff, also waved aside Groves's protests. "You have been chosen for the most important job in the war — the Manhattan Project," he said. "This is going to be an all-out effort to build an atomic bomb with truly incredible explosive power. A very small bomb will have the explosive power of twenty thousand tons of TNT. Think of it! You're to take over from Colonel Marshall and head up the Project."

Groves started to protest again, giving all the reasons why he shouldn't take the job.

"Groves," Styer interrupted, "you've been personally selected for this job by the Secretary of War, and the President has approved. The Project is in good shape — research and development are already done. Your job will be just to put the rough designs into final shape, build some plants and organize production. And when you're through, the war will be won."

As an officer Groves could only accept the assignment, but he remained more than a little skeptical about the whole thing. He had no idea of how far advanced the scientific side of the Project really was, nor whether any preliminary engineering had been started. Luckily, he did not know at the moment how overoptimistic Styer had been. In reality, things looked dark — the odds were heavy against success.

2

GROVES WAS in a black mood when he left General Styer and returned to his office in the new War Department Building. He was deeply disappointed; his dream of obtaining a combat assignment overseas had once again been frustrated and probably forever. This new job that had been urged upon him so unexpectedly would nail him down indefinitely to Washington. An extremely important job, Somervell and Styer had said. Yes, but after all, as Deputy Chief of Army Construction, he had been controlling work involving expenditures amounting lately to $600 million a month; the new project, as far as he knew, would probably cost only about $100 million altogether. It hardly seemed like much of a promotion.

Less than an hour after he had been assigned command of the atomic project, Groves had put aside his disappointment and gotten down to work. A man with an aversion for all delay, he had no intention of wasting an hour if he could help it. He called in Lieutenant Colonel Kenneth D. Nichols, Deputy Chief of the Manhattan District, and asked for a detailed briefing. What Nichols had to tell him was both fantastic and disturbing.

Since the splitting of the first uranium atom in Germany in 1938, it had been thought that a bomb with incredible destructive force might be built if enough fissionable material could be produced. This material had to be either U–235, a rare isotope of uranium, or plutonium, a newly discovered element, knowledge of which was limited to United States and British scientists. Both would be extremely difficult, if not impossible, to produce. Scientists in the United States and Britain had devised – in theory – several methods of producing large amounts of the two elements, but none had yet been tried.

The secret efforts of the laboratories engaged in the work were then being coordinated by the Office of Scientific Research and Development (OSRD), directed by Dr. Vannevar Bush, head of the Carnegie Institution in Washington. In early 1942, after receiving the advice of OSRD's Atomic Committee, called S–1, Bush had reported to President Roosevelt that production of fissionable uranium and plutonium — considered until then as a science-fiction dream — was probably possible.

On Bush's advice, the President turned the entire project over to the Army and ordered its transition from the research and development stage into the building of large-scale production facilities. In June 1942 the Army Engineers formed a special district under Colonel James C. Marshall, with Nichols as his deputy. To avoid attracting attention and because Marshall had chosen New York as his initial headquarters, the new unit was named Manhattan District.

Groves had known about the existence of the Manhattan Project; he had been the liaison officer between the new District and the Corps of Engineers. But his duties had been strictly limited to helping Colonel Marshall obtain anything he needed and advising him on plant sites, procurement and the selection of industrial firms. He was never told any scientific details and, being a disciplined officer, had never asked any questions. Now that he was in charge of the whole Project, Groves was greatly disturbed to learn that it was still in a very primitive stage of laboratory research and far from being ready for any production. The optimistic reports of the scientists seemed unrealistic and premature, and showed an almost total ignorance of engineering and industrial problems. Indeed, the scientists could not even state positively that fissionable uranium and plutonium could be produced at all!

That same day Groves and Nichols went to the Carnegie Foundation to visit Vannevar Bush, who still controlled the laboratories of the Project. The man who greeted them was tall and gaunt, with a humorous twinkle in his blue eyes and an unruly shock of hair falling across his forehead — in a way he resembled a clean-shaven Uncle Sam. At fifty-two the lean Yankee scientific engineer from Massachusetts had a highly distinguished career already behind him: an inventor with numerous electrical engineering patents to his credit, vice-president of the Massachusetts Institute of Technology and dean of its school of engineering until 1938, then head of the Carnegie Institution, a key research organization. Now he was overlord of United States scientific research in the war effort.

Groves immediately felt a certain reserve in the way the pipe-smoking director of OSRD received him. A typical New Englander's aloofness, he thought. But when Groves started asking direct questions about the atomic project, Bush's reserve immediately turned into icy coolness; he did not seem at all anxious to supply any information.

The visit did not last long. As soon as Groves left his office, Bush telephoned General Styer. "Who is this Colonel Groves," he demanded, "and just how much is he entitled to know?"

"You mean we did not inform you?" Confused and embarrassed, Styer apologized profusely. Somehow, no one had remembered to tell Bush of Groves's appointment, and the scientist had been totally unprepared for his visit. "What do you think of him?" Styer asked.

"He looks too aggressive."

"He is, but we thought that quality of his was what we needed most. Groves is a go-getter; he gets things done."

"I'm afraid he may have trouble with the scientists," Bush explained.

"You may be right," Styer conceded, "and you and I will probably have to keep smoothing things out. But the work will move — I can assure you of that!"

Bush remained unconvinced, however. After his conversation with Styer, he wrote a memo to Harvey Bundy, special assistant to Secretary of War Henry L. Stimson. It said in part: "Having seen Groves briefly, I doubt whether he has sufficient tact for such a job. I fear we are in the soup."

Two days later, on September 19, Colonel James C. Marshall, the District Engineer of the Manhattan District, arrived in Washington to discuss with Groves the current status of the Project. A slim, forty-five-year-old career officer, Marshall was to continue as District Engineer now that Groves had overall responsibility for the entire Project.* Marshall did not conceal the fact that ever since his first reading of the scientists' reports he had been disturbed by the figure of $85 million earmarked for the Project, including the construction of five industrial plants.

"How can they build even one of these plants for eighty-five million?" he exclaimed. "I've just come from a TNT plant in Pennsylvania that alone cost one hundred twenty-eight million to build!"

That afternoon Groves, accompanied by Marshall, went to see Vannevar Bush again. This time the OSRD director was very friendly and readily gave the two officers a brief history of the entire American atomic program to date. As he listened, Groves became fascinated by the story and gradually aware of the enormous challenge in his new assignment.

The first successful experiments in splitting a uranium atom had been carried out in the autumn of 1938 at the Kaiser Wilhelm Institute in Berlin. Within six months further discoveries by physicists in many countries pointed to an inescapable conclusion: a new form of energy — nuclear energy — might be achieved by the splitting, or fissioning, of the atom. This energy, which would be millions of times greater than any

---

* Manhattan *District* was the name given the unit within the Army Corps of Engineers. The Manhattan *Project*, on the other hand, covered not only the District but also the scientific, strategic and governmental aspects involved in the building and eventual delivery of the bomb.

hitherto known to man, might be used to generate power for peaceful ends; it might also be used to create a bomb of incredible explosive power.

The first scientists in the United States to become acutely aware of this danger were those refugee physicists who had fled Europe and Hitler's New Order. They had no doubt that Germany would bend every effort to develop such a superweapon. In the summer of 1939 three Hungarian refugee physicists — Leo Szilard, Eugene Wigner and Edward Teller — convinced Albert Einstein that the possibility of Germany's developing an atomic bomb should be brought to the immediate attention of President Roosevelt. To aid them in drafting a letter setting forth the dangers created by uranium fission, the scientists enlisted the help of Alexander Sachs, a highly erudite New York financier and a friend and economic adviser of the President's.

By some remarkable chance Sachs, whose extraordinarily wide interests ranged from the design of radio buoys to histories of the Napoleonic campaigns, had become fascinated by atomic physics and had read several articles on the subject in specialized publications. For several months he had unsuccessfully tried, using his unusually flowery rhetoric, to convey to Roosevelt the possibility of developing a nuclear weapon.

When the letter signed by Einstein was personally delivered to the White House by Sachs on October 11, 1939, the President, although he understood little of uranium fission, was already prepared by Sachs and was receptive to the idea of nuclear danger. He was impressed by the Einstein letter detailing the likelihood that Germany would try to develop an atomic bomb that would certainly lead to world conquest. He decided immediately to create a committee that would give Government financial assistance to American universities engaged in uranium research.

Despite the urgency of the problem, the program got off to a slow and modest start; a year later, only $300,000 had been allocated by the Government to sixteen research groups. Progress was dishearteningly slow in the laboratories. The central problem was how to develop methods that would produce sufficient quantities of fissionable material for a bomb.

By May 1942 research on five different methods was considered far enough advanced to justify a large-scale production attempt. Three of them — the electromagnetic, centrifuge, and gaseous-diffusion methods — involved the separation of uranium–235, a fissionable material. The other two methods involved the production of plutonium, also a fissionable material, by graphite reactor or by heavy-water reactor.

None of these five rival processes offered the certitude of success. Each was highly intricate and expected to be prohibitively expensive for the economy of a country fighting a war on two fronts. But if a bomb was to

) 10

be built before Hitler did it in Germany, if the weapon was to be used in the war, at least one of the five methods had to be chosen and developed in an all-out national effort. The question was, which one of the five?

As the country's commander-in-chief, President Roosevelt would bear the ultimate responsibility for the decision, and for such scientific matters he depended heavily on the advice of Vannevar Bush, who in turn relied on the counsel of the S–1 section — the Atomic Committee — of his OSRD. Bush's principal collaborator was Dr. James B. Conant, head of S–1, president of Harvard University.

James Bryant Conant, much like Dr. Bush, was a gaunt New Englander with a lock of hair hanging over steel-rimmed glasses, giving him a younger look than his forty-nine years. At first encounter he impressed people as being aloof, even cold, probably because of a certain austerity in his scholarly appearance. But the lack of demonstrativeness was hiding a great analytical mind and an incisive wit, much appreciated by anyone who became close to him.

Conant had served in World War I as a major in the Chemical Warfare Service, supervising the production of lewisite gas. In 1919 he became a professor at Harvard, and when in 1931 he was appointed chairman of the Department of Chemistry, he had already had some international recognition for his studies on chlorophyll and hemoglobin. His nomination in 1933 to the presidency of Harvard University was, however, met with surprise and criticism. Conant was only forty years old, a quiet, unspectacular man without much administrative experience. Many voices rose questioning his qualifications for the job. "An educational enigma," wrote the *New York Times*. But it soon became apparent that the sober pedagogue, who resembled a humble country schoolmaster more than the head of a $25-million-annual-budget university, possessed extraordinary qualities of administration and super salesmanship, combined with determination and fearless ability to act.

In 1940 Conant joined the National Defense Research Committee, and the following year he succeeded Vannevar Bush as its chairman. He was also a member of the commission that Roosevelt sent to England in 1941 to organize the exchange of scientific information of importance to defense. When the S–1 Committee was put in charge of the atomic bomb project, Bush asked Conant to become its head.

In May 1942 the members of the S–1 Committee met in Conant's Washington office to make the momentous decision as to which method of producing fissionable material would be developed. Besides Conant, the committee consisted of Professors Ernest Lawrence, Arthur Holly Compton and Harold Urey, all three Nobel Prize laureates; Dr. Lyman Briggs, director of the National Bureau of Standards, and Eger Murphree of the Standard Oil Company. An all-day discussion followed during which the leaders of the five programs* vehemently defended their rival production methods. But nothing was settled. It was obvious that the chances of success — or rather, the odds *against* each of the five processes — seemed essentially equal.†

Unaccustomed to making decisions directly affecting the industrial and economic power of the country, the members of S–1 were keenly aware of the frightening responsibility of their recommendation to the President. The pressure to make a decision was undeniably great. "The Germans are at present probably far ahead of us," Arthur Compton pointed out. "They started their program vigorously in 1939, but ours was not undertaken with similar vigor until 1941." Conant agreed: "If the new weapon is going to be the determining factor in the war, then there is a desperate need for speed. Three months' delay might be disastrous."

At this point the scientists abandoned their usual method of inquiry. Logically the task would be selecting the best of the five methods. The problem, however, was no longer which process would be the best — the success of each was equally improbable — but which would be the *fastest*. Unfortunately, there was no way of predicting this, nor was there any time for guessing wrong and trying all over again. The S–1 Committee then made one of the boldest decisions of the entire war. Since the members were unable to select one method over the others, they agreed that *all* five methods should be tried simultaneously. Such a program would entail the building of five large-scale plants such as had never been seen or even thought of before, whose equipment and technological processes would have to be invented and developed from scratch. Whole new industries would have to be created in a colossal scientific and technological adventure of incalculable consequences for the nation.

The S–1 Committee's bold, far-reaching recommendation was duly

---

* Arthur Compton was the leader of the plutonium program, which comprised development of the graphite pile and of the heavy-water reactor; Harold Urey headed the gaseous-diffusion program for uranium separation; Ernest Lawrence led the group working on the electromagnetic process; and Eger Murphree was in charge of the centrifuge method.

† Nine days before the meeting, Conant expressed his opinion in a letter to Dr. Bush: "All five methods will be entering very expensive pilot-plant development within the next six months; furthermore, if time is to be saved, the production plants should be under design and construction before the pilot plant is finished. To embark in this Napoleonic approach to the problem would require the commitment of perhaps $500 million and quite a mass of machinery. Anything less than this will mean either the abandonment or the slowing down of one of the methods. While all five methods now appear to be about equally promising, clearly the time to production by the five routes will certainly not be the same but might vary by six months or a year. Therefore, if one discards one or two or three of the methods now, one may be betting on the slower horse unconsciously."

approved by Bush, who then wrote a report and transmitted it to Vice-President Henry A. Wallace, Secretary of War Stimson and Army Chief of Staff General George C. Marshall. They approved the report and sent it on to the White House. It was returned almost immediately. In one corner was marked simply: *OK, FDR.*

When Bush came to the end of his briefing, Groves sat in silence for a few moments. He was relieved to discover that Bush was not what he considered a merely "academic" scientist; unlike many college professors, this was a man of action — decisive, confident and authoritative. They would work well together, he thought. And there was something else that had impressed Groves. He knew that Bush, like himself, was the son of a minister and seemed equally dedicated to serving his country. Unlike many intellectuals in Groves's experience, this lean Yankee scientist was not apologetic about his patriotism and seemed proud of America's moral values.

It was a necessary quality for the immense task ahead of them, for there was something essentially American about the scope of the Manhattan Project. They were going to have to launch a radically new style of solving scientific and technological problems of unheard-of proportions. A gigantic experiment on the scale of an entire continent would be performed. It would be the American way of solving the greatest problem of modern science; no other country in the world had the necessary resources and industrial power to attempt it.

To judge by Vannevar Bush's words, the country's leaders were absolutely determined to go ahead, no matter how great the obstacles and risks. It was just the kind of talk that Leslie Groves liked to hear.

3

Now FULLY aware of the urgency of his mission, Groves did not even wait for his appointment to become official before he began making decisions and sending a flurry of instructions right and left. His first concern was about the procurement priority that the Project had been given. "We're not going to be able to get the materials fast enough with just this AA–3 priority," he told Nichols.

Nichols agreed and showed him the draft of a letter, which had been prepared earlier, requesting the War Production Board to give AAA priority — the top — to the Manhattan Project. Groves took one look at the letter and shoved it aside. Then he took his pen and drafted a letter addressed to himself and to be signed by Donald Nelson, head of the War Production Board. When it had been typed, Groves himself took it to Nelson's office.

"No! Absolutely not!" Nelson exclaimed after glancing at the letter and listening impatiently to Groves's request for top priority. "We have too many other war projects of capital importance that are waiting desperately for higher priority ratings."

Groves stood up to leave, controlling his cold anger. "All right, Mr. Nelson," he said sternly. "In that case, I must recommend to the President that the Manhattan Project be abandoned because the War Production Board is unwilling to cooperate with his wishes."

The bluff worked. A few minutes later Groves left with the letter signed by Nelson and authorizing AAA priority for the Project.

Promoted to brigadier general, Groves officially took charge of the Manhattan Project on September 23, 1942. That same afternoon a top-level meeting was called in the office of Secretary of War Stimson. Surrounded by his closest advisers, including Bush, Conant, Generals Marshall, Somervell and Styer, Rear Admiral W. R. E. Purnell and Harvey Bundy, the Secretary of War had to decide what body would exercise supreme control over the atomic project. Stimson had still another reason for calling the meeting: he wanted a close look at the officer who had been so highly recommended for the job of running the Manhattan Project.

By age and by rank, Groves was by far the most junior person present, but he stated his opinions vigorously and without hesitation. Stimson explained that he himself, Vice-President Wallace and General Marshall were too busy with other duties to give much of their attention to so important an undertaking as the Manhattan Project. He proposed therefore the formation of a Military Policy Committee that would have overall supervisory authority. It would be composed of seven to nine high-ranking men from the Army, the Navy, and the Office of Scientific Research and Development.

"Such a large committee wouldn't be efficient," Groves protested energetically. "It would only cause delays and be a hindrance. Three is the ideal number. I could keep three people reasonably well informed and also obtain their advice much more readily."

After some discussion, Groves's view prevailed. Stimson also found a way of including both Bush and Conant on the committee of three — Bush would be the chairman, with Conant as an alternate; Admiral Purnell would represent the Navy, and Groves himself the Army.

At this point in the meeting, Groves did something that few officers would ever dare to do in the presence of their superiors. He stood up abruptly, glanced at his watch and announced, "May I be excused? I've got to get out of here if you're through talking. I don't want to miss my train to Tennessee — tomorrow morning we're deciding on a site at Oak Ridge for the first atomic plant."

For a moment everyone in the room looked startled; they all wanted Groves to move fast but hadn't expected him to move quite *that* fast. General Somervell and his deputy General Styer, who had recommended Groves in the first place, exchanged a smile.*

Groves was given permission to leave, but the meeting went on a while longer. One important change was made in the composition of the Policy Committee: the Army representative would be Styer, not Groves. It was obvious that the head of the Manhattan Project would have to make major decisions and accept full responsibility for them. At the same time it was necessary to have some very responsible persons to advise him and watch his work. Such a committee would have the ultimate power: the right to

---

* On Groves's return to Washington a few days later, Somervell told him, "That abrupt departure of yours for Oak Ridge was a smart thing to do! You made me look like a million dollars — I'd told them that if you were put in charge, things would really start moving!"

WESTFIELD MEMORIAL LIBRARY.
WESTFIELD, N. J.

recommend that Secretary Stimson fire Groves if they disapproved of the way he was running the Project.

Early next morning Groves arrived in Knoxville, where he was met by Colonel Marshall. They went immediately to inspect the Oak Ridge site, some eighteen miles from Knoxville and eight miles south of the small town of Clinton. The site, which had been selected by Marshall and Nichols in June, greatly pleased Groves. It answered all the necessary requirements for the future atomic plants: an isolated area with plenty of electrical power, abundant water supply, almost no population, good access by road and train, and a mild climate that permitted outdoor work the year round.

This portion of the quiet rural area was called Black Oak Ridge and was the northernmost of five principal oak- and pine-covered ridges around the meandering Clinch River. It was a verdant, beautiful country-side, with rolling hills covered with dogwood and full of partridge and deer. To the east were the Great Smoky Mountains, to the west the peaks of the Cumberland Mountains. The valleys were sparsely populated by proud, silent people of old Tennessee stock, some of whom still lived in log cabins, more or less as primitively as their forefathers. Economically, it was a poor region. Despite the dams built for the Tennessee Valley Authority, rural electrification had yet to be extended into most of the valleys.

"I knew this region looked good on the map," Groves told Marshall, "but this is even better than I expected."

Marshall nodded. "Yes, I liked it as much as everyone else who came down to see it. But I still didn't feel justified in acquiring fifty-four thousand acres of land for plants when the preliminary scientific work had yet to be done."

Groves knew the story. In June, when Marshall had taken the job of running the Manhattan Project, he had assumed that all the scientific preparatory work had been completed. The scientists had been proclaiming that they were ready to swing into industrial production as soon as plants were built. But it had taken only a couple weeks of visiting labora-tories for Marshall and his construction advisers, engineers from the Boston firm of Stone and Webster, to realize the bitter, alarming truth: *nothing* was ready for production, the whole Project was in an embryonic state.

A methodical, conscientious officer, Marshall considered the acquisition of land for plant sites as premature under the circumstances. He went along with the S-1 members, other than Conant, who wanted to delay the start of the plant construction because much data was still lacking. It was the displeasure of Bush and Conant with Marshall's reluctance that had led to his being superseded. (Another factor was Bush's desire to have an Army officer in charge who was more familiar with government circles in Washington.)

Groves agreed with Marshall that starting industrial production was illogical at this early stage. But Groves's methods were different, his self-confidence greater: he was ready to take the tremendous risk of putting everything into high gear simultaneously, to gamble by taking bold steps without waiting for the previous step to succeed. At the end of the day at Oak Ridge, orders went out for the immediate acquisition of the site.

Shortly after his return from Oak Ridge, Groves left Washington for Pittsburgh, where work on the centrifuge process was being carried out at the Westinghouse Research Laboratory. He wanted to inspect all the important laboratories and to figure out, insofar as possible, what the chances of success were for each of the five methods that might produce the all-important fissionable material for a bomb.

What he saw in Pittsburgh left him singularly unimpressed. The equipment for the centrifuge process had been developed by Professor Jesse W. Beams at the University of Virginia, then tested first by Westinghouse and then by Standard Oil Development in New Jersey. It consisted of big cylinder drums that were made to spin at fantastic speeds on the theory that the lighter uranium–235 isotopes could thus be separated from the heavier uranium–238 isotopes. But so far there had been no concrete results.

Groves was annoyed by something else, too. It was evident to him that the people in the Pittsburgh laboratory did not realize that the atomic energy program involved a grave national emergency. To Groves they all seemed to be working and, to be fair, working diligently, but Groves himself had a different idea of urgency. In his opinion, the people were going along at a relaxed, "academic" pace; they were not working harder than ever before in their lives. Groves was dumfounded to learn that the labs were closed on Sundays and holidays. The day of his visit, too, only one cylinder was running.

"Don't these things have to spin continuously?" he asked the laboratory head.

"Oh, yes."

"How long have you run this one?"

"Well, up to about fifteen minutes."

Groves shook his head in annoyance. "But why haven't you run it continuously if that is required?" It was both a question and a reproach.

"Well, we didn't think it was really necessary," came the reply. "Besides, maybe the cylinder couldn't stand up under the pressure."

Groves had already discovered that the work at the University of Virginia had also been proceeding at the same leisurely pace. He knew very little as yet about isotope separation, but he did not feel at a disadvantage among the scientists. After all, any engineer with good common sense could judge whether a process was feasible. The centrifuge process looked very possible, but it was so far behind in the laboratory stage that Groves did not feel it was a good approach to take. Then, too, there was no sense of urgency among the lab workers, no really hard-driving leader in charge of the program.

On his return to Washington, Groves told Conant that he felt the centrifuge method ought to be abandoned so that more attention could be devoted to the other four methods of producing fissionable material. Conant agreed, and later reported to Bush that though no one process had yet emerged as superior to all the others, the centrifuge was definitely the weakest. The program was dropped soon afterwards.

4

DISAPPOINTED by what he had seen in Pittsburgh, Groves next set out for New York City to inspect the work at Columbia University on the gaseous-diffusion method of obtaining fissionable material. His two top aides, Marshall and Nichols, accompanied him. All three officers wore civilian clothes so as not to attract attention; it was a practice that they were to observe from then on for all their university visits.

At Columbia the three officers talked first to the program leader, Dr. Harold Urey, who then showed them through the laboratories. Urey, with the prestige of his Nobel Prize, was the nominal head of SAM,* where the gaseous-diffusion method of uranium separation was being studied and developed. But the day-to-day work was led by an eager, thirty-five-year-old physicist, Dr. John Dunning, one of the pioneers of the process and the sparkplug of the program.

Dunning and his group probably knew more about gaseous diffusion of uranium than anyone in America. They had, of course, never tried it. At this early stage, they did not have the appropriate uranium gas, or the filters to push it through, or the material to make the pipes and the pumps. But they had studied the principle thoroughly and were working on the detailed design of the process.

To separate the uranium–235 isotope in uranium gas was an unbelievably difficult undertaking. But Dunning loved solving complicated problems. Ever since the age of ten, when he blew the main fuses of Shelby, Nebraska, by plugging his "electric arc" into the town's system, he had been looking for new ways to make things work. When Urey brought Groves, Marshall and Nichols to the laboratory, Dunning was more than pleased to describe his work to them. Each of the visitors' questions was followed by a deluge of detailed, optimistic explanations. The man was obviously in love with his method, and certainly very confident of its success.

The three Army engineers wished they could share Dunning's enthusiasm and Urey's confidence. As a laboratory experiment, gaseous diffusion

---

* SAM, standing for "Substitute Alloy Materials," was the code name for Columbia's nuclear laboratory.

was, no doubt, a fascinating challenge. But as a practical method for industrial production of uranium–235, the process presented so many technical problems that at this stage it could hardly be called feasible.

Before coming to Columbia, Groves had been briefed on the gaseous-diffusion process. The principle, fairly well known, was not too difficult to understand: if uranium were converted into a gas (composed mostly of isotope–238, with a very small percentage of isotope–235) and were forced through the microscopic holes of a filter, the lighter 235 molecules would pass faster than the heavier 238 molecules. Thus the gas on the other side of the filter, or "barrier,"* as it was also called, would be richer in 235–isotopes than the gas on this side of the barrier. If the operation were repeated several times, and the gas recycled through several consecutive filters, the result would be an almost complete separation of the lighter, 235–isotope. This was the one needed for the atomic bomb.

But to attempt massive separation (producing not micrograms but pounds of uranium–235) sounded to any engineer as unrealistic as a child's wildest fantasy. First of all, uranium is not a gas, but a heavy metal. Even if it were transformed into a gas, it would be so extremely corrosive that it would eat up any pipe, filter or pump. The amount of isotope–235 in uranium is so small (0.7 percent) that the diffusion would have to be repeated thousands of times before any concentration could be obtained. Several thousand filters would be needed, filters with billions of holes so small that molecules would pass through one by one.

To accomplish this, a fantastically big plant would have to be built. It would cover a huge area — larger than a city perhaps — filled with the most complicated equipment made out of still nonexistent materials. It was not a question of simply building several plants and laboratories. What was needed was to create an entirely new industry such as men had never seen before, with cities and towns swarming with engineers and scientists. New sciences would have to be developed, new technology, new metals, new tools. No country, perhaps not even the United States, could afford such a gigantic enterprise without running the serious risk of draining vital blood from its economy. And all this to obtain only a few pounds of uranium–235!

In spite of the gigantic problems, John Dunning's self-assurance seemed to be intact. Did he have any workable barrier, Groves inquired. Not exactly, was the answer, but Dr. Francis Slack was about to invent one. Maybe . . . And what about corrosion? Dr. Willard Libby's experiments in that field were very advanced, Dunning assured the visitors. And the pumps, were they invented? Practically, yes; Dr. Henry Boorse had

---

* British scientists used the term "membrane."

solved that one . . . more or less. As far as the intricate "cascade" of consecutive stages, each one richer in U–235 than the previous one, Dr. Karl Cohen was working on that, very successfully as a matter of fact, and Dunning hoped that very soon . . .

Dunning himself, with his colleague Dr. Eugene T. Booth, had actually designed the process. To listen to his exuberant, enthusiastic talk, one had the impression that from now on all the Project had to do was just translate on a larger scale the Dunning-Booth method. Dunning's personality appealed to General Groves at once, even though he was not at all reassured by the state of the gaseous-diffusion program. But in Groves's eyes, the dominating personality, the drive and the optimism of this scientist, could become an important factor leading to future success.

John Dunning had become involved in nuclear physics by accident. Like thousands of other American boys of his generation, his first passion was the radio. John, the brightest student in his small town, built his first wireless before he was twelve. After brilliant studies at Wesleyan College in Nebraska, where he moved more in faculty circles than among his fellow students, he decided to do graduate work in electrical engineering at Columbia. The reason: one of the idols of all wireless hams, the inventor Major Edwin H. Armstrong, was a professor there.

Armstrong happened to be sick the day that Dunning first went to see him at Columbia, so the disappointed student went instead to talk to the dean of the Engineering School, George B. Pegram. The school year had not yet started, and the newly built Pupin Building was almost empty. When Dunning located Pegram's laboratory, he found a handsome man in his late fifties standing behind a table cluttered with various instruments, tubes and wires. Pegram was deeply involved in an experiment and paid little attention to the young visitor.

As he silently watched Pegram at work, Dunning became fascinated by the experiment. Obviously something was wrong and the dean was getting more and more upset. Finally Dunning could hold back no longer. He gave the table a good whack with his fist — as he always did in his own experiments in case any wires should happen to be loose. He was lucky. The blow adjusted a bad connection; the current started to flow. Without saying a word, the dean and the student became involved in the experiment; ten minutes later, with Dunning's help, the mechanism worked beautifully.

Pegram was very impressed. "Young man, what did you say you wanted?" he asked.

"I'd like to enroll in graduate school."

"You better come with me and join the faculty!" Pegram exclaimed.

Dunning did, and found himself in the unusual position of doing graduate work as a student and being a member of the faculty at the same time. Gradually he inherited Pegram's work, started publishing scientific papers, and finally took his doctorate in physics. An extroverted, self-confident young man, he was cocksure in manner and had unusual drive. Dunning soon established himself as an authority in nuclear engineering.

In late 1942 the biggest single problem facing Dunning's group was to find a material suitable for the barrier. Almost by definition, the barrier seemed to be an impossibility. In order to let the molecules filter through one by one, the barrier material should contain literally billions of invisible holes, each one not larger than one ten-thousandth of a millimeter! The process would require several thousand such filters which, fantastically refined as they would have to be, must at the same time be strong enough to withstand the enormous pressure of the gas. The barriers also had to be completely impervious to the strongly corrosive action of the gas, and the microscopic holes must never clog. Such a filter, of course, not only did not exist; it had never even been conceived before.

Groves and his companions left Columbia with the definite impression that the gaseous-diffusion process, if possible at all, was certainly not for tomorrow. They also felt uneasy about the tense relationship they had noticed between Professor Urey and John Dunning, and they wondered if the program leader would be able to handle his younger, more dynamic colleague.

They felt happier and more at home in the less academic atmosphere of the Jersey City laboratory where the M. W. Kellogg Company was conducting research on the engineering possibilities of gaseous diffusion. At the beginning of 1942, the company had taken on a secret assignment from the S–1 Committee after President Roosevelt had ordered an all-out effort to push research on methods for uranium separation. Kellogg was asked to determine, in collaboration with the Columbia group, whether large-scale gaseous diffusion was possible.

Groves thought immediately that Colonel Marshall's earlier selection of the M. W. Kellogg Company was a very good one. At the beginning of the war, there were few people in America who could design and build modern petroleum refineries and chemical plants better than the engineers of Kellogg. Morris Kellogg had started the small pipe-manufacturing shop in Jersey City with $2750 in 1905. Quickly realizing the enormous potentialities of the infant oil industry, he began fabricating welded stills to replace the old riveted stills. Then he bought and developed a new process that the oil industry adopted avidly. By the time World War II broke out, the Kellogg Company was a multimillion-dollar business specializing in pure engineering — developing new processes and applying the latest inventions and most modern techniques.

The selection of Kellogg for the engineering research on gaseous diffusion was therefore natural, and so was the designation of Percival ("Dobie") C. Keith as head of the secret project. Highly individualistic, energetic and impulsive, the self-confident Texan was the company's enormously successful vice-president in charge of engineering. Like Dunning, Dobie Keith gave the impression of being extremely dynamic and enthusiastic. General Groves felt reassured to hear an engineer — and obviously an outstanding professional — speak with the same optimism as had the Columbia scientist. Groves was also pleased to see that the Jersey City laboratory was free from the strain he had noticed at Columbia. There was no doubt that the fiery, authoritarian Dobie Keith had his men well in hand.

5

RARELY HAD such an abundance of scientific brains been concentrated within the walls of a few buildings as on the University of Chicago campus in 1942. And rarely had there been a group as difficult to organize into a smooth, orderly administrative body as this conglomeration of brilliant, individualistic scientists. They were all very independent-minded, and a few were prima donnas.

Dr. Leo Szilard was unquestionably the *enfant terrible* of the Chicago group. A remarkably brilliant Hungarian, with a mind overflowing with original ideas, this paunchy, bespectacled, forty-four-year-old physicist led a restless life that amounted to a permanent crusade. Few scientists had done more to awaken American authorities to the inherent dangers of atomic energy than this farsighted prophet who had studied earlier in Berlin with Max Planck and Einstein. It was largely thanks to his insistence that Einstein had agreed to sign the letter that informed President Roosevelt of the likelihood that Nazi Germany was already working on an atomic bomb.

Modesty was not one of Szilard's qualities, however, and some people found him tiresome and pushy. But his crusades, they had to admit, were all for great ideas: the defeat of Hitler, the establishment of a world government and the development of nuclear energy. His passion for politics and philosophy was equal to his interest in science. Among the scientists assembled in Chicago, he was by far the most cosmopolitan and politically minded. His thinking was often unorthodox and original. "I am all in favor of the democratic principle that one person, even an idiot, is as good as one genius," he used to say. "But I draw the line when someone takes the next step and concludes that two idiots are better than one genius!"

Szilard regularly used to throw the university's Metallurgical Laboratory (the name had been chosen to mask the real nature of the work being carried on there) into a turmoil. He would rove through the labs, suggesting revolutionary approaches to problems, sounding the alarm about Hitler's military advances, and often asking some young scientists to switch from one experiment to another. Leo Szilard always seemed to leave a trail behind him like the wake of a cyclone.

Once, when everyone at the lab was commenting on the latest Szilard-ism, a dazzled scientist exclaimed, "I have a wonderful idea! I think I know what we should do with Leo. He should be put in a state of suspended animation under refrigeration, then taken out once a year and brought to life for two minutes — but no more. He could give us enough ideas to keep us busy for the rest of the year. For two minutes he'd be fantastic, but how marvelous life in the lab would be for the rest of the year!"

There was another brilliant Hungarian in the Chicago group: Eugene Wigner, a refugee physicist who had been teaching at Princeton. Greatly respected for his keen mind, Wigner was very much liked; he was without doubt the most polite man on the Project. His insistence on always letting the other person precede him through a door had become proverbial. "We hope your wife will never have twins," his colleagues used to tease him. "Poor woman! She would have to wait for months to deliver them because the babies would be exchanging polite invitations of 'After you, sir!' " An immaculately dressed and very shy man, Wigner never pushed himself. But behind his exquisite manners, he had strong determination and an uncompromising character. He had been seen to lose his temper only once, when a rude garage owner swore at him at length. Becoming exasperated, Wigner shouted from his car, "Go to hell!" — and then quickly added, "Please."

But the most extraordinary scientist in the Chicago group was un-doubtedly Enrico Fermi, the forty-year-old Nobel Prize winner from Italy. A friendly, simple man, he combined disarming personal modesty with an equally disarming, total self-assurance in scientific matters. With the growing complexity and specialization in physics, he was probably the only person capable of grasping the whole body of knowledge in the field; he was both a brilliant experimentalist and a great theorist. In confer-ences Fermi was usually the last to speak. He would not just venture an opinion; he would say how things *were* and what was going to happen next. And usually he was right, for it seemed that Fermi's brain was constructed in a special way, and his colleagues accepted the fact without any jealousy.

The amiable Italian scientist had his little vanities as a human being; but if he ever bragged, it was about what a great swimmer he was, or about how none of the younger scientists could outhike him in the mountains, or about how they could not guess before he did who the murderer was in a movie. But for Fermi there was never any guessing when science was involved. He loved to play a little game when calculations were being made on a hand calculator: he would stand next to the computer, his small slide rule in his hand, and would try to get the answer as fast and accurately as the machine. He was usually successful, to the delight of his assistants — and more particularly his own.

It had not been easy to recruit the impressive team at the Metallurgical Laboratory. "Shanghaiing" was a better word for the techniques used by Compton's emissaries in the spring of 1942. In March there had been only forty-five people in the newly formed Chicago group, including secretaries, guards and elevator operators. By June there were 1250, and the number was still rising. To persuade physicists and chemists to move to Chicago, without telling them what the Project was about, was a difficult mission. This was especially so because of the competition from other top-priority war projects, such well-established programs as the radar development at MIT and the proximity fuse at Johns Hopkins and the Bureau of Standards.

Arthur Compton had had to employ all his persuasive powers to bring the scientists to Chicago and thus centralize all work on piles* and plutonium. All through 1941 Enrico Fermi, helped by Herbert Anderson, had been experimenting at Columbia; Leo Szilard with Walter Zinn had been working there, too. They liked it in New York and preferred to stay there. Eugene Wigner was quite happy with his theoretical group at Princeton and really did not want to leave. Glenn Seaborg, discoverer of plutonium, and all his co-workers were busy at Berkeley. Samuel Allison was among the very few top scientists on the Project who was working at the University of Chicago.

But as the months went by, and as the self-imposed rule of secrecy increasingly impeded communications among the scientists, it became obvious that work on the different aspects of the problem had to be conducted in one place. Every group leader favored his university, and after long discussions with them, Compton had to make the decision. He chose Chicago after receiving a promise of help from Robert Hutchins, president of the university. All the scientists he invited to join the new Metallurgical Laboratory left their homes — some readily, some reluc-

---

* A "pile" (the first name used for the "nuclear reactor") is a device by which a fission "chain reaction" is achieved, by piling up natural uranium and graphite blocks. The neutrons emitted by the uranium cause the splitting of the nucleus of other uranium atoms — the fission. In addition to the two large fragments of the original nucleus, extra neutrons are emitted in the breakup.

When the nucleus releases two or more neutrons, which split still other nuclei, more nuclei are thus released, resulting in chain reaction. It was discovered, however, that fission would occur more readily if the neutrons were slowed down. For this reason, "moderators" were used to slow down the high-velocity neutrons. The first reactors were built with either pure graphite or heavy water as moderators.

tantly — and came to work in the Windy City. Among younger scientists, even more than in other professions, the prestige of a few illustrious names can work miracles. For them it was enough to know that the Chicago lab was working on a very important war project, and that people of the caliber of Fermi, Compton, Wigner and Szilard needed them badly.

The reputation of the laboratory's leader had been extremely important in that respect. Since the first days of any organized atomic effort in the United States, Arthur Holly Compton had played one of the principal roles on the scientific side, together with Bush, Conant, Lawrence and Urey. He came from an eminent family of intellectuals; his father and his two brothers were also professors; both his mother and sister also held college degrees and were active in missionary work. Arthur Compton was an enterprising scientist, who won the 1927 Nobel Prize in physics for his studies of X rays and became famous with his pioneering work on cosmic rays in the early 1930s.

A tall, vigorous-looking man of fifty (he had been a college football player), with a thick mustache and a strong chin, Compton was well liked in scientific circles because of his pleasant manners and considerate attitude toward others. He inherited deep religious feelings, abstemiousness, and a devotion to church work from his father, a Presbyterian clergyman and professor of philosophy at Wooster College in Ohio. Through his older brother Karl, who was later to become president of MIT, he became imbued with a passion for exploration in physics and began to associate, while still a youth, with some of the country's most prominent scientists.

Compton's bold scientific experiments in the new field of cosmic rays were carried out in the Himalayas, the Andes, in the Arctic and at the Equator; sometimes he even did research in planes flying at twenty-nine thousand feet, which involved considerable risk at the time. He became equally well known as a champion of the idea that scientific progress lends new strength to religion. "Science is the glimpse of God's purpose in nature," he wrote, "and the very existence of the amazing world of the atom and radiation points to a purposeful creation, to the idea that there is a God and an intelligent purpose back of everything." Compton taught Sunday school, was a deacon of his church and chairman of the Laymen's Missionary Movement.

In Chicago, Compton's role was that of organizer, coordinator and moving spirit for the scientists, as well as their liaison with the Government and with the Manhattan Project. Some of his colleagues jokingly stated that Compton was only half leader of the group, his co-leader being his energetic wife Betty. This rather large woman, with the looks and the voice of a Wagnerian heroine, was the only wife in the Manhattan Project authorized to share all the atomic secrets possessed by her husband. The Comptons were so devoted to each other that when the question of clearance first arose, the physicist admitted candidly, "If you clear me, you should clear my wife as well. I have always been one of those who must talk over important problems with his wife, and it would be unrealistic to suppose that I would keep from her matters that strongly affect me."

Betty Compton received the clearance. From that moment on, she accompanied her husband on a number of his trips and was present at many of his discussions, often asking questions and giving her opinion. She acted as hostess to the newly arrived scientists, helping them find accommodations and organize their lives in Chicago. In a short time Betty Compton became an influential, if unofficial, member of the Metallurgical Lab.

The purely scientific problems faced by the Chicago laboratory were staggering, but they were stimulating, fascinating problems. The chief cause of concern among the scientists, however, was the realization that the control and direction of their project was being taken rapidly out of their hands. This was obvious from the very first session they had with Marshall and Nichols in June of 1942. After the meetings, the officers talked privately with Norman Hilberry, Compton's top assistant and an expert on cosmic rays. "Now look, Hilberry, there is clearly a major misunderstanding here that has got to be straightened out," Marshall said. "It seems to us that all you folks are thinking in terms of making one or two bombs. Isn't that true?"

Hilberry confirmed this. The basis of the scientists' thinking was that if the atomic bomb worked at all, it would be such an incredibly destructive weapon that a single bomb or two would do the job and win the war. The psychological effect on the enemy would lead to his immediate surrender.

"That's all wrong," Marshall objected firmly. "There is a fundamental principle in military matters which — and I don't care how fantastic this atomic device may prove to be — is *not* going to be violated. This is one's ability to continue delivering a weapon, and it's this that determines whether the weapon is useful. If you folks succeeded in making only one bomb, I can assure you it would never be used. The only basic principle on which the military can operate is the ability to continue to deliver.

"You've got to sit down and get reoriented. The thing we're talking about is not a number of bombs; what we are talking about is *production capacity* to continue delivering bombs at a given rate. That, you will discover, is a very different problem."

Hilberry reported the conversation to his colleagues. Several scientists were shocked; they were simply unwilling to accept the concept that more than a couple of bombs would be necessary. But the arguments of the Chicago group could not be discarded out of hand, even for purely military reasons.

There was, first of all, the basic assumption that Germany was working desperately on her atomic bomb. The considerable delays that would be necessitated by industrial production in the United States might therefore place the nation in mortal danger. Suppose, for example, that Germany made only a few atomic bombs, then dropped them on the United States while we were still preparing for large-scale production? This became a deep, genuine concern for many of the scientists in the Project. They nonetheless felt that the military would impose its view in the end, despite all arguments. And yet the scientists were conscious of another truth: even the best scientific laboratory in the world, no matter how big, was not capable of large-scale, regular production of atom bombs.

Rumors had already reached Chicago that the job was going to be turned over to industry. A sense of frustration invaded the Metallurgical Lab. It was not only because of the hurt pride of men who viewed themselves as the originators of, and sole experts on, the new idea. Nor was it simply frustration born of a sense of possessiveness — the feeling among scientists that it was their "baby," that no one else would be able to understand nuclear physics. In most cases, opposition sprang from the sincere conviction that scientists could do the job better than industrial engineers.

By the nature of their science, physicists were very confident people. They had reached their eminence in the field by their own abilities; they had been faced with all sorts of difficulties and had found solutions. There was therefore no question in their minds: if left to their own devices, they *would* get the job done. They were deeply perturbed to see military and industrial engineers taking over something whose basic principles, almost by definition, laymen could not possibly understand. And these were fundamentals upon which success or failure would depend. The physicists also felt that it was courting disaster to turn over major responsibility for the Project's design and construction to people who could not possibly grasp the whole picture. Their concern could not be fully appreciated without putting it in context with their unceasing apprehension that the United States might be even one day later than Hitler.

The most voluble opponent of relinquishing direction of the Project to industry and the military was Leo Szilard. His anxiety, however, was shared in different degrees by Wigner, Fermi, Allison and almost all the

WESTFIELD MEMORIAL LIBRARY
WESTFIELD, N. J.

other important leaders. They were convinced that if a polished engineering job was started, as industrialists always demanded, there would be a day lost here to get drawings approved, a day lost there for something else. Scientists, however, could just go ahead and build the bomb.

The great majority of physicists had never had any experience with industry. They had never worked with engineers; the problems of industrial design and plant construction were entirely foreign to them. Physicists were rarely employed in industry before the war; mass manufacturing processes needed them only occasionally. Chemists, however, were in a very different position. New gigantic industries had been growing up in the United States before the war — most notably, the oil and chemical industries. Such industries had absorbed thousands of chemists, a fact which explains the better understanding of industrial problems by chemists at the time. But most physicists had no way of appreciating the entirely different problems of laboratory work as contrasted with those of large-scale industrial production. Seldom had the two spheres anything in common: a successful laboratory experiment was of little use to industry, especially when it had to be translated to a scale 100,000 times larger, or more.

Arthur Compton, head of the Chicago group, was in deep sympathy with his academic colleagues. At the same time, he himself had had some previous industrial experience, and he had to admit that in this crucial situation, the military people seemed to be right. It was obvious that his physicist friends had very incomplete, sometimes even naïve, ideas about the truly enormous engineering and construction problems that the Project would have to face.

6

As USUAL, Mrs. Jean O'Leary, General Groves's chief secretary, accompanied her boss on the train as far as Baltimore, so that he could dictate memos and letters for a while longer.

A bright, pretty young woman of thirty, who had worked earlier in New York as a secretary for *Time* magazine, she had come to Washington in 1942 with her small daughter, heartbroken over the sudden death of her husband, a journalist. After working for General Styer for a short while, she was transferred to Groves more than a year before he took charge of the Manhattan Project.

During the war years secretaries had not lasted too long with Leslie Groves. A strict taskmaster, he took the uncompromising view that a secretary should devote her entire time to the job. Long coffee breaks were frowned upon, personal problems were not to be discussed at the office. Distant in manner, Groves was the kind of boss who had no time for anything but business. This suited Jean O'Leary perfectly. She wanted to forget her personal sorrow by burying herself in work. She deliberately avoided any social life and new friendships. After the first few months, she was no longer intimidated by the general's blunt, impatient ways. Despite his demanding attitude, she quickly gained his confidence and established herself as one of the key figures in the office. Little by little, Jean O'Leary became his Washington executive assistant, especially when he traveled outside of the capital.

Groves's reputation for toughness and his lack of consideration were well known. The construction people often complained that he was too hard on them. In the Army he was criticized for his lack of subtlety and tact. And most people described him as a man with an inflated ego. Groves was well aware of his reputation, but being unpopular didn't bother him. All he cared about was getting the job done. And he would see to it that the job *was* done, even if it meant stepping on a lot of toes. Most of his subordinates feared him; only a few liked him. But he preferred it that way; all he demanded was respect. And respect Groves had — from superiors, from subordinates and from colleagues.

Ever since he graduated fourth in his 1918 West Point class, Groves had been known for his exemplary work, his efficiency and total devotion to the Army. When a task was assigned him, his commander felt certain the job would be done if it was humanly possible — and done well and on time. But *how* Groves did it was another story. If necessary, he could be blunt and ruthless, tyrannical and severe. He had no patience with procrastination, no tolerance for sloppiness, no time or talent for polite formality. With his own extraordinary capacity for work, he drove everybody to the maximum, not sparing their strength or feelings — but never sparing himself either.

Groves's subordinates in the Army had no choice but to put up with his hard-driving ways. But even the construction companies and industrialists with whom he had to work were treated in exactly the same way. Often he would ask a civilian engineer to accompany him on a tour of construction projects and, to the civilian's dismay, Groves would choose a train with some outlandish departure time like 1 A.M. Thus they would manage to arrive at their destination at, for example, 6 A.M., and when the exhausted companion would hope at least to have a decent breakfast after a nearly sleepless night, Groves, looking completely rested, would say cheerfully, "We have no time for breakfast, do we? Let's go straight to the meeting."

Because of his capacity to get things done on time according to specifications, Groves had been put in charge of the construction of the Pentagon and, as deputy to General Thomas Robins, also supervised all other military construction in the country. Although in many cases Groves's superiors did not like him, they appreciated his courage and sense of responsibility.

On his first trip to Chicago on October 5, Groves was to exhibit the same qualities of frank speaking and straightforwardness in his dealings with extremely eminent scientists. Arthur Compton with Colonel Marshall met Groves and Nichols at the station, took them straight to the lab and showed them the various divisions and introduced to them his principal colleagues. The visit took the whole morning.

Groves was immediately struck by the number of different approaches toward the problem of cooling the graphite pile. Several entirely different methods were under consideration, and cooling, obviously, was still at the talking stage. This indecision was delaying all other decisions about future reactors. When Groves talked to Szilard and some of the other scientists working on the cooling problem, he managed to convince them that they must drop all but one or two of the proposed methods and concentrate all efforts on these. As the result of one morning's visit, two cooling systems were chosen right away: one using helium, the other using air.

A meeting with the Chicago scientists was set for the afternoon in a large and well-furnished room in the laboratory. It was an impressive group of men: three Nobel Prize winners — Fermi, Compton and Franck; some of the best experts in the field like Wigner and Szilard, and a dozen younger scientists. The important question to be discussed was the definition of how much fissionable material would be needed for an atomic bomb.

One after another, the scientists went to the blackboard and covered it with complicated equations. It was Groves's first experience of watching nuclear physicists work at the blackboard. In spite of his fairly good background in mathematics, Groves found the equations hard to follow. The figures were scribbled in an illegible manner, like the handwriting on a physician's prescription. Suddenly, trying intensely to follow them, Groves noticed one small figure in an exponent that seemed to be copied incorrectly on the following line. For a moment he wondered whether he was being trapped — whether they just wanted to see how much he knew. But then, after a few moments, he decided to make the plunge.

"Excuse me," he interrupted, "but I don't understand how you got from equation No. 5 to equation No. 6. How does 10-to-the-minus-6 become suddenly 10-to-the-minus-5?"

The scientist took a quick look at the blackboard. "Oh, you're right — that's an error," he said, and erased the wrong exponent with a finger. Groves was surprised to see some of the greatest physicists in the country making an error in simple math; somehow he felt more at ease now, with his self-confidence returning.

Finally, the scientists at the blackboard came up with an answer concerning the amount of material needed for the bomb.

"How accurate is this figure?" asked the general.

He did not expect to be given a precise estimate; as an engineer, he anticipated hearing that the answer was correct between 25 and 50 percent. But he was stunned when the scientists said the figure was accurate to a factor of 10! He had never heard that term used before. It meant the true amount could be anything from ten times *less* to ten times *more* than the estimated figure.

Groves found it hard to believe that scientists were willing to work with such slipshod calculation. It was just as idiotic, he thought, as sending for a caterer for a wedding reception, then telling him, "We don't know how many guests are coming — maybe somewhere between ten and a thousand — but see to it that you have the right amount of food for them!"

The general was shocked by this unrealistic thinking. He couldn't help saying, "How do you expect me, if I needed so many bombs per month, to build a factory based on your vague figures? Shall we design for, say, three bombs a month, or for three-tenths of a bomb, or for thirty bombs?"

The Chicago physicists were unable to answer him.

Before he left the meeting, Groves decided he had to put the relationship between himself and the scientists on what he believed to be the right basis. Showing no inferiority complex because he was talking to Nobel Prize winners, the self-assured officer told them bluntly, "There is one last thing I want to emphasize. You may know that I don't have a Ph.D. Colonel Nichols has one, but I don't. But let me tell you that I had ten years of formal education after I entered college. *Ten* years in which I just studied. I didn't have to make a living or give time to teaching. I just studied. That would be the equivalent of about two Ph.D.'s, wouldn't it?"

Nobody said anything. There were a few embarrassed smiles. Leo Szilard, puffing with annoyed impatience, could hardly wait for Groves to leave so that he could vent his indignation.

"You see what I told you?" he said to his colleagues. "How can you work with people like that?"

7

Professor Ernest O. Lawrence was waiting to meet Groves at the railroad station in San Francisco. He shook his hand cordially and said, "We're going straight to Radiation Hill, General. You're going to have a surprise! You've been listening to all those theories in Chicago and at Columbia. But out here, you'll see separation actually going on."

Groves, who was making his first visit to Berkeley, was delighted to hear this. "It's more than I expected, Dr. Lawrence," he admitted.

The long train trip across the country had given him a good opportunity to study the reports and technical papers on Lawrence's electromagnetic method of separation; it had not been very encouraging reading. Groves now understood, though, why the engineers of Stone and Webster, who had been assigned by Marshall to solve the engineering problems of the process developed at Berkeley, liked to work with Lawrence. He was obviously a man who would get things done; he was an "engineer's scientist," someone a technical man could talk to, and not at all one of the academic "longhairs" that engineers find so hard to cooperate with.

Lawrence was a tall, boyish-looking man with blond hair and high color. There was something enormously vital in his movements, in the energetic way he walked. His light-blue eyes sparkled behind rimless glasses with the eagerness of someone afraid that time would be too short for all the marvelous things he wanted to do. He was not the older, more sedate man most people would expect. Lawrence's healthy California tan, his young face, the sports coat, gray flannel slacks, his informal manner — all this certainly did not correspond to the popular image of a Nobel Prize winner.

Lawrence's car, with the professor at the wheel, took the road to the Berkeley campus. Groves was to remember the trip for years to come as one of the most hair-raising experiences he had had in the war. Lawrence's atrocious driving petrified him. Pressing the accelerator down to the floor and keeping his face turned toward his passenger, the talkative professor threw the car forward in jerks and spasms, swaying from one side of the road to the other, cutting corners at full speed and paying no attention whatever to the other cars they passed. Groves made a mental note to issue an order as soon as he returned to Washington that would assign Government chauffeurs to the major scientists — Lawrence, Fermi, Compton — whether they liked it or not.

Still ruffled by the ride, Groves followed Lawrence into the building where the "calutron" was installed. He had never seen a calutron before; in fact, almost no one outside of Berkeley's Radiation Laboratory had either. The word had been coined by Lawrence as the name of his new invention: "calu" for the University of California, and "tron" for cyclotron, the atom-smashing machine for which he had become a Nobel laureate in 1939.

The calutron was a peculiar-looking gadget, combining the 37-inch magnet of Lawrence's cyclotron and a crude vacuum chamber, shaped like the letter C, which was installed in the eight-inch gap between the poles of the magnet. "This is the old machine," Lawrence said proudly. "I wanted you to have an idea of our earlier calutrons. But wait until you see the new one!"

A handful of young men, postgraduate students in checkered shirts and sneakers, were swarming around the machine. They followed Lawrence's every word with the reverence of disciples hearing the Gospel. The whole atmosphere of the Berkeley lab was youthful and alive. But Groves was impatient to see the new giant machine that made Lawrence enthusiastic for he had already read enough disturbing reports about the lame performance of the old 37-inch calutron.

The first reports had been written at the beginning of 1942, when Stone and Webster sent engineers to Berkeley to find out the state of the electromagnetic program. What they learned there filled them with anxiety. They did not know much about atomic science — theories were not their business. But they were among the few engineers in the United States who had been told, in highest confidence, that a tremendously destructive weapon could be built if enough uranium–235 were ever separated.

Their opening question, after Lawrence had demonstrated how his calutron worked, was right to the point: "How much U–235 have you separated?" They got their first shock when the professor replied proudly that in February his laboratory had produced three samples of 75 micrograms each. Micrograms! Was Lawrence talking seriously? That was a speck the eye could scarcely see! Then Lawrence announced, still with the same pride, that each sample contained 30 percent of uranium–235. The engineers could not hide their disappointment: so the dust speck was not even pure!

From the scientific point of view, Lawrence's electromagnetic process was certainly fascinating, the engineers felt, and they could not help but admire the ingenuity of its inventor. But they found it difficult to see even a remote connection between the clever gadget and any serious industrial operation. How did Lawrence intend to separate *pounds* of pure fissionable uranium–235? How had Stone and Webster ever gotten involved in these laboratory experiments? Where would engineers be expected to come in? If the separation of a few micrograms required the biggest magnets and round-the-clock work of several dozen Berkeley scientists, it would have to be multiplied by thousands and thousands of magnets, tens of thousands of Ph.D.'s working day and night over acres of incredible instruments and using colossal amounts of uranium — in order to produce just *one* pound of U–235.

Before Lawrence had answered these questions, the engineers were beginning to wonder how the leaders in Government and science could have considered such a fantasy as any serious possibility. But it was enough to hear Ernest Lawrence speak about his projects once, to understand why the professor had become one of the most influential figures in American science.

His explanation was an illuminating exercise in self-confidence and bold imagination. For the realistic, down-to-earth engineers from Stone and Webster, it was an unusual experience. As Lawrence described his vision of gigantic industrial complexes and laboratories, armies of specially trained scientists and arsenals of newly invented tools and instruments, his voice rose with enthusiasm. It was contagious enthusiasm that overwhelmed doubt and drowned all sense of reality in a flood of buoyant optimism. For a moment the mesmerized engineers felt as though their ties with practical common sense were being cut. Somewhere deep in their minds they knew that all this was too fantastic to be feasible. But while Lawrence was talking, it was impossible not to fall under the almost hypnotic spell of his enthusiasm.

When the spellbound Stone and Webster representatives came down to earth, however, the reality frightened them. The company had already agreed to design huge production plants; preliminary engineering had to start immediately. Before the end of 1942 construction had to be under way. And yet nobody seemed to know what the electromagnetic process would look like, or whether it would even work!

No company had ever undertaken such a task before. What would the size of the future plant be, what shape, what specifications? What kind of equipment would be needed? No one at Berkeley or in Washington knew. The only definite words were "extreme urgency." No time for tests, no time for pilot plants. Stone and Webster suddenly realized that a whole new industry had to be built before methods, machines and instruments had even been invented.

To General Groves, Lawrence readily admitted that the production from the first calutron had hardly been spectacular so far. "But that was just the beginning," he said with great assurance. "We're replacing the old 37-inch machine. We have already a huge 184-inch experimental cyclotron up on the Hill. But the country's at war — cyclotrons for experiment must wait! So I'm using its magnet for the calutron. You've never seen such a magnet — it's the largest in the world! Come, I'll show you!"

Once again Groves endured the perils of Lawrence's driving as the car climbed the narrow road that wound up the green hill overlooking the campus. Far below, beyond the gardens and lawns of Berkeley, the bridges of San Francisco Bay shone in the sun. Lawrence preceded Groves into the newly built round dome atop Radiation Hill. Under the circular white ceiling, with iron beams arranged like the spokes of a bicycle wheel, the giant magnet towered twenty feet above the floor. A huge red crane hung horizontally over the unfinished cyclotron. Members of Lawrence's team were working with the separation equipment installed between the poles of the magnet. It was an impressive machine, obviously far more powerful than the 37-inch calutron.

Lawrence was visibly thrilled by his creation. "Here is the uranium gas, General, and on this side we have the electric source. It's ten times more powerful than the old model!"

He drew Groves closer to the machine. "Let me show you how it works. You see, the atoms are accelerated through the vacuum tube to a speed of many thousands of miles per second. At this speed they enter an intensely strong magnetic field." He gesticulated to the operator. "Jimmy, turn it up stronger — stronger, for Heaven's sake!"

He turned back to Groves. "By the pull of magnetic force," he went on, "the atoms are curved into circular paths. As you know, uranium has two kinds of isotopes: 238, and a lighter one, 235. So the lighter 235-atoms are bent into a different circuit than the heavier 238-atoms. Do you follow me? It's like throwing two stones of different weights with the same force: one will go farther than the other. Here, at the end of the arc, we have separate containers, one to collect the heavier atoms, the other to collect the lighter."

Lawrence pulled Groves even closer to the machine. "And now you look through here, General. See that arc? It's that arc going around that makes the separation."

Groves looked through and saw the electrical arc. "But how long does this thing have to run to get real separation?" he asked matter-of-factly.

"Well, it takes a long time to make a vacuum in the machine itself. It'll take from fourteen to twenty-four hours to get a vacuum that's sufficient."

"But how long do you run it?"

"It's never been run for more than ten or fifteen minutes."

The enthusiastic Lawrence could not understand what he had said to make such a look of disappointment come over the general's face.

"What about separation? How much do you get in the baskets?" asked Groves, with only faint hope in his voice.

"Well, actually, we don't get any sizable separation at all. I mean, not yet. This is still all experimental, you see . . ."

8

IT WOULD BE difficult to imagine two men so opposite in every way. One was a frail, emaciated-looking young professor with an intense face and magnetic blue eyes that radiated extraordinary sensitivity; the other a heavyset, self-confident general with a wholesome air. If they had belonged to two entirely different species, the theoretical physicist from Berkeley and the Army engineer from West Point could not have had less in common either in background or in education. There was no similarity in character, taste or thinking. Ostensibly they were speaking the same language, but each had different nuances of meaning for the same word.

Normally, people so disparate never meet. Or if they do, they have nothing to say to each other. Or even worse — one may quickly catalogue the other as a "long-hair leftist intellectual crackpot" while, at the same time, being set down as "reactionary Prussian militarist." Strangely enough, it did not work that way for Dr. J. Robert Oppenheimer and General Leslie Groves — quite the contrary. As conversation progressed in the uncomfortable roomette aboard the Twentieth Century Limited from Chicago to New York, the two men became more and more interested in each other. Colonel Marshall and Lieutenant Colonel Nichols were also crowded into the tiny compartment, and the three officers were fascinated by the scientist's brilliant reasoning.

Groves had met Oppenheimer once before, briefly, and had been struck by the remarkable intellect of the reserved, pipe-smoking, thirty-eight-year-old scientist. His very first impression had been that this was a monastic professor with a wide knowledge of theoretical physics and possessed of an exceptional intellect. As Oppenheimer talked now on the train, the general became aware of his remarkably broad culture, his knowledge of the arts, literature and philosophy. He was impressed to hear that Oppenheimer, who spoke fluent German and French, had learned ancient Sanskrit just for the intellectual enjoyment of it. Groves became fascinated by the quick, incisive mind of the young professor, by his grasp of problems. At the same time, he was surprised by the very limited notions Oppenheimer had of subjects like the American system of government and the way it operated; about industry, construction, the problems of management and labor. Indeed, brilliant as he was, he seemed to be as ignorant of American military history as Groves himself was of symphonic music or Hindu poetry.

At that time, Oppenheimer was helping the Manhattan Project only on a part-time basis; but now Compton had asked him to take charge of theoretical problems concerning the design of the bomb itself. Like all the physicists of his generation, Oppenheimer had followed with great interest the developments triggered by the fission of the atom in 1938, and, in a "very romantic way" as he used to put it, had often discussed the problems of critical assemblies* with his colleagues. But he had not been brought into the secret until September 1941, and then only by the indiscretion of an English scientist, who was talking to Lawrence in Oppenheimer's presence. Assuming that Oppenheimer already knew about the bomb project, the visitor suggested he be used in a more active way. Lawrence agreed that this should have been done and the next month took him to a meeting in Schenectady, New York, where problems of assembly and critical mass† were discussed. On the way, Lawrence kept raving about the possibilities of his electromagnetic method of separation.

Oppenheimer became intensely interested in the whole project. He gave Lawrence a hand with the design of the magnetic-field circuit, but acted only as a consultant, without formally joining his team. Instead, he continued teaching at the university.

After Pearl Harbor, Oppenheimer was invited to the meetings in Chicago, where Compton was organizing the Metallurgical Laboratory. Even then Compton felt that, independently of the work on "slow fission" of the pile, some group should start looking into "fast fission" — in other words, the actual problems of constructing an atomic bomb. He asked Oppenheimer to take charge of this part of the work and organized a small team of theoretical physicists.

No one had even an approximate idea of the probable design and size of the bomb. Many scientists thought that working on its design was extremely premature until there was definite knowledge that uranium-235 could be separated in quantity, or that a weapon might be made out of plutonium. One skeptic was Berkeley's Ernest Lawrence. "It's wrong to start this now," he said, "because we'll be taking men from the biggest job of all, which is getting the fissionable material, and putting them on work that is premature. In three months," he told Groves, "thirty scientists could design this bomb if we had the fissionable material."

---

* Critical assembly: sufficient fissionable material to sustain a chain reaction.

† Critical mass: the smallest amount of fissionable material that will support a self-sustaining chain reaction.

WESTFIELD MEMORIAL LIBRARY
WESTFIELD, N. J.

The general, obsessed by a fear of losing even one day in the race with German scientists, disagreed completely. He felt that such an attitude either underestimated the difficulties of the bomb design or overestimated the abilities of Lawrence's fellow scientists, and that the Manhattan Project should not wait for the bomb material before doing something about a design for the weapon itself. He agreed when he heard scientists say that the problems would be very difficult. There *were* formidable questions involved. How much material, for example, would be required for a critical mass? What should be its shape? How could it be detonated? Could the force of the explosion be predicted? Maybe something essential might be overlooked, or some unforeseen obstacle might crop up that would take a year to surmount. It would be absolutely unforgivable to have the fissionable material all ready, and then to hear the scientists say, "But we don't know how to make the bomb!"

Most scientists, indeed, recognized the need for prompt determination of the probable critical mass, which was why Compton had assigned the study of theoretical aspects to Oppenheimer and other groups. But it was still a program lacking coordination — different phases of the problems were being studied by independent groups of scientists scattered around the country, and most of them were working only on a part-time basis while continuing to carry out their academic duties.

Groves did not like the situation at all. Such a halfway approach, without rigid deadlines and efficient organization, was contrary to his temperament and method of work. Unofficially he summed up his feelings with the remark: "We can't just sit on our fannies and meditate!" It was the reason he was so interested to hear Oppenheimer express his worries about the bomb-design program. The wording was not the same — one of Oppenheimer's striking talents was his superb mastery of literary English. However, the concern of both men was very similar. The professor, too, was disturbed by the uncoordinated research in bomb design and Groves had asked him to spend a couple of hours on the train from Chicago with Marshall, Nichols and himself and give them his frank opinion.

What bothered Oppenheimer most about the bomb-problem study was the lack of contact and exchange of information among different laboratories. He did not think that any appreciable results could be achieved without closer contact among scientists. Weren't there, perhaps, some exaggerated regulations about secrecy that were seriously handicapping the researchers?

The officers listened carefully. Geographical separation was a major problem, indeed. Oppenheimer, in fact, was describing some of the disadvantages of physical separation, but he was not challenging the Project's basic principle of "compartmentalization."

Compartmentalization consisted simply of allowing each person or group in the Manhattan Project to know only as much as was necessary for him to do his own job. There was no need, it was felt, for the thousands of engineers, scientists and workers to know that they were working on an atomic bomb. The people in the Metallurgical Laboratory, for example, had no business knowing about gaseous diffusion. Nor was there any reason to tell the electromagnetic people at Berkeley the details of the work being done somewhere else on plutonium. Even in the same laboratory, each person should know only about his particular experiment; he should not know what was going on in the next room. The rule applied to everybody, even the highest-ranking scientists and engineers. With the nation at war, they were not inclined to ask probing questions about military secrets anyway. But even if they did, strict orders had been issued that they were to be told only as much as they needed to know.

The advantages of the system were obvious, and the instructions supporting it, issued by Roosevelt and supported by Stimson, General Marshall, Admiral Ernest J. King, Bush, Conant and Groves, were categorical. On the other hand, compartmentalization was criticized as bearing in itself the seeds of unfortunate mistakes, duplication of research and ridiculous exaggerations. Inevitably, in some cases, scientists might waste time and effort solving a problem that had already been solved in another laboratory. They did not know it, however, because they had not been permitted to exchange information.

Groves and his aides were well aware of the situation. Nevertheless, they were firmly determined to protect the secrecy of the Project and enforce the strictest rules of security in spite of protests and criticism from scientists. Groves had another reason for insisting on compartmentalization: he wanted to keep the scientists working strictly on their specific jobs and not "to establish a great university where they discuss their new ideas and try to learn more from each other."

There was only one possible way to reconcile the conflict between scientific communication and military secrecy: bring together, in one place, all scientists working on the actual problems of the bomb itself, and then let them exchange ideas and information as much as necessary. But they would have to be isolated from the outside world. Groves discussed the idea with Oppenheimer, whose own thinking went along very similar lines. Bush and Conant had already been asked for their opinion; both men agreed that all research on the weapon should be concentrated in one place.

By planning a unified bomb laboratory, Groves was nonetheless stepping for the first time outside the sphere of responsibilities originally assigned him. When he first received command of the Manhattan Project, the idea was that he would be mainly in charge of the construction and operation of plants producing fissionable material. He had no formal authority beyond this. But neither did anyone state that he should *not* assume responsibility for the new problems that would inevitably emerge. Gradually, quietly, Groves took authority for more and more decisions that had originally not been staked out for him. He was only applying his basic personal belief: "When in doubt, act!" Each step that remained unchallenged was going to be followed by another and longer step on the upward path leading to the ultimate success of the Project.

Having received the approval of the Military Policy Committee, consisting of Bush, Conant, Styer and Purnell, Groves made the decision to set up a bomb laboratory. There remained, however, the major problem of finding the right person to organize it and lead it successfully. The fact that Compton had assigned Oppenheimer to conduct preliminary theoretical research on the weapon did not constitute any obligation to select the Berkeley physicist as leader of the new program. The members of the S–1 Committee had all expressed the wish that Compton choose an eminent scientist for the theoretical research, one with enough authority and prestige to attract the best people available and coordinate their work.

Unfortunately, though, none of the Nobel laureates could be spared. Compton already was doing more than his share; without the personal leadership of Lawrence, the electromagnetic process would have hardly any chance of success; Urey was a chemist, and this was primarily a job for a physicist. And it would be questionable to assign the most secret military program to a foreign-born citizen or refugee like Fermi, who anyway was badly needed in Chicago.

In the absence of a more important figure, Groves was in favor of selecting Robert Oppenheimer. At each contact, his respect for the scientist's intelligence and for his grasp of the situation increased. Groves did not feel, however, that Oppenheimer was the ideal choice. He did not have any administrative experience and seemed to be too much of a purely theoretical academic scientist; his previous lack of interest in the nation's background and its history could also be considered a mark against him.

Neither Bush nor Conant was overly enthusiastic about selecting Oppenheimer. Compton and Lawrence also had their reservations about his capacity as a leader and administrator. But who else was there? Groves's position was straightforward. "Find me another Ernest Lawrence, and we'll appoint him! But where do you find such a man? With Oppenheimer, we at least have a first-rate theoretician and an extremely brilliant mind." Then he added, "As for the administration, *I* will see that it works!"

The days that followed, however, were days of delay for Groves. A new, highly disturbing element had appeared, one that made the decision even more difficult. The FBI had informed the Manhattan Project chief that it did not think that Oppenheimer, because of his background, should be used in the Project at all. The Manhattan District had its own security service, which worked very closely with J. Edgar Hoover's agents. The FBI, in accord with its usual policies, could give only information and advice — the final decision would remain Groves's. Since the case was too important to rely entirely on the conclusions of others, Groves, as he often did, read the complete file himself.

Oppenheimer's background was very interesting. Born in 1904, he was the son of a successful New York businessman who had come to the United States from Germany at the age of seventeen. The child grew up on then fashionable Riverside Drive, in a family with wide cultural interests. He was a precocious boy who, rather than playing with other children, collected butterflies and stamps, read poetry, and experimented with a microscope.

By the age of eleven, he had arranged his collection of minerals and was carrying on a wide correspondence, always by typewritten letter, with geologists in such a mature way that he was invited to deliver a lecture at the Mineralogical Club in New York City. When he arrived at the meeting in the company of his parents, no one could believe that the speaker of the day was the boy, not the father. But the lecture given by the eleven-year-old was a great success, and the delighted audience gave him an ovation.

Oppenheimer received his bachelor's degree *summa cum laude* at Harvard, then went abroad to study at Cambridge and at Göttingen, Germany, where he took his Ph.D. After a year's fellowship at Harvard and at the California Institute of Technology, Oppenheimer spent another year studying abroad, this time in Leyden and Zurich. On his return to the United States in 1929, he received invitations from several universities and accepted appointments as an assistant professor at both Pasadena's California Institute of Technology and Berkeley's University of California. For the next twelve years he taught theoretical physics, particularly quantum theory, nuclear physics and relativity, at the two schools.

Oppenheimer led an intensely intellectual life and paid little heed to social and political issues of the period. As he himself was later to say, describing those years: "My friends, both in Pasadena and in Berkeley, were mostly faculty people, scientists, classicists, and artists. I read very widely, mostly classics, novels, plays, and poetry; and I read something of other parts of science. I was not interested in and did not read about economics or politics. I was almost wholly divorced from the contemporary scene in this country. I never read a newspaper or a current magazine like *Time* or *Harper's;* I had no radio, no telephone; I learned of the 1929 stock-market crash only long after the event; the first time I ever voted was in the presidential election of 1936. To many of my friends, my indifference to contemporary affairs seemed bizarre, and they often chided me with being too much of a highbrow. I was interested in man and his experience; I was deeply interested in my science; but I had no understanding of the relations of man to his society."

What worried the FBI the most was Oppenheimer's past involvement with certain left-wing causes and friends. He had never been a Communist himself, but he had often been associated with members of the party, especially during the period of the Spanish Civil War. The security file on J. Robert Oppenheimer was full of details about his contributions to leftist organizations and also about each acquaintance who was a member of the Communist party. To the FBI and to the Manhattan District's own security service, then largely controlled by the War Department's counterintelligence, the dossier seemed much too disturbing. They would definitely refuse to issue formal clearance to a man considered a security risk, and they most certainly would not approve his assignment to the leadership of the most sensitive war project. The scientists on the Project, on the other hand, were not at all interested in Oppenheimer's political past. If they had some reservations about him, it certainly was not because of his earlier leftist associations.

The man who had to decide now whether Oppenheimer should be cleared and appointed as head of the bomb laboratory was General Groves, a man who from childhood on had suspected anything and anybody connected with the left wing, and who had always had a strong aversion to Communism. Groves — and for that matter, Marshall and Nichols, too — belonged to the category of conservative Americans who believed that any connection with Communist groups was not only unpatriotic but also showed very poor judgment and questionable intelligence.

An important decision had to be made, and it was for Leslie Groves to make it, without delay.

9

BACK AGAIN at his desk in Washington, General Groves turned his attention to the problem of procurement of crucial materials for the Manhattan Project. The Berkeley electromagnet gave him particular concern. Suppose that Lawrence's extravagant electromagnetic installations could be built on an industrial scale, where could the enormous amounts of copper be found that were needed for magnet coils and electrical conductors? With the wartime demand and scarcity of copper, it was simply impossible. Groves called in Lieutenant Colonel Nichols for a briefing on the copper situation.

"I think we've solved that particular problem," Nichols said with a broad grin. "Since copper is so hard to come by, Lawrence and his boys said, 'Why not use silver?' It was as simple as that — silver is an excellent conductor of electricity! But where to get such large amounts of silver? In the U.S. Treasury, of course. So we went to the Treasury."

Nichols related the unusual details of this procurement. He had received the task from Colonel Marshall in August, one month before Groves's appointment. Nichols was the right man for the delicate mission. Though self-confident and capable of being tough, the thirty-five-year-old West Pointer could also be tactful and diplomatic; he usually had his way with civilians. A highly intelligent man, he had had a fine education — the Point (where he ranked fifth in his class), a Cornell master's degree in engineering, a fellowship in Berlin's Technische Hochschule, and a Ph.D. from Iowa State University. Nichols had also developed a talent for articulate expression during a four-year tour of duty as an instructor at West Point.

In the Treasury Department the colonel was received by Under Secretary Daniel Bell, a tall, well-dressed man in his early fifties. The red, gold and white flag of the Treasury stood behind his massive walnut desk. The whole office had a solemn, impressive look of high Federal authority.

"Colonel Marshall has told us that you wanted to discuss an important matter," Bell said in a friendly voice. "What can I do for you?"

"We need large amounts of silver, Mr. Secretary."

"What for?"

"It's top secret, Mr. Secretary," Nichols said. "All I can reveal is that it's for an important war project directed by the Army Engineers. It has the very highest priority."

Bell did not ask questions. He and his department were used to dealing with the Army, and especially now in wartime they had learned to restrain their curiosity about people with the right credentials.

"How much do you need, Colonel?"

Nichols hesitated before replying, because no one knew for certain how much conductor material Lawrence would need for his yet uninvented, undesigned magnets. But after everybody had made guesses, Marshall and Nichols had decided upon a quantity that seemed reasonable, at least to start with.

"Six thousand tons of silver," Nichols answered firmly.

For a moment the friendliness disappeared from Bell's face. His eyebrows rose and his voice became icy. "Young man," he said, weighing each word, "*you* may think of silver in tons, but the U.S. Treasury will always think of silver in troy ounces."

This time Nichols found himself over his head. He hadn't the slightest idea what a troy ounce was. "Mr. Secretary," he said bravely, "does it really make any difference whether we call it tons or pounds or troy ounces, as long as you know the amount we need?"

Bell, the perfect gentleman, was shocked but much too polite to tell the young officer that it was like talking of strings and ropes to a schooner captain instead of sheets and lines. He made the distasteful compromise of converting, for the officer's benefit, the troy ounces to tons. He admitted that the Treasury had enough silver to satisfy the demand without difficulty, provided necessary authorization were given. The Treasury had already had some dealings with the military, who had borrowed silver for their Defense Plant Corporation, a government agency, to use as bus bars in aluminum plants. Treasury Secretary Henry Morgenthau was also favorable to any contribution to the war effort, even if the letter of the rules was not strictly respected.

Bell assured Nichols that the Manhattan Project could count on the Treasury's assistance and promised to find a solution as soon as possible. Immediately after Nichols had left his office, Bell asked for the Director of the Mint, Dr. Leland Howard, a chubby, pleasant man with tortoise-shell glasses who knew everything about silver. Howard did not need much explanation: he was already familiar with the lending of Treasury silver to the Defense Plant Corporation. The Treasury had no right, without Congressional authorization, to sell the silver that backs the national currency. But it could make available 47,000 tons of what was called "free" silver without asking the Senate Silver Committee. And there was no reason not to apply the same rules to the mysterious Manhattan District as to the Defense Plant Corporation.

Secretary Morgenthau approved Bell's decision after receiving a letter signed by Secretary Stimson. The silver was to be taken from the West Point Depository and to be returned in the six months following the end of the war. The agreement specified that no information would be given to the press on the removal of the silver, which would continue to figure on the Treasury's daily balance sheets.

The silver was removed by regular trucks hired in the name of the Defense Plant Corporation, which already had taken silver out of the West Point Depository and was therefore less likely to arouse suspicion. The bullion bars were delivered to the Defense Plant Corporation at Carteret, New Jersey, where they were cast into cylindrical billets. These were then sent to the Phelps Dodge Copper Products Company at Bayway, New Jersey, where they were extruded and rolled into strips 40 feet long, 3 inches wide, ⅝ of an inch thick. They were rolled into coils which, wrapped individually in paper, resembled automobile tires ready for shipment. Finally the coils went to Allis-Chalmers in Milwaukee for winding on the magnet casings.

The Army Engineers did not seem to know what they really wanted: every few days they changed their silver requirements, switching from one figure to another, with differences in thousands of tons. The Treasury people could not know that every day Professor Lawrence at Berkeley was modifying the design of his extravagant magnets; but it certainly sounded like poor organization and indecision.

Once the silver left the iron gates of the concrete, bunkerlike West Point Depository, it became the full responsibility of the Army, and a very detailed accounting system was organized. Once a month Colonel Nichols had to sign a statement that he still had all the silver — down to the hundredth of an ounce. Strict security precautions had to be taken; special guards were assigned to accompany each shipment and watch the precious metal while it was being processed. It was important that the Army's interest in silver remain secret. All shipments were therefore sent to nonmilitary addresses; officers wore civilian clothes when inspecting the plants; coded commercial bills of lading were used; and all correspondence and telephone conversations avoided the mention of the word "silver." The Army Engineers were taking no chances with security.

Nichols also gave General Groves a detailed report on uranium procurement. All American plans for producing fissionable material had been based on the assumption that large amounts of uranium could be readily obtained. Incredibly, however, the report from Colonel Nichols stated clearly that this metal ore was actually scarce, and almost impossible to

WESTFIELD MEMORIAL LIBRARY
WE____ ELD. N. J.

92469

find in the free world. Early in September 1942, Thomas K. Finletter, special assistant to the Secretary of State, was informed that a Belgian named Edgar Sengier had a large quantity of uranium ore that he had shipped out of the Belgian Congo. Sengier was president of the Union Minière du Haut-Katanga, the world's largest producer of uranium ore. He knew that the United States Government was looking for uranium and contacted Finletter, who in turn alerted Colonel Nichols. Finletter did not have the slightest idea why the Army Engineers would need uranium, but to the Manhattan District the tip was of capital importance. On September 18, with the consent of the S–1 Committee, Nichols went to see the Belgian in his New York office.

Sengier was an abrupt though very polite man in his sixties, with an unusually pale face and sparse hair. Nichols introduced himself, but before he was invited to sit down, he was asked, "Do you have any identification? You say you are from the military and yet you are wearing civilian clothes."

Nichols produced his identification card. The Belgian glanced at it and waved his visitor to a chair. "Now what do you wish to see me about, Colonel?"

"I understand you have some uranium, Mr. Sengier."

"Are you a contracting officer?" Sengier asked. "Too many people have been around here about this uranium, and they just want to talk. Do you have any authority to buy?"

"Yes," Nichols replied. "I have more authority, I'm sure, than you have uranium to sell!"

The Belgian thought for a moment, then demanded abruptly, "Will the uranium ore be used for military purposes? I will not sell it for commercial reasons, you see. Military use is the only one I'm interested in."

Nichols hesitated. He was in a quandary: how could he tell an alien anything about the country's most secret war project?

"You don't need to tell me how you'll use it," Sengier went on without waiting for an answer. "I think I know. All I want is your assurance as an Army officer that this uranium ore is definitely going to be used for war purposes."

"You have that assurance," Nichols said solemnly.

"Good, then let's make a deal, Colonel! My company, the Union Minière, has twelve hundred tons of uranium ore stored on Staten Island."

Nichols could hardly believe his ears. While they had been searching desperately for uranium all over the world, the precious ore had been lying unused in New York, right on their doorstep! Nichols was not only delighted but extremely puzzled. "Tell me, Mr. Sengier, how does this ore happen to be in the United States?"

"Very simple, really. In 1939 some European scientists informed me of uranium's potential military value. A year later, when Belgium fell, I had the twelve hundred tons of ore shipped to this country for safekeeping. It has been stored in steel drums in the Staten Island warehouse since 1940."

To Nichols it was now absolutely clear that the Belgian knew how the uranium ore would be used. Was he going to ask any questions about the Manhattan Project?

Sengier smiled as if he knew what was in the officer's mind. "Come now," he said briskly. "I suggest we come to terms on price."

In less than a half hour they had agreed on the conditions of the sale. The contract consisted of eight sentences, written in longhand, on a yellow pad. The price was fixed at $1.60 a pound, the lowest market price. Arrangements were also made to ship to the United States all uranium ore stockpiled above ground in the Congo.

After both men had initialed the agreement, Nichols said happily, "Well, I want to start hauling that uranium away tomorrow."

"Quite all right with me," Sengier replied. "Our lawyers can work out the formal contract later."

The lawyers completed the contract three months after Nichols and Sengier had initialed the agreement, long after the Staten Island ore had been turned over to the Manhattan District. One day shortly afterward, Sengier's lawyer came to Nichols's office and complained, "You know, Mr. Sengier forgot to charge you the commission. The price should have been 15 percent higher for the American market."

"That's just too bad!" Nichols replied. "You go back and ask Mr. Sengier whether he doesn't accept everything we initialed on that yellow pad!"

The lawyer shuddered. "God, I wouldn't have the nerve!"

The matter was closed, and the Manhattan Project had an ample supply of the ore needed to make the bomb.

To have uranium ore was one thing; to have purified uranium metal of the type needed for the atomic pile was an entirely different thing. Dr. Arthur Compton, head of the Chicago laboratory, remembered that the only place in the United States where a few very small ingots of fairly pure uranium were produced was Westinghouse's Lamp Division. Dr. Harvey Rentschler and Dr. John Marden, with whom Compton had collaborated in the past, had experimented with uranium for eventual use as filament for light bulbs.

Early in 1942, Compton visited the Westinghouse laboratory in Bloomfield, New Jersey. "What I'm asking you is very confidential," he told his former colleagues. "We need your help in making some uranium metal of unprecedented, nearly absolute purity. Believe me, the entire course of the war may now depend on you!"

"How many grams do you need?" asked Rentschler and Marden. "All we've produced so far amounts to a few small ingots of the size and shape of a cashew nut."

"That won't do at all. What I need is not several grams but several *pounds.* And that's only to begin with!"

The Westinghouse scientists gaped, and finally managed to say, "But that's absolutely impossible!"

Compton shook his head and looked at Rentschler closely. "Don't you remember that when you were my boss, your favorite maxim was 'Nothing is impossible'? You used to tell me, 'Formulae, equations and rules are made to be challenged; they exist only because some scientist or engineer challenged the rules that came before.' What has changed you?"

A few days later, strange activities began to take place on the roof and in the basement of Westinghouse's Building 6. Well-dressed, bespectacled gentlemen raided hardware stores around Bloomfield, buying every available garbage can and bringing them to the Lamp Division building. Large vats from a nearby brewery were rounded up and placed on the same roof. Since the elevator went only as high as the fifth floor, the heavy equipment had to be carried up the stairway to the roof on the narrow shoulders of a few Ph.D.'s. There, using simple automobile jacks instead of cranes, impatient research scientists set up the cans and vats in long rows. The work was carried on at a feverish pace. At the same time, in the basement of Building 6, furnaces were rapidly improvised out of ash cans as stern-faced guards were posted at each door to keep away the curious. One day even the firemen were turned away when the basement caught fire and white smoke poured out of the windows of the five-story lamp factory. "We have no fire here, it's a false alarm," the Westinghouse people said. The surprised fire chief pointed to the smoke. A few security men emerged from the building. "Go back to the station — there's no need to worry," they told the chief while at the same time discreetly flashing their badges. "We can handle this ourselves."

The overworked Westinghouse people knew that the hush-hush job they were doing was extremely urgent, but they did not know its ultimate purpose. Rather than wait for proper apparatus, they executed the whole operation of purifying the uranium under primitive, amateurish conditions, using any makeshift equipment that came to hand. The process they were carrying out so frenetically would normally be described as photosynthesis — using sunlight to speed up the reduction to metal of the greenish salt solution which filled the pails. But the scholarly Greek word seemed almost too pompous to describe the laundrylike activity atop this shabby New Jersey building — especially on a rainy day, when at the first few drops of rain scientists would rush to protect their precious vats, covering them with tarpaulin, with sheets, or even in some emergencies with their own shirts.

Through these efforts, Westinghouse scientists produced some uranium metal of a purity never before believed possible in industry — and in time for Chicago's atomic pile. Rentschler and Marden learned something else: that uranium was really not suitable for lamp filaments. As far as electric bulbs were concerned, all research and experiments proved utterly useless. But the erroneous assumption of some Westinghouse lampmakers had made possible the building of the first atomic pile.

WESTFIELD MEMORIAL LIBRARY
WESTFIELD, N. J.

10

THE STATELY board room on the ninth floor was impressive: fifty feet long, it had an ornamented plaster ceiling with three huge crystal chandeliers — the ceiling seemed as high as a cathedral's. Whoever had conceived the room possessed a dramatic sense of decor: the proportions were intimidating, and the enormous red carpet drowned all noise except the tick of the tall grandfather clock. At the large French windows, heavy red curtains trimmed with gold hid the dreary view of a Wilmington, Delaware, street.

The thirty members of the board of directors were seated around the glistening, thirty-three-foot mahogany table — an oval table shaped, appropriately enough, like the oval trademark of E. I. du Pont de Nemours and Company. On the walls hung life-size oil portraits of past presidents of the company: nine stiff-looking Du Ponts with strange first names, starting with *Eleuthère-Irénée* (*1802–1834*).

The thirty men had assembled for an important decision. In a few minutes they would declare yes or no to a momentous proposition. If the decision was yes, hundreds of millions of dollars would flow into the national economy, tens of thousands of people would change their jobs, huge construction projects would go up, chimneys would soon start smoking above new factories, and — who could say? — the whole course of the war might change for the better.

According to the original plan, the Boston construction firm of Stone and Webster was to handle all engineering work for the Manhattan Project. A contract had been signed with them for $78 million out of the $80 million available, and Marshall and Nichols had told their top men John R. Lotz and Russell Branch, "You are our engineers for everything. You are to give us every service we need. But after we learn just what has to be done, we'll take out pieces and hand them to other firms, too. The only assurance we give you is that when it's all parceled out, you will have a piece. We'll decide who does what."

The first doubts about the efficiency of such an overall contract came from Arthur Compton. Watching the Stone and Webster people working on the plutonium project in Chicago, he soon realized that they did not have the chemical know-how for some of the future operations. When Colonel Nichols came to Chicago on one of his weekly visits, Compton took him aside. "We'll need a chemical company," he said. "Stone and Webster are good for the other jobs, but if we succeed with the reactor, they'll get plutonium all mixed up with the other chemicals. How are they going to separate it? Will they ladle it out? No, it will have to be separated chemically." Compton thought a minute, then said wistfully, "We ought to have somebody like Du Pont."

"All right, we'll get Du Pont!" came Nichols's swift reply. "I've been working with them, I know these people."

Nichols called upon a man he knew — Thomas H. Chilton — one of the topflight technical men in Du Pont's Design Division. "We want someone," Nichols and Compton told him, "to come up with a design for separating an unknown element, plutonium, from a mess of other stuff. We want you to put some people on it."

"What will it cost?" asked Chilton.

"About a million dollars," answered Compton.

Nichols did not hesitate for a minute. "Let's sign a letter of intent for that," he said as he took out his pen.

In September 1942, Du Pont was thus signed up for the chemical separation of a yet unseen substance to be produced by still-to-be designed reactors. Two weeks later a furious Chilton burst into Nichols's office in Washington.

"You took advantage of me!" he shouted at the officer. "God, they don't even have this stuff yet! It's not in existence. How do you build a plant when you don't even know what the end product is going to be? Who's your boss?"

"We have a new boss — General Groves."

"Well," said the Du Pont engineer, "I want to see him about this. My company is not going to risk its neck on something we don't even know will work!"

General Groves not only had no intention of relieving Du Pont of this relatively limited task, but by that time he was seriously considering the company's involvement on a very big scale. Groves was beginning to realize that the Manhattan Project was going to be an enormously greater industrial undertaking than he had foreseen from statements by scientists and official committees. It seemed to him that present achievements were being unrealistically overestimated; that the tremendous technological and engineering problems were not understood; that it was naïve to think that a single engineering company — Stone and Webster — could possibly carry the whole burden, even with all the subcontractors they could get. In his search for ways to reduce pressure on the company, he thought that the whole plutonium project — construction, engineering and operation — should be assigned to another firm. And he believed that there was only one company in the United States capable of such a job: Du Pont.

Willis F. Harrington, a sixty-year-old senior vice-president of Du Pont and member of its executive committee, received a telephone call from Groves on October 30. The general apologized for being unable to come to Wilmington and asked Harrington to come to Washington to discuss a very important and secret matter. There was such urgency in the Army officer's voice that Harrington agreed to come the very next day and bring a Dr. Stine with him.

Charles M. A. Stine was the chief research man and technical adviser for Du Pont. A Lutheran clergyman's son, he had become professor of chemistry at the early age of twenty-two. Two years later, when only a handful of organic chemists were enrolled in American industry, he started to work for Du Pont. After a brilliant career he was now, thirty-six years later, the vice-president in charge of all research.

The discussions next day in Groves's office were very frank. Groves and Conant explained the secret project to the two Du Pont vice-presidents, insisting on the importance and urgency of the atomic weapon, and yet not concealing the enormous problems and uncertainties involved. They made it quite plain that they needed — rather, the country needed — Du Pont's help in developing plutonium processes and in building a whole new industry. As far as the other processes and the work on the bomb itself were concerned, Harrington and Stine were told nothing, except that they existed.

The Du Pont men did not in the least like what they heard. First of all, they were chemists, not physicists, and the proposed job required great experience in physics. Second, the whole undertaking sounded more like science fiction than a feasible industrial process. When Conant and Groves asked them for their opinion of the chances of building a large-scale operation in a short time, the two experienced technical administrators said frankly, "The entire project seems beyond human capability."

It was not the answer that Groves wanted to hear. "We are inclined to share your feelings," he said bluntly, "but we are going ahead anyway. The stakes are too high. We need the best advice and help we can get, and we thought we had come to the right place for it. In any case, until the process is proved unfeasible, the design, construction and operation will be carried through to the fullest extent of our ability."

Though still highly skeptical about the whole idea, Harrington and Stine nevertheless promised to gather more technical data from the

Chicago scientists, then submit the request to Du Pont's president Walter Carpenter and to its executive committee.

Stine went to Chicago and carefully studied the work being done on plutonium. A chemist with unusual industrial experience, and a thorough background in basic science, he knew what he was talking about when he met Dr. Compton and Colonel Nichols.

"I don't think you have a Chinaman's chance of getting this thing done in five years," Stine told them at the end of his visit. "And yet I don't see how the nation can afford *not* to try it. I just think it's too big, too difficult." Then he smiled ruefully and added, "If there's any company in the world that can do the plutonium end of it, it's Du Pont. But I'd prefer to have no part in it."

Stine returned to Wilmington to present his report to Walter Carpenter. The first thought that came to Carpenter's mind when he heard about the atomic project was "perpetual motion." To him, the idea of recovering the power of the atom and using it seemed as provocative, fascinating — and impossible — as the centuries-old dream of *perpetuum mobile*.

On November 10, when Groves asked the company officially to consider its involvement in the Project, Carpenter found himself in a dilemma. But he was impressed by Groves's opening remarks. "There are three basic military considerations involved in our work," said Groves, seated in a comfortable chair in Carpenter's plush office. "First, it's very possible that Germany will soon produce some fissionable material. We have no evidence to the contrary. Second, there is no known defense against a nuclear weapon. And third, if we succeed in time, we'll shorten the war and save tens of thousands of American lives."

As the general spoke, Walter Carpenter was studying him with great interest. Intelligent, he thought; dedicated, aggressive, sincere — and tough. The two men were completely different in appearance. The thin, suave president of Du Pont was an elegantly tailored gentleman of fifty-four, with gaunt cheeks, a sallow complexion and an impressive, shiny skull. There was a certain distinction emanating from the courteous smile in his intelligent eyes, from the way he gestured with his well-manicured hands. Opposite him, the bearlike Army officer, with his mustache and his thick curly hair, talked bluntly, almost ignoring the amenities. They had never met before. But strangely, these two men, so different in manner and appearance, trusted each other immediately and completely.

Walter Carpenter had many reasons for not wanting to engage his company in such a risky undertaking. Du Pont was already deeply involved in war production, building new plants, producing explosives, supplying the armed forces with numerous chemical products. The new atomic project sounded much too hazardous, with many colossal obstacles and little chance of success. To accept such a perilous adventure in a field in which Du Pont had had no experience whatsoever would be to put the company's prestige in grave jeopardy. There would be no time for pilot plants, no time even for extensive laboratory experimentation; a whole new industry would have to be created.

Groves was aware of Carpenter's reluctance. "The Government considers the Project to be of the utmost national urgency," he said firmly, "and this opinion is shared by President Roosevelt, Secretary Stimson and General Marshall."

"And you, General — you personally — do you agree?"

Groves was surprised by the question but answered without hesitation, "Absolutely and without reservation!"

There was another reason for Du Pont's lack of enthusiasm. The memory of the Nye Committee investigation in 1934 was still fresh in the minds of the company's directors, and the manufacturing of munitions was still an extremely touchy subject for them. They could not forget the violent campaign against all arms manufacturers during the 1930s when the Du Pont family had been called "merchants of death."

Set up under Senator Gerald P. Nye, a North Dakota Republican, the Senate Munitions Investigating Committee was an expression of the great wave of pacifism that spread over much of the Western world in the years following the First World War. Disillusionment about everything military took on dramatic proportions in the United States, particularly in the liberal press. The economic hardship caused by the Depression pushed this feeling to a new high. Twenty-five thousand youths staged a Student Anti-War Strike and pledged themselves not to support the Government in any future war.

Three Du Pont brothers had to take the witness stand and testify in public hearings. The brother who stole the show was blue-eyed, pipe-smoking Irénée, a calm man of unshakable self-confidence. He did not feel his company had anything to apologize for. "If we had not shipped powder to France and England," he told the committee, "the possibilities are that Germany would have won the war, and we would have been taken next and become a German colony."

The Nye Committee hearings revealed the enormous profits made by Du Pont in World War I. "Until 1917 it was Europe's war, not ours," Irénée Du Pont replied in his company's defense. "We couldn't be expected to risk money on plant expansion for the sake of other countries. But when the United States entered the war, we did have the production facilities ready because we had been expanding during the previous three years." The argument was valid, and Du Pont came out completely cleared. But war profit-making nevertheless remained an unpleasant part of Du Pont's public image.

Walter Carpenter was particularly aware of this; few men had contributed as much as he to the transformation of Du Pont in the period between the wars. During the remarkably swift rise which had brought this Pennsylvanian to the presidency of Du Pont, a position that only members of the Du Pont family had occupied before him, Carpenter had in effect grown up with the company. At the early age of thirty-one, he became a member of the company's executive committee. World War I had just ended, and the men on the committee then felt that the company needed younger blood in the executive echelon. They decided to step down and were replaced by a group of younger men, one of whom was Carpenter.

In the twenties and early thirties, the entire American chemical industry was behind Europe's and Du Pont had only one department: explosives. Many chemical products — the badly needed dyes, for example — were imported from Germany. In terms of development, the German chemical industry was perhaps fifty years ahead of that in the United States. Only at this time did Du Pont begin to expand into fields other than explosives.

Many of these new products came through the Development Department. Carpenter was lucky enough to be in this department in the years of Du Pont's great transformation from a purely explosives company to a broadly diversified chemical company. After being Du Pont's director of development, Carpenter was named treasurer and by 1940 rose to the presidency, largely through his financial acumen. By then the Amercian chemical industry, as a whole, was rapidly catching up with Europe's, and Du Pont considered itself equal or superior to the best European firms.

"General, I'm afraid we must go and join the members of our executive committee," Carpenter said as he stood up to lead the way. The conference was interrupted, and yet Groves still did not understand whether his polite host had said yes or no.

Du Pont's eight top executives were waiting for their president and General Groves, who with his associates — Compton, Nichols and Norman Hilberry — took places next to them in leather armchairs around a polished conference table. After being introduced, Groves went straight to the heart of the problem, repeating the points he had just made to the president.

The meeting was not a long one. Each member already knew the pros and cons of the proposal — or rather, the long list of cons, because there were few things to be said in favor of Du Pont's involvement in the risky venture. Walter Carpenter added a new argument: nobody knew how great the danger of explosion would be if a reactor were built. Supposing the chain reaction worked, would it be possible to control and check it? How sure could they be that a terrible conflagration would not destroy the whole plant, even the whole surrounding area? "We'll have thousands of people working for us, perhaps tens of thousands," he said. "An explosion would be catastrophic."

Compton and Hilberry, the only physicists present, admitted that at such an early stage no 100 percent guarantee of safety could be given; but they assured the committee that all scientific theory, calculations and experiments virtually excluded the possibility of a disaster. Du Pont nevertheless asked that in view of the totally unpredictable hazards involved, the Government provide equally unusual protection against all costs, expenses, claims and losses that might be sustained by Du Pont in the event of an explosion. Groves accepted this condition without hesitation. But he and his friends still did not know whether their mission was successful or not, even when the report of Du Pont's brief investigation in Chicago was read.

The comments of the Du Pont men who had inspected the progress of the Chicago group were hardly encouraging. The graphite pile, in their opinion, might possibly work, though it had yet to be demonstrated. But the program was hampered by a lack of engineers and an inadequate supply of metal. Furthermore, the Du Pont experts did not believe that any valuable data would be obtained from the first two models of piles; they also doubted that Pile No. 3 would work as designed. The several proposed cooling systems presented enormous problems, too. In case the graphite pile failed altogether, the heavy-water method of separation was recommended; yet this would prove very expensive — four heavy-water plants would have to be constructed at once, each plant costing $10 million.

The final recommendation of the executive committee was hardly the logical conclusion to the long litany of doubts and fears. The men of the Manhattan Project were already getting discouraged when Walter Carpenter interrupted a long silence. "However great the problems are, gentlemen," he said quietly, "I think we really have no alternative but to go ahead. After all, we are an American company; we have a long history of contributing to the country's defense in times of emergency. It is a record that goes back more than a hundred and fifty years. . . ."

Carpenter paused for a moment; nothing would have embarrassed him more than to appear overly emotional. "General Groves has described the extreme importance and urgency of the project," Carpenter continued in a businesslike tone. "The first nation to solve this problem could force a victorious end to hostilities. Since the Germans are seeking to solve the same problem — and since, in the opinion of the Government, Du Pont's assistance is needed — we cannot refuse to attempt the work. Therefore we will propose acceptance of the contract, and the Company's board of directors will then make the final decision."

Groves and his aides felt tremendously relieved. They had leaped the first hurdle; they were confident of the committee's ability to convince the board of directors.

"We'll recommend one condition," continued Carpenter, thinking back to the public outcry against Du Pont at the time of the Nye Committee hearings. "We wish to make no profit out of this. We'll sign a contract for a fixed fee of one dollar if the Government agrees to pay all costs of the project. And any patent rights developing out of the work should become the property not of Du Pont, but of the U.S. Government."

Several days later, Carpenter and the thirty members of the board met to make their momentous decision. As he spoke, a folder lay on the table in front of him; it contained all the Manhattan Project's top-secret technical information. Groves had felt that the participation of Du Pont was of vital importance to the Project; he had therefore entrusted Carpenter with the responsibility of using his discretion and divulging the Project's ultimate purpose — building an atomic bomb — if the board members insisted on knowing it.

Carpenter informed the board that the President and the country's highest officials considered the Manhattan Project essential to victory. It was a top secret, he said, but any board member had the right to ask questions before voting — the documents were all there. He also stressed that the undertaking was so risky and uncertain that its possible failure might well destroy the company. Then, speaking for the executive committee, Carpenter strongly recommended Du Pont's acceptance.

The Du Pont directors were no more patriotic — and no less so — than most Americans. At the same time they were shrewd investors who had never put a dollar into a corporation before studying all the details. They had on many occasions made difficulties for the executive committee over much smaller issues. By training they were hardheaded businessmen who felt a keen responsibility to their stockholders. And now they were being asked to approve a venture that was supremely risky and whose details remained unknown.

Yet nobody asked a question; the folder with the top-secret documents remained unopened. Then the thirty capitalists voted yes, in unanimity, to a proposal that might destroy their company.

The meeting on the eighteenth floor of Kodak Towers in Rochester, New York, had lasted nearly all day. The chief executives of Eastman Kodak and their two Army visitors — General Groves and Colonel Marshall — had left the conference room only to go to lunch, then immediately returned.

Groves was determined to get Tennessee Eastman, a subsidiary of the company, to operate the future electromagnetic plants at Oak Ridge, but the idea of a new war project did not seem to appeal to the Kodak executives at all.

Groves, impressed by the job they were doing at the Holston Explosives Plant near Kingsport, Tennessee, had first phoned James C. White, Tennessee Eastman's general manager, to make the proposition. White declined the offer, saying that his corporation did no initial research for new processes. But Groves assured him that all he needed was industrial experience. "We're not looking for scientists. We have so many Ph.D.'s now that we can't keep track of them." But White obviously could not make the decision without consulting the home office, and he arranged a meeting for Groves in Rochester.

Eastman's executives had listened patiently to Groves's forceful talk, which was a cross between a science course in uranium separation and a lecture on patriotism and civic duties. Most of them thought that the company was already overextended in war work and simply could not provide the necessary personnel. "The operation won't need more than twenty-five hundred people," insisted Groves.

The most vigorous questioning came from Eastman's British-born director of research, Dr. Charles K. E. Mees, the only scientist present with any previous experience in the field. A man of strong convictions, he argued that the project was scientifically very uncertain — risky, to say the least. Mees had worked on radioactivity before, and his colleagues would naturally rely on his opinions in this scientific field.

The group appeared tense and undecided when the chairman, F. W. Lovejoy, turned to the two officers. "Gentlemen, it's a grave decision for us. Would you mind stepping out for a moment? We would like to discuss this among ourselves."

The officers left the room, and in the corridor outside they gazed at the panoramic view of Rochester and Lake Ontario through the window. "How do you think I did?" Groves asked Marshall.

Marshall looked worried. He hesitated, then said, "It wasn't too bad, General. But how did you manage to mispronounce, time after time, the same word — the key word! For Heaven's sake, it's 'isotope,' not 'isotrope'! It wouldn't have mattered if there had been no scientists present, but that Dr. Mees squirmed each time you said 'isotrope.' I don't think your scientific explanations convinced him . . ."

When the officers were called back into the board room, Eastman's president T. J. Hargrave announced gravely, "If the Government insists, we can do nothing but accept the assignment. Perley Wilcox, the head of Tennessee Eastman, and Jim White, our general manager, will be in charge of the operation."

One of the members shook his head grimly. "You two have just put us in the biggest trouble we've ever been in!"

As they left the building, Groves and Marshall were beaming. "How did you say it again?" the General asked mischievously. "It's not isotrope, but isotope, eh?"

WESTFIELD MEMORIAL LIBRARY
WESTFIELD, N. J.

The Untold Story of the Making of the Atomic Bomb

II

Muscular and tanned, the boys of the Los Alamos Ranch School were the picture of health as they rushed noisily out of class at the sound of the three-o'clock bell. In spite of the cold November wind, they all wore shorts: the founder and director of the school, Ashley Pond, was an enthusiastic advocate of the vigorous outdoor life and did not even believe in heated sleeping quarters. Each boy at the school was assigned a horse, and swimming, ice-skating and pack trips along the Yemez River occupied a major part in the education of students, who were most of them sons of rich Easterners.

A military car drew to a stop in front of the porch of the main building, an unusual log structure in which hand-hewn timbers were used like Greek temple columns. The four men who stepped out did not look like visiting parents, and after the first stares of curiosity, the schoolboys quickly lost interest. Both General Groves and Major J. H. Dudley were in uniform, but officers were not an unusual sight in those war days. The appearance of the other two men — Dr. Oppenheimer and Dr. Edwin M. McMillan — held nothing intriguing for the boys.

The four men inhaled the fresh mountain air deeply as they looked around. The fifty log cabins of the Ranch School were scattered amid pastures and cropland. It was a lovely place, this clearing in the pine trees on top of an isolated mesa eighty-five hundred feet above sea level. Against the horizon, the broken line of high mountains rimmed the vast circular plateau, which was shaped like a gigantic volcanic crater that had been eroded millions of years ago into mesas separated by deep canyons. A few miles off, the surprisingly unimposing Rio Grande River — not at all grand at that point — wove its way through a dry, rocky bed.

When the group left Albuquerque that morning, they had had no intention of visiting Los Alamos. Their original destination was the area around Yemez Springs, situated north of Albuquerque and recommended as a site by the local Army engineering office. Before choosing New Mexico, some consideration had been given to two localities in California, but both were deemed inadequate. One of the main requirements for the site of the future bomb laboratory was isolation, and California's large and growing population would have made secrecy very hard to maintain. Since 1929 Oppenheimer had had a ranch high in the Sangre de Cristo Mountains of New Mexico; he was well acquainted with the area and had warmly recommended it to Groves. Major Dudley had made an extensive field search of the whole Southwest and had come to the same conclusion.

The Yemez Springs Valley they had visited in the morning did not look right. It was too narrow, and Oppenheimer found it gloomy and depressing; he felt that few scientists would like to come and live at the bottom of a canyon where the sun rarely shone. If the laboratory intended to attract many of the leading physicists and chemists of the world, some thought had to be given to the attractiveness of the surroundings.

Groves found fault with it, too. It was an Indian settlement of little farms, and the general immediately thought of the delicate problem of displacing such families and the unfavorable publicity that would ensue. Some of the other requirements were missing too, and the disappointed group decided to drop this location. Before going back, Groves turned to Oppenheimer. "I don't want to waste the day," he said. "Let's look some more. Do you have any idea where we might find something?"

"Well, we can go back to Albuquerque by way of the Los Alamos Ranch School, and you might be interested in that. It's about fifty-five miles from my ranch over a very rough trail. We've often ridden across by horse, so I know the place."

They crossed the mountain range in the direction of Santa Fe, stopped for a sandwich on the roadside, and arrived at the top of the mesa on which Los Alamos was situated. Groves liked it immediately. The flat green mesa, separated from the rest of the plateau by the vertical walls of two deep canyons, offered perfect isolation. The sunny site was as pleasant as a mountain resort, with a magnificent view reaching to the Jemez Range and the peaks of Sangre de Cristo.

The Ranch School buildings could provide living accommodations for the first scientists to come. Groves asked about the water supply, which seemed to be enough for what their needs would be. The only serious problem was road communication; there was only one poor road leading to Santa Fe, twenty miles to the southeast. This posed the important question of whether heavy laboratory equipment could be transported there. Groves took a good look at the road to see if it could be improved and if it was possible to do this without tremendous alterations that would consume precious time. He had had enough experience with road construction to conclude, after a half hour's reconnaissance, that improvement was possible even though the steep gradients and rough terrain would pose problems. Another advantage of the site was that no population would have to be relocated other than the teachers and the students at the school. But what if the owners refused to sell it? Luckily, the school was in financial difficulty and the owners were quite happy to close it down for a good price.

Oppenheimer was pleased with Groves's favorable reaction to the site. Ever since he had discovered New Mexico at seventeen, he had been in love with these mountains. It would be a good place to work, he thought.

At this point, Oppenheimer still did not know definitely whether he would be the Project's leader or only one of the principal members of its team. The hesitation over his appointment had lasted for weeks, and the situation was still confused. But during this time Oppenheimer had gained Groves's admiration as a scientist and as a man. In the security dossiers the boss of the Manhattan Project had found no reason to doubt Oppenheimer's loyalty to the United States. To Leslie Groves, anybody who got involved in Communist-supported causes was a fool. But he remembered that during the Depression years and during the Spanish War, most liberals in America had shown sympathy for pro-Communist causes. They saw nothing wrong with Communism and no reason to fear it. Groves considered Oppenheimer a brilliant scientist and humanist but politically naïve.

According to regulations Oppenheimer, because of his background, ought not to receive clearance for the most classified work of all. But the cases, Groves felt, could not be judged under standard regulations. Oppenheimer was an exceptional man, a scientist very badly needed for the Project, and, in any case, he already knew a great deal. All through his career Groves had relied on his ability to judge people. After reviewing the qualifications of the several other possible candidates, he concluded that Oppenheimer was the right man to lead the new laboratory. And because it was impossible for a man with such a dossier to get security clearance through normal channels, the general took the responsibility for ordering that Dr. Oppenheimer be cleared immediately. The order, which was in no way a mere suggestion, caused consternation among security officers of the Manhattan District; they tried to have it changed. But for General Groves, once he had made his decision, the matter was closed.

Colonel Marshall and Lieutenant Colonel Nichols, who knew in detail all the objections against the Oppenheimer appointment, agreed whole-heartedly with General Groves. The official letter to the security service, demanding the scientist's clearance, had to be written by Marshall in his capacity of District Engineer. Nichols was in his office when Marshall, just before leaving on a trip, dictated the letter to his secretary. When she finished typing the letter, she realized that Colonel Marshall had already left and forgotten to sign it.

Nichols knew that waiting a few days until Marshall's return would delay issuance of the clearance. It was desirable to avoid all delay in view of the violent opposition of the security people. He had full authority to act on behalf of Marshall — they had exchanged official letters to that effect. Nichols did not hesitate. He took the letter over to a light table and then, using an order that Marshall had signed, he traced his superior's signature above the typewritten name and sent the letter off immediately.

Two days later it was returned with this remark by the chief of the security service: "Because the matter of Dr. Oppenheimer's security clearance is so serious, we carefully examined the letter here enclosed. We have suspicions that the signature is forged. Please confirm."

Nichols dictated a new letter, this time under his own name, confirming that the first letter was quite in order.

12

At the Chicago railroad station Arthur Compton hailed a taxicab and gave directions: "To the university, please, and drop me on the west side of Stagg Field."

"Very bad wind today," the cabbie said in an attempt to start a conversation, but Compton, absorbed in his thoughts, was not listening. His mind was still in Washington, and the voices of General Groves and Dr. Conant were still echoing in his ears. He remained silent until the cab stopped in front of the crenellated towers which rose above the stands of Stagg Field.

"Too bad they don't play football here any more!" said the driver. "I've heard President Hutchins doesn't like football."

Stagg was a concrete structure partly covered with ivy, and under the stands there were lockers and shower rooms for the teams, and also a racquets court.

The men who greeted Compton on his arrival could easily have been taken for coal miners or for some kind of black-face minstrels. Not only were their hands completely black and shiny, but their faces, shirts and trousers were covered with fine black powder. It also covered the floor of the court, making it as slippery and polished as a dance floor. The activity these men were absorbed in was hardly intellectual: they were merely carrying blocks made of graphite and piling them in the center of the court, in orderly layers the same way bricklayers build a wall.

A few of the group leaders surrounded Compton in a corner of the room.

"We just had a meeting of the S–1 Committee," Compton informed them, "and things are going to move faster now. I told them that we are going to try it right here on the campus, and that we can't wait any more for the Argonne Forest building* to be ready."

"How did they take it? Were they scared?"

"You should have seen it! When I told them what we were preparing to

---

* The Argonne National Forest, twenty miles from Chicago and named after the famous World War I battle, had been selected as the site for the first piles. The building was to have been completed by the end of October 1942, but labor difficulties had caused a delay.

perform here, in the middle of Chicago, Conant's face turned white. And Groves didn't like it at all. He rushed to the nearest phone to ask the Army people whether Argonne could be ready. But they didn't try to stop us. They're as much in a hurry as we are. And I explained, of course, that the risk is really very small, and that Fermi is positive now that it will work."

It was true that Enrico Fermi had reached the positive conclusion that a chain reaction could be produced and kept under control. Two weeks earlier, at the beginning of November, he had informed Compton that all calculations and theoretical work had been checked and rechecked, and that the danger of an accident or an uncontrollable reaction was practically nil. Not until then did Compton give the green light for the construction of the pile on the university campus.

But in spite of the assurances given by a man of genius — and everybody in the Chicago group considered Fermi one of the few true geniuses of modern physics — Compton was faced with a great responsibility. No matter how small the risk, the danger of an accident could not be ruled out completely. How could he be absolutely sure that some unknown phenomenon would not appear when the chain reaction began? All precautions would be taken, of course, and the reaction would be performed very slowly, step by step, with the control rods released an inch at a time. An atomic explosion was not possible — unless all the science, the mathematics and the logic of the best brains in the Chicago group were completely wrong. And yet some unexpected radioactivity, for instance, or some effect that had never been observed before?

In taking such a risk right on the grounds of the Chicago campus, Compton knew that his duty was to ask the permission of the university's president, Robert Hutchins. But he also knew it would be unfair to ask Hutchins to take the responsibility for an experiment when the background, the theory, and the chances of success were completely unknown to him. It was obvious that the president's answer, under the circumstances, would be no. The man in Chicago who would bear this responsibility was the head of the Metallurgical Laboratory himself. And Compton took it.

He had another reason to be in a hurry with this experiment. November was the critical month when it had to be decided which one of the proposed methods for producing bomb material should be abandoned.* Groves and Conant had just appointed a Reviewing Committee with the

---

* After discarding the centrifuge method and selecting the graphite pile (rather than the heavy-water reactor), the Manhattan Project concentrated efforts on *three* of the original five methods for producing fissionable material: gaseous diffusion, the graphite pile for producing plutonium, and the electromagnetic process.

task of reappraising the entire S–1 Project. In large measure this had been done because of Du Pont's feeling that they had been assigned the worst, most thankless task in the Manhattan Project. With the idea of showing them that the Berkeley and the Columbia methods were as difficult as the plutonium project, three Du Pont engineers were invited to become members of the Reviewing Committee. Du Pont, however, had already accepted the job.

For its chairman, Conant proposed Dr. Warren K. Lewis, famous for his capacity to evaluate chemical processes and recognized as the leading authority in the country. Groves agreed immediately, aware of the prestige Lewis had among industrial chemists.

Compton was upset and irritated by the report that Du Pont vice-president Dr. Charles Stine had made after studying the work of the Chicago group for a few days. "There is not more than one chance in a hundred that it can lead to anything useful in this war," he had told General Groves. The Lewis committee was due in Chicago on November 26, and their first question was going to be: "Is a self-sustained chain reaction possible? Can you prove it?"

Compton feared that unless the Chicago group made a uranium pile work in the next few weeks, before General Groves could hear the final conclusions of the Lewis committee, the Project would not receive full support. Priority might be given to other methods; the Chicago scientists would have to spend many more months trying to convince anyone of the merits of their project.

Construction of the Chicago reactor called Chicago Pile One (CP–1) started on November 7, 1942. There was nothing ceremonial about it. A couple of men finished sweeping the rubberized canvas that was to serve as the floor of the construction. Somebody shouted jokingly, "Well, Enrico, why don't you lay the cornerstone?" Fermi grabbed a graphite brick and, with a grin, placed it in one corner.

The structure, designed by Fermi, Walter Zinn and Herb Anderson, was extremely simple in appearance. It consisted of lumps of uranium, spaced 8¼ inches apart by graphite blocks. The major problem was the procurement of large quantities of materials possessing the high degree of purity necessary. Forty thousand graphite blocks were needed, each one 4⅛ inches wide and deep and 16½ inches long. Each layer of solid graphite blocks alternated with a layer of graphite blocks in which holes had been bored for pieces of uranium. According to the design, the pile had to be shaped approximately in a spherical form, about 24 feet in diameter. The structure was partially supported by a wooden cradle, so that the graphite structure could be built as a sphere, thus saving perhaps 20 percent of the material.

) 70

Obtaining huge quantities of high-grade graphite had been the special task of Norman Hilberry. The degree of purity required was unheard of; such graphite was not being produced anywhere except in minuscule quantities for electrodes, and the Chicago scientists needed tons and tons.

For two years Leo Szilard had been badgering the graphite companies to try to turn out pure graphite. The Speer Carbon Company in St. Mary's, Pennsylvania, with whom he had been working, had discovered that by using petroleum coke they could get a purer graphite than by using mineral cokes, which contained boron — something that had to be kept out, since it absorbs neutrons. Speer succeeded in making some better graphite, but the output was only half as much as a furnace normally produced.

Since Speer had only a few furnaces, Hilberry went to the National Carbon Company, a subsidiary of Union Carbide, to see if they could make the stuff in quantity. Union Carbide was already heavily booked up building electrodes for the production of aircraft fuel and for the electric steel furnaces. Even so, Hilberry went to the company's offices in New York City and spoke to John Nolan, manager of development for National Carbon. After describing what kind of graphite he needed, Hilberry apologized for not being able to give any concrete details about the project other than to say that it was the most important war project of all.

"Well, how much do you need?" Nolan asked.

"To start with, we can get by with two hundred and fifty tons of graphite — of the utmost purity — but then we'll need much more later." Nolan was left speechless. "I know it's a messy business to use petroleum coke," Hilberry went on. "It will cut your capacity by half, but this condition is a *must* if we're to get the purest type of graphite. Another thing: we will have to get the graphite as soon as possible — by next week."

"But it takes us six weeks to make a batch of the stuff!" Nolan exclaimed.

Hilberry nodded gravely. "I know, but that's too long. If you need priorities, I can give you an A—priority right now. If you have to have one of those special X—priorities, I'll have it for you tomorrow."

Nolan was stunned to hear the size and difficult requirements set forth by the scientist. "I think we'd better talk to Harry Drevinstet," he said weakly. He rose from his chair and escorted Hilberry down the hall to the office of the Union Carbide executive in overall charge of graphite production.

After hearing what Hilberry wanted and the priorities he could obtain, Drevinstet was no less stunned; he suggested that they lunch the same day with a company vice-president at the old red-brick Murray Hill Hotel at Fortieth Street and Park Avenue. There, over a meal of the hotel's famous corned beef and cabbage, Hilberry again stressed the supreme importance of his project. At the end of lunch, the three Carbide men, now completely persuaded, agreed to do everything possible to produce the necessary graphite.

When Hilberry returned to Chicago, his secretary stopped him at the office door and said, "Washington has been trying to get you for hours! You're to call back some man on the War Production Board."

But even before Hilberry could put in the call, the telephone rang again; it was the same WPB official. "Professor, I understand you were in New York yesterday visiting the National Carbon Company," he said. "I think you ought to know that nobody slept in New York last night — they sat up all night trying to rework their production schedules. They had me on the phone the whole morning. It was a big jolt, you understand, to have this new demand for graphite. There's only so much capacity, and when you told them two hundred and fifty tons, you just took the wind out of their sails."

"Well, that's just a starter," Hilberry replied calmly. "If the first shipment of two hundred and fifty tons of graphite does what I think it will do, we'll soon be asking for five-thousand-ton lots, not two-hundred-and-fifty-ton lots." The WPB man was silent for a moment, then said, "Something is going to have to be done about graphite production then. We just don't have that capacity." Then, just before hanging up, he added, "There's one other little matter, Professor. Would you please let *me* handle priorities?"

"Of course. I don't know much about priorities anyhow."

"That's what I thought! You don't seem to know that until a higher priority order is filled, all the other orders have to wait. The highest priority that has been given for graphite so far has been a C. When you told them in New York that you would give them an A–priority on the spot, and an X the next day, you turned the entire graphite business upside down!"

Transportation of graphite from the railroads to deserted Stagg Field caused some difficulties. For security reasons, covered vans had to be used. One day a full load was delivered, but when the empty truck was leaving the field, it rode too high for the arches of the masonry fence and crashed. The van lost its top and the drivers declared that they would refuse to go through the gate from then on. In order to placate them, Professor Zinn personally led a commando of scientists armed with sledgehammers to make more headroom through the brick entrance.

Earlier experiments had proved that the air contained in the graphite had a bad effect on the reaction. So the builders of the pile decided to assemble the whole structure inside a sealed balloon-cloth bag, the air from which had to be evacuated when the reactor was ready to operate.

People at the Goodyear Tire and Rubber Company in Akron, Ohio, thought that Herbert Anderson was a harebrained young fellow when he came to them to order a balloon. He wanted a square balloon, and was very fussy about its specifications. Goodyear, which had had extensive experience in building rubberized balloons for the armed forces, tried in vain to convince the frail young scientist that square balloons would not fly well. "Why don't you have it round, like everybody else?" But Anderson, who had been forbidden to disclose the purpose of the bag, was obstinate. Several weeks later, the square balloon was delivered, neatly folded, to Stagg Field.

The huge bag, when unfolded, filled the racquets court. It was hung from the ceiling, with one side left open; then, in the center of the floor, a layer of graphite blocks was placed in a circle and braced by a wooden frame. So began the piling of the reactor.

The main difficulty was the procurement of uranium metal pure enough to satisfy the requirements. The metal simply did not exist in the needed quantities. The bulk was furnished by Westinghouse, whose primitive methods of production had been improved and speeded up considerably. Metal Hydrides Company had started their production of purified metal, and Frank H. Spedding was making some good metal at Iowa State College. But these few tons were not enough; Hilberry and Richard L. Doan were turning gray trying to find more of the pure metal. The pile could not wait. Then it was decided that purified uranium oxide could be used together with the metal itself. Walter Zinn developed a hand press for preparing the oxide in the required size and shape, and Mallinckrodt Chemical Company of St. Louis began to send the purified material to Stagg Field. Each uranium lump weighed six pounds. The more efficient uranium — the metal — was placed in the center of the pile where its effect would be greatest; the oxide was used for the outer portions.

Fermi had the overall direction of the building of the pile. It was his brainchild and he was the undisputed leader of the project. Two of his lieutenants, Walter Zinn and Herb Anderson, headed the two construction crews, and Volney Wilson was responsible for the instrument work. The details of construction were developed as the pile grew, and many problems had to be solved along the way.

As the Reviewing Committee's date of arrival drew near, work in the racquets court became hectic. Scientists left their laboratories in order to give a hand to the thirty technicians, mechanics and student helpers at Stagg Field. The two crews worked around the clock in the slippery, messy, drafty room. It was November and bitterly cold, but the scientists could not ask the university to run the heating system beyond the normal working hours for fear of attracting suspicion.

No one outside of Fermi's team knew about the crash program being carried out under the west stands, but curiosity was soon aroused by the increasing number of trucks that arrived at the field and unloaded material. Then, too, there were those voices and strange noises coming out of the racquets court day and night. One day Professor Allison called Walter Zinn in and said, "Can't you do something about the disturbance in the middle of the night? People in the neighborhood are calling up the chancellor of the university and complaining they can't sleep." Zinn protested that they didn't run saws or other noisy machinery at night. "It's not the machines," Allison said, "it's the singing." It turned out that the night crews were singing to relieve the boredom of their grueling work.

The graphite, which was received from the manufacturer in long bars with rough surfaces, had to be cut into bricks right on the spot and then smoothed off. The work was done with ordinary woodworking machines by the crew of an expert cabinetmaker, August C. Knuth, of Local 1922, United Brotherhood of Carpenters. Then holes measuring ¾ inch in diameter had to be drilled in half of the blocks to permit insertion of uranium into the graphite. Twenty-two thousand holes were drilled, at the rate of sixty to one hundred holes an hour.

The scientists who came to help Knuth found that the old shower room once used by football players was extremely gratifying after eight hours a day of machining graphite. But one shower would remove only the surface graphite dust. About half an hour after the first shower the dust in the pores of the skin would start oozing. "This is the cleanest dirt that has ever existed!" the scientists used to say, referring to the highly purified graphite.

Day after day the odd-looking pile, made up of enormous quantities of highly purified material, rose higher toward the ceiling of the racquets court. "If people could see what we're doing with a million and a half of their dollars, they'd think we were crazy!" the scientists used to say while scrubbing their blackened faces with soap in the shower room. "If they knew *why* we were doing it, they'd be sure we're crazy!" With practice, the scientists developed fairly good techniques for handling bricks, and their human chain looked almost professional. Some took particular pride in their adroitness in catching the slippery blocks while standing high up on the pile. Everyone had a few fingers smashed, but it wasn't considered cricket to talk about it.

Still, nobody knew for sure that the reactor would work as expected, whether a chain reaction would occur. Thirty small piles had already been built and torn down by Fermi, but these were subcritical models called "exponential" reactors, with just enough uranium and graphite to perform some experiments and testing but not enough to start a reaction. From such results the behavior of the future big pile had been calculated or simply guessed. Fermi— the "Pope"— was confident that it would work. His fellow scientists just took his word for it. Was Fermi really infallible?

It was all a matter of faith.

WESTFIELD MEMORIAL LIBRARY
WESTFIELD, N. J.

13

As THE TRAIN raced across the endless Midwestern plains, the four men locked in the double compartment were too absorbed in reading secret technical documents to look out the window. Time had passed slowly since the members of the Reviewing Committee had left Chicago Thanksgiving night, but the long ride to San Francisco would provide an excellent opportunity to familiarize themselves with the intricacies of Lawrence's electromagnetic separation method.

Warren K. Lewis was explaining a few points to Crawford Greenewalt, the handsome and reserved young Du Pont engineer. It reminded Lewis of the old days when he was Greenewalt's professor at MIT. The other two Du Pont men, Roger Williams and Tom C. Gary, were studying confidential papers describing the separation processes.

The Reviewing Committee which Lewis headed had started its investigation six days earlier in New York, where Urey, Dunning and Keith had explained the gaseous-diffusion method. They were impressed by what they saw at Columbia. There were still no results, of course, but as chemical engineers they saw the possibilities of the process. The committee left for Chicago convinced that the gaseous-diffusion method could be successful if enough time and effort were put into it. But the organization seemed to be weak — on one side, the Columbia scientists did not give the impression of being a united team; on the other, Dobie Keith's group of Kellogg men were doing their design and engineering research quite independently of the scientists.

Since the three Du Pont engineers had already inspected the plutonium project, the stopover in Chicago had been mostly for Lewis's benefit. Compton managed to have Hilberry finish a hundred-page report just in time for the visit. Very optimistic in tone, the report not only concluded that production of the necessary quantities of plutonium was feasible but also gave a precise timetable: 500 grams of plutonium in 1943; first bomb ready in 1944; regular production within the same year. But Compton and Fermi still could not demonstrate a chain reaction.

In a sense, Tom Gary was the most remarkable member of the Reviewing Committee. A peppy, practical, "give-'em-hell" type of man, he had achieved extraordinary prominence in his field despite very little formal education. At fifty-two he was head of the Design Division of Du Pont, and yet he did not have a doctor's degree, had never gone to college, and indeed did not even have a high school diploma!

Gary had quit high school in Virginia two months short of graduation, even though teachers had offered to help him through college. But since he had a mother and sister to help support, he went to work as a rodman on the Chesapeake and Ohio Railroad in Richmond. At nineteen he became masonry inspector of the railroad and was really resident engineer, too. In the next ten years he put in long hours of study at the night school run by the Virginia Mechanics Institute in Richmond. Then he went to Cleveland on another railroad job and from there changed to the Grasselli Chemical Company. When Du Pont bought Grasselli in 1928, the enterprising Virginian began to move up rapidly.

Tom Gary was a strong believer in hard work and continuous self-education. And he was very fortunate in being exposed to fine senior engineers, patient men who would take hours to explain things to him. He learned almost entirely by listening, asking questions and listening. Transferred to Du Pont's Engineering Department in Wilmington in 1932, Tom Gary, the self-taught engineer, made such an outstanding record that he was named head of the Design Department only seven years later. The fact that Gary, with no formal education behind him, now had to evaluate the work of some of the world's most eminent scientists did not disturb him at all. He was a hard-boiled, practical engineer, used to contact with Ph.D.'s and professors. And, speaking in his Virginian drawl, he would recognize his debt to them: "After all, that's how I learned everything I know. I've always stuck around the kind of men who, even when I asked a silly question, wouldn't give me a silly answer. They would patiently explain it to me, always."

On Saturday morning, November 28, the four tired members of the Reviewing Committee arrived in San Francisco and, after taking a shower, went to the Radiation Laboratory at Berkeley. Lawrence was waiting for them in the Cyclotron Building, surrounded by his staff and as excited as a general before battle.

Things had changed very much in the last few months. Lawrence's dream — the huge 184-inch cyclotron — was being transformed in order to adapt its magnets to Lawrence's calutrons. Two new vacuum tanks had been installed in May, and the controls of the ion source, of the power supply and the cathode's position were improved. After a satisfactory single beam had been obtained, Lawrence tried to install a source containing three beams in the same tank. But the arcs, 1.25 inches apart, were interfering with each other, and, in spite of incredible effort and painstaking adjustments, results were poor throughout the summer.

Several more young scientists in their twenties had joined the team since the beginning of the year,* but jobs and responsibilities were distributed in a very informal manner. Looking at Lawrence in shirt-sleeves, climbing the green slopes of Radiation Hill and surrounded by youths in dungarees and checked shirts, made the review committee think of a Boy Scout picnic rather than nuclear scientists on their way to work.

But few scoutmasters were as demanding as Lawrence. The rules of the game were very simple: E.O.L., as they called him, expected men and machines to perform continuously and at maximum capacity. Nothing less than their very best was good enough. He was as exacting with himself as with others. No one could figure out when he slept. His men worked, in different shifts, around the clock, and the "owl shift" was accustomed to seeing him appear in the Cyclotron Building in the early hours of the morning. "I couldn't sleep, so I thought I'd come over to see how things are going," he would say at 3:30 A.M.

Often he would go to the workshop in the middle of the night to give a hand to a discouraged mechanic. The door would fly open and E.O.L. would stride in, changing an atmosphere of gloom by the sheer force of his infectious optimism.

"How are you doing, George?" Lawrence would ask cheerfully, for he made a point of knowing the first name of every technician, every janitor.

"Not so good, Professor Lawrence. This damned thing won't work! We've been trying for days, but no results."

"Let me try!" E.O.L. would say, turning the machine up full speed. "What do you mean it doesn't work?" he would say excitedly as the machine, much to the technician's dismay, seemed on the point of falling apart. "You're doing a great job! Never mind if it breaks — we can correct that. But your design is terrific. You can't expect to succeed the first time, can you?" Smiles reappeared as Lawrence moved on to cheer up someone else who was stumped by a problem.

---

* The first Lawrence team working on the calutrons was composed of Robert Thornton, Byron Wright, Duane Sewell, Edward Lofgren, Elmer Kelly, Frank Oppenheimer, Fred Schmidt and many others — most of them graduate students still in their twenties. Wallace Reynolds acted as manager of the group: William Brobeck was in charge of engineering. Lawrence's closest associate and personal friend was Dr. Donald Cooksey, who acted as his confidant, troubleshooter and chief of staff. Cooksey, a quiet and selfless man, was so impressed by Lawrence's genius that he gave up his own scientific career, moved from Yale to Berkeley and devoted several years of his life to helping his younger colleague.

Always rushing things and living in an atmosphere of perpetual tension, Lawrence nevertheless managed to remain a surprisingly uncomplicated person, a family man who enjoyed spending time with his four children and who gave everyone the impression of being happy and at peace with himself. In spite of his restlessness, he loved to play host to friends at Trader Vic's restaurant and enjoyed a good game of tennis. His friends worried that he wouldn't be able to keep up the frenzied rhythm of his work indefinitely and that one day his health would break down. But Lawrence himself was not the worrying kind: responsibilities and hard work never seemed to disturb or frighten him.

Friendly as he was by nature, E.O.L. could also be very tough and impatient, especially when he thought that somebody wasn't giving himself 100 percent to the job. Such a man would be ruthlessly removed, even if Lawrence liked him. The young scientists were terrified of him at the beginning and, at the same time, full of admiration. He was their teacher, their idol in a sense: the inventor of the cyclotron atom-smasher and the Nobel Prize winner. More importantly, he was the laboratory's undisputed leader, a man who encouraged and helped them in their experiments — and gave them full credit for their work, even when the original idea had been his. During one of Groves's visits, a graduate student working on the cyclotron overheard the general say to Lawrence, "No, I think you're wrong on this point." Lawrence's young disciple, not believing his ears, later confided to friends, "I thought a bolt from heaven would strike the general down. But then Lawrence calmly answered, 'You may be right,' agreeing with Groves that he — the great E.O.L. — could be wrong. Well, I felt that part of my own personal world had collapsed."

Lawrence expected the utmost effort and performance from every-body — and all the time. Jimmy Vale, the frail, softspoken operator of the cyclotron, was a fairly good pingpong player in his off hours. One weekend Lawrence came by to play awhile. Vale had just finished beating another fellow, Joe McMorrow, very easily, and handed Lawrence his paddle. Lawrence lost, then asked Jimmy Vale to play him. After a heated game, Vale won by only a reasonable margin. Lawrence threw down his paddle angrily. "Now wait a minute, Jimmy!" he shouted in a furious voice. "You played Joe and you skunked him, and Joe beats me pretty easily. Then you play me, but you don't skunk me. You weren't trying your hardest! Why? You have no right to do that to me!"

If Lawrence took games seriously, he became profoundly serious when it came to science and anything concerning electromagnetic separation. The day of their arrival, the members of the Reviewing Committee spent hours listening to Lawrence's vivid explanation of the method. There was no doubt in his mind that one day it would work, and certainly large amounts of uranium–235 could be produced by it, if not very economically. Bursting with optimism, he nevertheless admitted the difficulties he had had in obtaining several beams in the same vacuum tank; but he announced that since September he had found a way to focus the beams very sharply. "We'll continue this study in 1943," he told them. "Now we are on the right track."

Progress had also been made in the design of a better collecting receptacle, and small quantities of uranium–235 were already trapped in some of the improved collectors. The use of multiple sources naturally complicated the process; to catch the multiple beams, multiple collectors were needed. But in October it had been discovered that results were much better when the face of the collector was set at a 45-degree angle rather than perpendicular to the beam, and the experimental model operated successfully. Lawrence, therefore, was positive that the electromagnetic method could be used on an industrial scale if enough money and effort were expended.

The next day was Sunday, and Lawrence took the visitors up the hill to see the giant calutron. As Lawrence sat down at the control desk for a demonstration, Jimmy Vale crossed his fingers: E.O.L. was always pushing instruments to the limit, and sometimes, after one of Lawrence's visits, he would have to spend the whole day trying to get the strained machine back into shape. But today the professor was more careful; he had to answer the questions of the visitors. Roger Williams asked most of the questions on the scientific aspects of the process, but Lewis and Greenewalt also demanded several explanations. Tom Gary was interested strictly in the engineering aspect; it was too early to discuss this, so he kept silent most of the time.

In spite of Lawrence's enthusiasm and articulate explanation, it was obvious to the four visitors that the yield from magnetic separation was extremely small. Calculated on the basis of the calutron's present results, an industrial operation would require enormous power, several thousands of operators and unbelievable equipment. It would be fantastically expensive. The whole method seemed not only excessively extravagant but inefficient as well.

It was late in the evening when the inspection ended. The four visitors rushed off to catch the eleven o'clock train to Chicago. They were exhausted by the whirlwind pace of their visit. "We behaved like the Supreme Court," said Tom Gary. "We just tormented the life out of those people, asking questions."

"What do you think of Lawrence?" Lewis asked him.

"If that guy had been born in England," Gary replied, "Churchill wouldn't have had a chance to be prime minister."

"And what do you think of his electromagnetic separation?"

The men looked at one another and shook their heads.

14

WESTFIELD MEMORIAL LIBRARY
WESTFIELD, N. J.

14

THE TEMPTATION was almost irresistible, and once or twice Herbert Anderson felt his willpower weakening. But he knew he shouldn't do it, and that this was almost a matter of honor. The night of December 1 was very cold, and the temperature inside the Stagg Field racquets court was just above zero, but Anderson was so excited that he didn't pay any attention to his frozen hands as he adjusted the sliding graphite bricks. It was unusually quiet in the vast, drafty room; only the silhouettes of half a dozen men could be seen around the black pile.

Enrico Fermi had worked until four o'clock that afternoon, helped by Walter Zinn and his crew. The pile had already reached forty-eight layers, and five hundred tons of graphite bricks were stacked around the fifty tons of uranium. During the day the instruments had reacted strongly when each new brick was added; it was obvious that the critical mass was about to be reached. Control rods absorbing neutrons were inserted in order to hold the pile in check. It looked as if the critical size would be reached sooner than had been expected, and it was not going to be necessary for the pile to reach as high as the ceiling.

The clicking of the counters speeded up, and every now and then the scientists put aside the bricks and stopped to check the instruments and compute the reaction in the pile. Fermi took his small 6-inch slide rule out of his pocket more often than usual. He would scribble a few figures on the back of the slide rule, then compare his hasty calculations with the results given by the instruments and machines and look pleased when his figures proved almost identical. The moment was quickly approaching when the long-expected experiment with the pile could be performed.

At 4 P.M., when the Anderson team arrived to replace the Zinn crew for the night, Enrico Fermi suddenly interrupted his measurements. "Let's call it a day!" he said as he walked out of the racquets court. "Tell everybody to come tomorrow morning at eight-thirty. But we won't need the mechanics and the students."

Before he left, Fermi took Zinn and Anderson to the adjoining room. "That's almost it," he said. "All calculations now indicate that at the fifty-first layer the pile will be in a critical condition." He turned to Anderson:

"You'll finish the piling tonight. But when you reach the fifty-first layer, put in the rods, lock them and go home! Don't start the reaction until I come!"

"OK, Enrico," Anderson said.

But as though reading the young man's mind, Fermi gave Anderson a close look and, wagging a finger at him, said laughingly, "You promise you won't do it without me?"

"Of course I won't! I wouldn't think of it!"

Fermi had left, and most of the scientists had finished work for the day. Herb Anderson and his men started working with the slippery bricks, adding one more layer, then another. The counters started clicking madly. He checked his instruments, then made his calculation on a piece of paper and looked again at the counters. The neutron activity was increasing tremendously. Like a mason on top of a brick wall, Anderson was catching the black blocks in the air and arranging them in a last layer. The fifty-first layer. It was about eleven o'clock at night.

"That's all for tonight!" he told his crew. "Everybody go home!"

As his men left the racquets court, Anderson checked all instruments once more. He was all alone in the silent drafty court. As he prepared to lock the safety rods before turning off the lights and leaving, his eyes fell on the control rod and remained fixed on it as though he were hypnotized. His mind was working feverishly. The pile had become critical, there was no doubt about it. If the control rod were removed — or just pulled out a little, one foot or two — who knew? The chain reaction might start right away.

A chain reaction — the key to everything! The dream of every nuclear physicist in the world, the prophecy of Joliot-Curie, and of Fermi, coming true! The answer to the great question that the Chicago group had been investigating for months! Would the splitting of each atom trigger in turn the splitting of other atoms, spreading like a brush fire until the chain reaction was self-sustained; or would the neutrons be lost, one after another, like dying sparks, without igniting the fire? In the first case, enormous nuclear energy would be created with which a bomb might be built one day. In the second case, the atom-splitting would remain merely a laboratory experiment without much practical use.

Standing in front of the pile where the critical mass would be achieved for the first time in history, this eager, twenty-eight-year-old scientist felt enormously tempted. His fingers touched the control rod, his eyes remained fixed on the instruments. He was so close to the answer to the questions that had been burning in his mind for three years. It would take just seconds to pull out the remaining few inches of the control rod; then he'd be the first man ever to witness an atomic chain reaction! What a marvelous climax to the career of a Columbia electroengineering student who had switched to physics only because during the Depression the National Youth Administration found him a part-time job with a professor in the Physics Department! What a long way from the poor Bronx boy who had ridden the elevated every day for an hour and a half to go to Stuyvesant School on the Lower East Side!

Anderson was born under a lucky star. One day in 1939, while he was working alone on the Columbia cyclotron, Professor Niels Bohr, who had just arrived in New York, burst into the lab to tell Fermi the great news about the splitting of the uranium atom. Since he could not find Fermi right away, the excited Dane unburdened himself to the young physicist. Receiving the news from one genius, Bohr, and later working with another genius, Fermi, could a young physicist dream of a better experience?

But the first man to see a chain reaction? Anderson was dying to be that man, and he had to keep his hands from grabbing the rod. But he knew it wouldn't be right. It was Fermi's pile, after all. He, and only he, should have the honor of conducting the first performance. Reluctantly Herb Anderson turned his back to the pile and tried not to think of the temptation. Then he started counting the hours that remained until morning.

Coming back from Berkeley, the Reviewing Committee headed by Warren Lewis arrived in Chicago Wednesday morning, December 2, 1942, and went straight to meet Compton at the university. It was an unpleasant winter morning. People in the crowded buses were reading the headlines about French Admiral Jean Darlan assuming rule in Tunisia, and about General Jimmy Doolittle's Flying Fortresses bombing the docks of Bizerte.

During the long train trip from California, the four members of the committee had written the draft of their report on the work in Columbia, Chicago and Berkeley. Now they were on their way to present it to General Groves.

Compton, Hilberry and a few of their colleagues were waiting for them in a conference room at Eckhart Hall. The first thing Lewis noticed was Fermi's absence. "Where is he?" he asked. "We want to discuss some of these things with him."

"Fermi asked to be excused," answered Compton. "He has an important experiment going on in the laboratory and cannot join us."

The discussion of the report began without delay. It was a good, realistic report, and as far as Chicago's work was concerned, Compton and his friends were relieved to hear that the Reviewing Committee recommended vigorous continuation of the project. They were disappointed, on the other hand, that no immediate production of plutonium was recommended. The committee felt that it was still premature to talk about production when no pilot plant had been built and there was still no evidence that the process could be successful.

In the middle of the discussion, the telephone rang. It was Volney Wilson calling Compton from Stagg Field. "I thought you would want to know that Fermi is ready to start the critical experiment."

Compton could hardly hide his excitement. "Could I bring them?" he asked. But Wilson said that the place was already too crowded; if Compton brought more than one person, the experiment might be disturbed.

When he hung up, Compton turned to the members of the Reviewing Committee. "Gentlemen," he said, "Fermi is about to try the chain reaction. Tests show that the pile, only about three-quarters of the size that had been thought necessary, is ready to give a chain reaction."

Compton wasn't a very good speaker, and he was jumping from one unfinished phrase to another. "Reaction — held down by control rods coated with cadmium — swallows up all neutrons within reach. To make the reaction work, only necessary now to pull these control rods out of the pile. It's a fortunate coincidence, gentlemen, that the experiment happens to be ready on the day of your visit," Compton concluded.

One of the committee members had to be selected to see the first pile experiment. Compton's eyes fell on Lewis, but he discarded the idea immediately; it would be better to choose one of Du Pont's men, not another university professor. Gary? Roger Williams? Then he decided on Crawford Greenewalt. He's the youngest, Compton thought, and he probably will remember longer than the others what he will see.

When Crawford Greenewalt, the patrician, forty-year-old Du Pont chemist, entered the racquets court under the west stands of Stagg Field, he was thrilled to be present at the first experiment with Fermi's pile. Keenly interested in science himself, and one of the first men Du Pont's Stine had talked with about the recent developments, he well appreciated the scientific importance of a chain reaction. If Fermi's first experiment didn't succeed, it would probably be due to insufficient purity of the materials rather than to any basic error in theory.

Greenewalt was mentally prepared for the failure of the pile; many first experiments didn't work, but that didn't mean that the theory was wrong. If the experiment fails, he thought, they'll find some way of overcoming the difficulty and will try again. It would not mean, so far as the Reviewing Committee was concerned, that they would recommend that the whole reactor project be abandoned.

Walking next to Greenewalt, Dr. Norman Hilberry was absorbed in his own thoughts. He was not worried that the pile would not go critical that afternoon; the evidence that it would do so was already overwhelming. Nor was he worried by the possibility of some catastrophic accident; there was undeniable experimental evidence that the reaction could be controlled. Only the possibility of some previously unknown and unimaginable new physical law suddenly emerging at the point of criticality could cause concern. No, the experiment itself provided no cause for real concern as to its safety, or for doubt as to its success.

About twenty people were assembled on the balcony erected ten feet over the north end of the racquets court, with Enrico Fermi, surrounded by Zinn and Anderson, standing at the center of the group, directing the experiment. Fascinated by the activity in the strange laboratory, Compton and Greenewalt took their places next to Fermi and his two assistants.

On the other side of the court the pile was standing twenty-eight feet high, covered on all sides but one by the useless gray balloon, which had proved unnecessary but couldn't be removed once the hundreds of tons of bricks were piled on it. The unfinished pile had an odd shape — the base was square like a quadrangular, windowless brick house, but the top was tapered in the form of a roughly flattened sphere, and left unfinished as it neared the ceiling.

It was a very cold morning, and the heating wasn't working. Volney Wilson had asked for an electric heater for his instrument room. But the university people had answered, "Not possible to get you one, Dr. Wilson. Don't you know there's a war on?"

A bridge connected the pile and the balcony, and under it a young scientist, George Weil, held the control rod sticking out of the pile. A spontaneous reaction was being prevented by three sets of control rods, one of which was automatic and could be controlled from the balcony. The second safety rod was for emergency; it was hooked up with a big weight on one side and its end was attached by a rope to the balcony. Hilberry was standing by with an ax in his hands, ready to cut the rope in case the reaction got out of control. The third rod, the one Fermi intended to withdraw step by step until the reaction began, was handled by Weil. No major accident was expected, but just in case something completely unexpected did happen, a three-man "suicide squad" stood by on a platform above the pile, with buckets in their hands. These men — Harold F. Lichtenberger, Warren E. Nyer, and Alvin C. Graves — were prepared to flood the pile with a cadmium solution which would absorb the neutrons and stop the reaction, in case the control rods failed.

At 9:45 A.M. Fermi ordered the electrically operated control rods withdrawn. Everybody stopped talking; only Fermi's voice could be heard in the silence. Then, as the rods went out of the pile, the clicking of the counters stepped up and all eyes fixed themselves on the dials indicating the neutron count. At the same time, the neutron activity inside the pile was traced by the pen of a recorder, resembling the seismographs recording an earthquake.

At 10 A.M. Fermi asked Walter Zinn to withdraw the emergency rod, called "the zip," and as the zip went out and was tied to the balcony rail, Hilberry, with the big ax ready to cut the rope, felt slightly ridiculous. But nobody was laughing, and the tension in the room mounted steadily as the clicking of the neutron counters accelerated. Now the only obstacle standing in the way of the chain reaction was the cadmium rod held by George Weil. The rod bore the markings of the number of feet and inches remaining within the pile.

Fermi was absorbed in reading the meters and quickly comparing them to his predictions. His previous calculations fitted with astonishing precision. "Pull it to thirteen feet, George," he ordered at 10:37. The pen of the recorder moved up sharply, and the clicking increased. Fermi's fingers were moving quickly over his small slide rule as his eyes followed the meters. As usual, he looked completely self-confident, in his natural, unassuming way. His lieutenants continued comparing the figures of his theoretical predictions with the readings of the counters. So far, everything was going exactly according to theory.

"The trace will go to this point and level off," Fermi said, indicating a spot on the graph. In a few minutes the pen stopped at the position he had predicted and moved no higher.

That day, Enrico Fermi was very much onstage. He had prepared every detail of the experiment very thoroughly as usual, and was going to make a good show of it. He wanted to demonstrate how completely he understood the entire process. With a marvelous sense of showmanship, he wanted to prove that every step in the experiment was well calculated and well understood, that his predictions based on the theory would materialize to the last detail. He was not only a witness to a new phenomenon; he was going to be its master. Every ten or fifteen minutes he ordered the rod pulled out a few more inches, and each time the clicking of the counters increased. Each time he indicated the point at which the graph's pen would level off, and each time he guessed right. It looked as if the pile would behave exactly according to theory.

Everybody was growing tense as the moment approached when the reaction would become self-sustained. Then, unexpectedly and very calmly, Fermi announced, "I'm hungry, let's go to lunch."

It was a good idea, he felt, to relieve the tension before the final experiment. At the student cafeteria, everybody was silent on the subject of the pile and the conversation turned to unrelated topics. Some of the scientists played their usual gambling game with the numbers on the check stubs.

At two o'clock the experiment resumed. The automatic rod was reset and George Weil stood ready at the control rod. During the lunch hour, word of what was going on got around to the other laboratories working on the project, and when the scientists went back to the stands, they found that many more people had gathered, filled with expectation. As the tests proceeded, the instruments began to read higher and higher but were still leveling off at each new position of the control rod. Enjoying himself tremendously, Fermi continued predicting what would happen each time the rod was pulled out and showing exactly where the meters would go on the instruments.

William Overbeck settled down at the secondary control panel, and as each reading was relayed to him, he repeated it. Before long, a faint echo of cheers went up each time he repeated a reading. It was coming from the group of people behind the pile who were unable to see what was going on but who had somehow managed to manipulate the switches on a nearby communicating set so they could hear the readings. As Overbeck repeated them the cheers became part of a general excitement that was beginning to affect everyone present.

"Move it six inches," said Fermi at 3:20. The counters nearly jammed, but again leveled off. Five minutes later Fermi ordered, "Pull it out another foot!"

As Weil withdrew the rod, Fermi turned to Compton: "This is going to do it! Now it will become self-sustaining! The trace will continue to climb and will not level off."

Everyone set aside pencils and slide rules just to watch the meters and see what would happen. Overbeck continued to announce the readings over the teletalk system, and everyone was mentally comparing each reading with the previous one. The rate of increase was phenomenal with each new reading.

It looked as if a real chain reaction was beginning. The counters registering the rays from the pile were now clicking so fast that the sound became a rattle. Fermi computed the rate of rise of the neutron counts over a one-minute period. If the rate was constant and remained so, it would mean that the reaction was self-sustaining. If anything unpredictable was going to happen, now was the moment.

Under the ceiling, the "suicide squad" waited nervously, ready to pour their liquid cadmium onto the pile. But nothing happened. Tense but calm, Fermi was operating his slide rule with extraordinary speed. Three minutes passed, and he calculated the rate of rise again. The scientists on the balcony crowded in around the instruments, anxious not to miss any reading, while Overbeck's voice called the neutron count for the people behind the pile. The click of the counters was already too fast for the human ear and a steady noise was coming from the instruments.

At the control rod Weil was watching Fermi and didn't dare move his eyes from him, waiting for orders. Fermi's face was motionless, his eyes darting from one dial to another. His expression was so calm it was hard to believe. Then, suddenly, his whole face broke into a broad smile. Fermi closed his slide rule. "The reaction is self-sustaining," he announced happily.

For twenty-eight minutes the group had watched tensely as the pen steadily drew a straight upward line. There was no leveling off. For the first time a nuclear chain reaction had been produced.

At 3:53 P.M. Fermi interrupted the experiment. "OK – zip in!" he ordered Zinn. As the emergency rod was reintroduced into the pile, the rattle of the counters died down to an occasional click, and the pen steadily drew an upward straight line.

"Lock the control rods to the safety position and come back tomorrow morning!" said Fermi. His face showed no particular sign of elation. He wasn't surprised that the pile had worked exactly as expected. His theoretical calculations were confirmed, and now he had a new tool for experiments for the next job, the hard job.

At that moment Wigner stepped forward and handed Fermi a bottle of Chianti. Fermi, delighted, uncorked the bottle and somebody produced paper cups for everyone. Fermi poured a little wine in each cup, and they all drank to success. "And let's hope that we are the *first* to succeed!" one scientist exclaimed pessimistically, thinking of Hitler's physicists. After the bottle was empty, all witnesses of the first chain reaction autographed its straw basket.

Compton went back to his office and called Conant at Harvard. "Jim," he said, "you'll be interested to know that the Italian navigator has just landed in the New World. He arrived sooner than he had expected."

Conant's voice betrayed his excitement. "Were the natives friendly?" he asked.

"Everyone landed safe and happy," answered Compton.

WESTFIELD MEMORIAL LIBRARY
WESTFIELD, N. J.

15

WHEN PROFESSOR UREY invited his former student, Edward Adler, to join the Columbia group on an extremely important war project, he did not mention anything about an atomic bomb. Adler, a fiery, twenty-six-year-old New Yorker who taught chemistry at City College, was told only that different porous materials were being tested for an unbelievably fine membrane, or barrier, to be used in some kind of gaseous-diffusion process. Dr. John Dunning, the originator of the gaseous-diffusion program, gave Adler a classroom laboratory in the Havemeyer Building, introduced him to Dr. Francis Slack, who was in charge of barrier research, and told him that because of his experience in electrochemistry, he was to continue Slack's work on possible barrier materials.

So far, all tests had failed. Many porous materials, metals and alloys, had been tried, but none came even remotely close to meeting the fantastic requirements. Most materials were immediately corroded by the uranium hexafluoride, the gas to be used in the diffusion. Some brilliantly ingenious ideas had been suggested, however. Why not try, for example, to obtain porosity by using metal alloys, in which one component would be etched out — like taking zinc out of brass sheets — thus leaving porous holes in the remaining copper? Another suggestion: since thin layers of copper electroplating were porous, it might be possible to "spoil" such plating, deliberately, by introducing removable impurities.

These and many other ideas were investigated, but all through the winter and spring of 1942, Adler was unable to report any success. With every passing month the risk grew greater that unless some breakthrough miraculously occurred, the whole gaseous-diffusion program would come to a standstill.

One afternoon Dunning called Adler into his office. "I want you to try something different, and a man is coming to see you about it," Dunning said. "Franz Simon and some other British scientists have brought him to my attention, and I think he is a man we need. His name is Edward Norris."

"Is he a chemist or physicist?"

"Neither. Norris is a decorator — an interior decorator."

To Adler it sounded like a joke — who needed a decorator!

Dunning opened a drawer and pulled out a small piece of thin metal smaller than a dime. "This man Norris has invented some material that may work for the barrier. We've tried it, and at first sight it looks damned good!" Dunning leaned forward eagerly. "But Norris has had only two years of high school and knows very little about science. So please help him!"

Edward Norris, a reddish-faced, balding Englishman in his early forties, had been born in London and came to Connecticut at the age of three. His father became a decorator in Greenwich, Connecticut, and the son continued the family tradition, but without enthusiasm. Edward Norris might have been a good decorator, but he certainly was not a happy one.

One source of dissatisfaction for him was the type of spray gun he had to use to paint walls. He hated the guns. He tried to find a finer sprayer for more even painting, but none was on the market. So he made one himself, a spray gun that did not involve air. Since he needed a very fine, flat screen for his centrifugal painting machine, he invented one in 1934, a metal mesh made by an electrodeposition process. It was so successful that the C. O. Jelliff Company, manufacturers of woven wire, bought Norris's invention and hired him to make the screens for them.

When the British started developing their gaseous-diffusion program, somebody thought of Jelliff's "Lectromesh," which was already known commercially. In the summer of 1941, during a visit to the United States, British scientist Franz Simon called on Norris and asked him to make a small, half-inch-square screen with a half-million holes in it. Norris succeeded and was then taken to Columbia to meet Dunning.

The mysterious talk about "the secret" intrigued Norris. He remembered having glanced through an article in the *Saturday Evening Post* some years before that had mentioned gaseous diffusion. After some searching, he found a copy in the library in Southport, Connecticut. He read it carefully and at last understood the nature of the secret project.* The ex-decorator set up some equipment in his home workshop, and by the end of 1942 had produced two samples of material more suitable than the fine screens Jelliff was making for the British. He took these samples to Dr. Dunning for evaluation.

When Norris joined Adler (at first only on a part-time basis), several groups were studying different aspects of the problem in the same large

---

* Later, security officers of the Manhattan Project checked every library in the country to find out the names of people who had borrowed this particular issue. Among the names on the "suspect" list was that of Edward Norris!

laboratory room in the Havemeyer Building. In one corner Willard Libby tested the corrosion of uranium gas; in another corner George Cady worked on fluorine compounds; Francis Slack tested the separation qualities of various materials, using helium and carbon dioxide instead of the actual uranium hexafluoride.

Adler moved into a small room in the basement of Pupin Hall, a few doors from the cyclotron room. Norris used to come several times a week to watch Adler's progress. The two formed a good team. Both were men of ideas, both very empirical in outlook; they always went ahead with any approach that looked good at the moment, even though it followed no particularly logical pattern.

Norris's lack of formal training often showed up when intricate chemical problems arose. But his intuition was remarkable, especially in electrochemistry. He was the quieter of the two, but he had a forceful, determined personality and strong, definite opinions.

Edward Adler threw himself into work on the Norris barrier idea with all the energy of his explosive temperament. He literally lived in the laboratory, arriving sometimes at 7:30 in the morning and staying until midnight, six days a week. His assistant, Elliott Charney, did the same. Before Norris knew it, he had joined them, becoming a full-time worker, taking off for only short lunch breaks with Adler at the nearby cafeteria. Dunning was constantly in touch with them, asking for progress reports.

When the work increased, the group was moved from the basement to the sixth floor of Pupin. In a few days the new laboratory looked as messy as the old one. The ex-decorator and the chemist were by no means meticulous workers. With no patience for cleaning up, they jumped from one experiment to another, leaving tubes and bottles all over the place. Adler was especially disorderly, moving from corner to corner, a lock of thick black hair falling over his forehead, his clothes soiled by chemicals, and working at tables littered with several days' debris. Young Charney tried to clean up from time to time and put the place in some order, but it was a losing battle. Both Adler and Norris were impatient men, more the intuitive, impulsive type of researcher than the methodical scientist; both detested red tape and administration.

One after another, most metals and alloys were eliminated as possible barrier material. Glass also was ruled out. The choice was extremely limited to begin with, because practically no material resisted the corrosion of uranium hexafluoride gas. By the end of 1942, almost all effort was being concentrated on nickel, one of the few metals impervious to corrosion. Though their barrier was still by no means ready to separate uranium isotopes, the Norris-Adler technique, continually improved, became more and more promising. The Dunning group could hope that it would eventually produce a good nickel barrier. For the moment, the delicate material was much too fragile to withstand any gas pressure and too brittle to be assembled in the diffusion system. But the porosity was quite good and the holes very fine.

One problem was that many pinholes were being made as the result of impurities and defects during production. No matter how fine the millions of pores were, one or two large pinholes on the same set were enough to make it unusable. Before the barrier was tested in the laboratory, the pinholes had to be mended by hand; it used to amuse other lab workers to watch the impatient Adler painstakingly filling holes under the microscope, using an ordinary needle. He looked like a black-haired Mexican revolutionary working clumsily on some delicate needlepoint.

But serious questions remained. Would the Norris-Adler barrier ever be strong enough for use in a large-scale plant? Would its porosity be sufficient? Would it clog after a few days — or hours — of operation? How would the pinhole problem be solved without trying to mend acres of barriers by needle? No one knew the answers. But good or bad, the Norris-Adler barrier seemed to be the best and most advanced so far.

At Bell Laboratories in New York, where he was working on a different type of barrier, Foster C. Nix disagreed. A handsome, blue-eyed giant of thirty-seven, Nix was an independent-minded, highly opinionated Alabamian with a sharp tongue. He divided humanity into two groups: the decent people with morals, manners, taste and traditions; and the left-wingers, phonies and parvenus. And he was not a man to let Yankees step on his toes just because they had won the Civil War. A conservative, Nix was often upset by the way the nation was led by "the S.O.B.'s in Washington" and was misinformed by "the slanted pink press"; and he seldom hesitated to express his views, bluntly, openly and directly.

Nix had been working at Bell Laboratories in New York as a research physicist when John Dunning and Booth contacted him in November 1941 and asked him to help with some neutron research. He had known the Columbia physicists for a number of years, and had done research with Dunning before. An informal working relationship began with the Columbia group, and soon after Pearl Harbor, Dunning let him in on the secret. Nix switched to full-time work on the barrier. He was well qualified for the job; and it is to Dunning's credit that he was able to recognize Nix's potential value for barrier work. Nix had studied mining geology at the University of Alabama, but took his master's degree in metallurgy. In 1929 he went to the University of Berlin to study physics and received his Ph.D. there. This combined experience in metallurgy and solid-state physics, plus his creative intelligence, put Nix in one of the leading positions in barrier research.

But his work in the first months of 1942 was unsuccessful. He continued to work in his small laboratory at Bell, but had regular contacts with Dunning and the group. The top people at Bell had been told of the nature of his work; they agreed to take part in the Project by contributing Nix and his laboratory, to which fifteen assistants were attached.

Nix was a dedicated and enthusiastic worker, but also a very individualistic one who could operate well only if given a free hand. He was not a good organization man, and did not at all like to work under the supervision of others. Luckily for him, both Bell and Columbia gave him a free hand in trying out his ideas and methods. In the summer of 1942, when Columbia tests proved that nickel was the only metal resistant to uranium hexafluoride, Nix also switched to this metal but had the idea of trying compressed nickel powder. Knowing metallurgy, he ordered some specially made powder which could only be obtained in England and sent to him via diplomatic pouch. Nix's method was entirely different from the Norris-Adler technique. The two groups worked completely independently of each other, and since the techniques had so little in common, there was scant interchange of ideas. But Nix's relations with Norris and Adler were very friendly, which was not always the case in his dealings with other Columbia people. Asked once for his opinion on the work of a certain scientist, Nix quickly retorted, "He is worth at least two Nazi divisions for all the harm he is doing to the Project." But the important thing was that the tall Southerner liked both Dunning and Booth as well as Adler and Norris, and their cooperation was perfect.

The powder tests during the summer gave Nix hope. The new material did not have the weaknesses of the Norris-Adler barrier; indeed, its structure was very strong. But its separation qualities were still in doubt; its porosity did not have the degree of refinement of the Norris-Adler barrier. Besides, Nix's special technique of making it in the laboratory could not be used in large-scale production.

Every day Foster Nix worked on the improvement of his barrier, adding or changing something in the technique. But progress was difficult to follow, because Columbia still did not have good ways of testing and measuring the separation characteristics of a new barrier. The real gas could not be used in the tests, nor could the real pressure nor the real assembly. But somehow Foster Nix was convinced, even at this early stage, that he was the one on the right track.

16

FOR ALMOST a year, Mrs. Manson Benedict had been seeing less and less of her husband in their Westfield, New Jersey, home. His work in the M. W. Kellogg Company's laboratories in Jersey City, where he was head of Process Development, had increased tremendously — in addition to six long working days, he now spent three evenings a week on the job.

This evening followed what had become a regular pattern for the Benedicts. They were just sitting down to a late supper when the telephone rang. "Not again!" Mrs. Benedict sighed in exasperation. Her husband rose slowly from the table and walked to the phone with an air of tired resignation. They both knew who was calling; it happened almost every evening.

"Yes, Mr. Keith," said Benedict, without waiting to hear the voice at the other end of the line.

The boom of Dobie Keith's voice brought the man almost physically into the room. Nobody would ever have suspected that the ebullient Kellogg vice-president had just put in another grueling ten-hour day of work and decision-making. Nearly every night Keith, speaking with great gusto, made his "emergency" call to Manson Benedict, then to other top men of the team — Clarence Johnson and John Arnold.

"How did it work? What were the results?" was Dobie Keith's usual question. The urgency in his voice gave the feeling that his own life — indeed, the course of the whole war — depended on the answer. He asked the same questions even about experiments several days short of first results. This did not seem to make sense; but many people suspected that Keith was doing it on purpose, to maintain an acute sense of constant emergency throughout the whole operation.

He was setting the example. Nobody could possibly work longer hours or put more fire into the job than this exacting Texan dynamo. He was the kind of man who enjoyed the challenge, who was not afraid of responsibility or risks. "Dobie is not the type who *gets* ulcers," said his subordinates. "He *gives* ulcers!"

Manson Benedict was in charge of the industrial design of the large-scale gaseous-diffusion process. It was his responsibility to produce a workable cascade composed of thousands of diffusion stages through which uranium gas would be pushed, enriched each time in U–235 content, until the pure isotope was obtained. Gaseous diffusion of uranium had never been tried before; nobody knew whether it could be done at all.

Designing a successful cascade was the all-important crucial task; without it, Kellogg was incapable of answering the question the Government had asked — was the gaseous-diffusion process possible from the engineering and industrial point of view? Dobie Keith was glad to have Benedict working on it; there was no man better suited for the job, and Keith had selected him personally.

Dr. Manson Benedict, a tall, serious-looking man of thirty-four, had come to Kellogg in 1938. At the time, the company was having difficulty with some hydrocarbon mixtures, and a number of young men with experience in petroleum refining were hired to help. The modest, soft-spoken Benedict solved the problem in a brilliant way, and in an unexpectedly short time.

Dobie Keith knew talent when he saw it. "This quiet fellow from MIT seems to have a mind that works differently from most people's," he remarked as he watched the young scientist reduce highly complicated problems to simple, orderly solutions. From then on, each time a difficulty arose, Keith would send Benedict to the trouble spot. Silently, the scientist would sit down to work, as precise and methodical as a computer, and some original solution — what scientists call an "elegant" solution — would shortly be forthcoming.

Neither the appearance nor the manner of Manson Benedict was spectacular. A hundred versions of the same long face and the same rimless glasses are seen in colleges and laboratories, usually hidden behind thick technical books in the silence of reading rooms. His father was the chief metallurgist at the Calumet, Hecla Company in Lake Linden, on Michigan's Upper Peninsula, a little town with one industry: copper mining. A bookish boy, he grew up in a modest, middle-class family. The greatest revelation of his childhood was Slossom's *Creative Chemistry*, a book he read several times until he knew some paragraphs by heart. Manson and his brother started a small laboratory in their basement, supplied with chemicals and test tubes their father brought from work. He was sixteen when he left the small town for the first time, to go to study in a boys' prep school; later he went to Cornell and then to MIT for graduate study.

For Manson Benedict chemistry had become his life. He entered it as monks enter an order — with all his heart, and for life.

Manson Benedict, of course, did not invent the diffusion cascade. The principle was well known, and had been ever since 1829. In the 1920's German chemist Gustav Hertz had separated neon isotopes by recycling the gas through many stages. The principle was straightforward: if a gas were forced through a porous barrier, the lighter isotopes would pass more rapidly than the heavier.

John Dunning's group at Columbia was most advanced in research and well organized for studying the possibilities of diffusion of the uranium gas UF–6. Assisted by Eugene Booth, Aristid V. Grosse and a few others, Dunning had designed in early 1942 a cascade in which UF–6 gas (the uranium of which contains only 0.7 percent of the needed U–235) had to be propelled by pumps through thousands of stages until the U–235 became concentrated at the top of the cascade, while the U–238 concentrated at the bottom. But no adequate barrier had yet been invented, no workable pump, no pipe which would resist the corrosive effects of uranium. Hence all Columbia experiments were still performed with other gases, not with uranium hexafluoride, and on a very small laboratory scale. But theoretically, at least, the Dunning-Booth process was possible.

When the Kellogg Company became involved in the gaseous-diffusion process, the logical place to look for information was Columbia. A sustained collaboration grew up between Dr. Dunning's scientists and Kellogg's engineers. Because the problems of industrial production went beyond those encountered in the laboratory, Keith decided to assign Kellogg's own scientists, headed by Benedict, to design a feasible cascade for large-scale separation.

The difficulties were incredibly complicated. Natural uranium contains more than 99 percent of uranium–238 — but this was the heavier isotope, which would not produce fissionable material for an atomic bomb. It was that 0.7 of one percent of natural uranium — the lighter 235–isotope — that was needed. Enormous quantities of gas, therefore, had to be pumped through the lower stages of the cascade in order to obtain very small quantities of U–235 at the top. Theoretically, volume, pumps, barriers, pipes — everything had to be of a different size for the thousands of different stages. Extraordinary mathematical calculations had to be made before a design could even be envisaged.

In this work, the main help came from another Columbia scientist, Karl Cohen, a brilliant young mathematician and a friend of Urey's. Before the Kellogg engineers began work on their design, Cohen had calculated not only the number needed for the ideal cascade — five thousand stages — but also the quantities of gas at each of the stages, and had plotted a graph giving the values.

For the practical design of a plant, however, the equipment should not run into several thousand types of pumps and valves for each stage.

Cohen and Benedict plunged into the problem of how to reduce and simplify the equipment and still meet the theoretical requirements. Although the theoretical blueprint for the cascade was made in 1942, there were serious problems to be overcome before industrial production could ever become a reality. The most insurmountable obstacles seemed to be the barrier and the pumps for circulating the gas through the many stages of the cascade.

Scientists at Columbia, at Bell Laboratories and at Kellogg were all still trying desperately but unsuccessfully to solve the barrier riddle. Eger Murphree's planning board on the S–1 Committee had charged Dobie Keith, one of its members, with the task of seeing which company could develop high-speed pumps (or compressors, as gas pumps are technically called) without any leaks whatsoever. At Columbia a very ingenious scientist, Henry Boorse, was showing some progress in his research on new types of reciprocating pumps.

But new, thorny problems kept cropping up every day. Thousands of compressors of differing size were needed for the different stages of the cascade. These had to operate at supersonic speed; they had to be made out of some material impervious to the UF6 gas, which corroded almost every metal. And the pumps could not be lubricated because the gas would become explosive on contact with any grease whatsoever. The pumps also had to be hermetically sealed, with no possible change of leakage, and could never be opened for repair once they were installed. Such pumps did not exist. Keith tried all manufacturers, but nobody could make such a compressor. Most companies assured him it simply could not be done. Finally Keith convinced the Ingersoll-Rand Company to try, and they reluctantly started research on new centrifugal pumps, but with no tangible results.

For months in 1942, Manson Benedict, his right-hand man, Arthur M. Squires, and their group were "playing," as they put it, in the Kellogg laboratories in Jersey City. "Playing" meant that they made several designs — maybe ten, twenty, thirty — and then tore them up: They had to explore the maximum number of ways of putting together this still imaginary equipment. They did not know what pressures to work on, nor what temperatures: whether to anticipate a multitude of little pieces of equipment or a few big ones.

So many choices had to be made with so many independent variables, all demanding innumerable mathematical calculations and very good judgment. The word for this work was "optimizing." Until December 1942, all that the Kellogg group did was a continuous "optimization" of the cascade design.

Benedict's team consisted of Arthur Squires, the Chief Process Engineer Charles C. King, mathematicians Elliott Montroll and Joseph Lehner, and a dozen assistants. They started by using the Columbia lab's theory, but soon their work continued independently in a sort of friendly race with the parent team. There were frequent meetings and a regular exchange of reports; everything they did was written up and sent to Columbia at once. The Columbia scientists, however, were not really working on the engineering aspects of the cascade at all; they were not designing a plant. Their approach was more scientific, more analytical; they were more interested in the theory and mathematics of the problems.

Benedict's approach was more empirical and practical. He wrestled, for example, with the problem of barrier efficiency — in other words, how would thousands of square feet of barrier in a future plant behave, as compared with the performance of the one-inch laboratory model of the same barrier? Kellogg solved this problem by using the empirical methods known in chemical engineering. Meanwhile, working simultaneously at Columbia, Karl Cohen took one of the latest, most sophisticated hydrodynamic theories — Carman's Boundary-Layer Theory — and came up with a brilliant solution, and was astonished to learn that precisely the same results had been obtained by the Kellogg group in a far humbler way.

During all this period of "optimizing," the driving force behind Benedict's group was Keith, with his urgent telephone calls, inquiries and incessant demands for tangible results and greater speed. Relations between the impulsive, hard-driving engineer and the cool, intellectual scientist — two men of greatly contrasting temperaments — were based on mutual respect. Benedict was impressed by the intuition and decision-making courage of the great engineer; Keith considered the young chemist a genius and was relying on him for solutions of most of the theoretical problems.

Often Dobie Keith showed little patience with people, especially with those he considered "no-idea" men. Full of ideas himself, directed in his work more by impulse and intuition, Keith had little understanding or interest in orderly, organization-type bureaucrats. When he wanted to know something, he ignored all established channels and called his subordinates directly in their offices or at home. This created some conflicts with his chief assistant, Albert L. Baker. A huge, vital man of enormous energy, Baker had a character as strong as Keith's, but a completely opposite method of working. He believed in organization and order. Precise and methodical, he was often exasperated by Keith's flamboyant, disorderly leadership, his constant changing of orders and new demands.

Baker's job as project manager was to see that the ideas of Keith and his braintrust were followed up and executed. He was the man who had to implement every decision, to translate it into practice. But at each corner he was bypassed by the impatient Keith, for whom all hierarchy, memos, channels and committees were just unnecessary red tape and a waste of time. It was fortunate that Kellogg's Project X was headed during this period by two such formidable people as Keith and Baker — but it was not always smooth sailing.

I7

FROM A GASTRONOMIC point of view, the dinner at the French restaurant in New York City was excellent — and a waste. Leslie Groves would have been just as happy with a hamburger and apple pie, and wine didn't appeal to him. Dobie Keith had chosen the menu with great care, for he himself was not only a good host but also a keen connoisseur of French cuisine. Among his leisure-time skills, the vice-president of the M. W. Kellogg Company was an excellent chef, and one of his proudest possessions was a rare original edition of the classic cookbook written by the great French chef Escoffier. But when a plate of sizzling snails was served at a nearby table and Groves snorted, "How in the world can people eat those things!" Keith definitely crossed gastronomic pleasures off the evening's agenda.

Keith had heard many stories about the general before he met him, and some of these were not very flattering. Many people who had worked with him considered him bossy, inconsiderate and sarcastic. "Very efficient, but tough and obstinate as a mule," was one verdict. From their brief encounters at earlier conferences, Keith had already formed an opinion of Groves as a dedicated officer of unusual energy and integrity. Their first long tête-à-tête tonight at the restaurant confirmed this impression. The general did not make the slightest effort to please; he offered no small talk, no preliminary words; he did not waste one smile on politeness. As brutally as a bulldozer, he went straight to the point.

Keith, a sophisticated man, was impressed by the fact that Groves could talk about things like patriotism, duty and moral values in the same matter-of-fact way in which he discussed construction, machinery and roads; to Groves the reality of the first was as definite and concrete as that of the second. Yet, whether it was because of his candor or his total assurance, his words did not seem at all falsely sentimental.

The general was doing some sizing-up, too. At forty-two, Dobie Keith already had the reputation of being one of the three or four top chemical engineering authorities in the country. He was a rather handsome, dark-haired man with thick eyebrows, light-blue eyes and a tone of command in his voice. Because of Keith's expansive way of talking, many people wondered, on first meeting him, how serious the cocky engineer from Texas really was. But Groves, after listening to him for a while, was convinced that Keith was a capable, imaginative man who thought in big terms and would not shirk responsibility for bold decisions. Before dinner was over, there was already a bond of understanding between the two men.

The December night was cold when they stepped out of the restaurant and strolled up Fifth Avenue. Keith was about to make the greatest decision of his life, and after all the meetings and conferences of the day, he still had some doubts and questions. Groves had come to New York to arrange the last details for the launching of one of the boldest industrial adventures of all time. He was to give the green light for the design and construction of the most fantastic technological complex ever built in this country: the gaseous-diffusion plant for separating U–235.

Until now, Columbia scientists and Kellogg engineers had been investigating only the *possibility* of large-scale gaseous diffusion; there had been no order for actual production. Now the Military Policy Committee had agreed to the order, and General Groves was given full power to execute it. It was a bold and extremely risky decision to proceed with the engineering and the building of the actual plant before the tremendous problems of barrier, pumps, process design, corrosion and perfect airtightness were even remotely resolved. To carry it out successfully, most of the general's advisers had recommended the M. W. Kellogg Company and its go-getting vice-president, P. C. Keith.

Keith's childhood had been indelibly marked by the influence of a swashbuckling French officer, Captain Le Tellier. Educated at France's famous military schools of St. Cyr and École Polytechnique, Le Tellier had become French military attaché in Washington during the Civil War and was sent as an observer to Lee's army. He fell in love with a Southern belle, married her and volunteered to serve under General Stonewall Jackson. After the war he moved to Sharon, Texas, and became a teacher.

Keith's father was a well-to-do, Scottish-born pharmacist in Sharon; his mother wrote poetry in her free moments. Both wanted their son to have the best of educations. At six Percival Keith was precocious, but his parents believed he was still too young for public school; so they sent him to Kidd Key College, a girls' school. In his second year there, his geography teacher lost her temper and slapped the child's face. The boy, who had a temper too, hit her back with a geography book. When the superintendent insisted that the boy apologize publicly or be expelled, Keith's father was furious. "You don't have to expel my son," he retorted, "I'm taking him out of your school!"

It was then that Captain Le Tellier, already seventy-two, became Percival's tutor. He was an extraordinary teacher. "Almost everything I know I learned from Le Tellier," Keith often said later on. "He taught me how to concentrate. He used to put me against the wall and slowly read a very long, complicated sentence; then I had to repeat it word for word. Impossible at the beginning, it became very easy for me after long training. Later I got the reputation for having an unusual memory — but it was only a matter of training."

Le Tellier used to give him complicated arithmetic problems that the boy had to solve in his head. When he wasn't paying attention or wasn't trying hard enough, the captain used to hit him on the hand with a black ruler. The child worked six hours a day with him, and Le Tellier developed his taste for history, philosophy and science.

Until the boy was eight, his mother kept his hair long and dressed him in velvet pants with buckle shoes. Other children used to make fun of him, and one day two boys waited in front of his house to beat him up. Old Captain Le Tellier rushed to his aid, grabbed one of the boys and shouted to Keith, "I'm holding this one, but if you don't beat up the other, I'll break your neck!"

After majoring in English at Harvard, he enrolled in a course on short story writing and simultaneously took courses at MIT. When the course at Harvard was suddenly canceled, the would-be author took, almost by accident and with mixed feelings, the road of chemical and electrical engineering. His literary interests remained later on, however, in his habit of quoting Dante and using Renaissance examples when discussing power plants and pipe circuits.

For one year, Keith had been a member of the planning board of the S–1 Committee under Eger Murphree. He was familiar, therefore, with the secret developments of isotope-separation methods. But he had also had an opportunity to appraise the incredible difficulties involved in large-scale gaseous diffusion. Basic knowledge was still very incomplete, much too inadequate to begin the construction phase. Thus, when his company was asked to proceed with the design and building of a production plant, Keith's first impulse was to refuse the assignment. Not that he was afraid; he had a solid reputation for making bold decisions and looking for challenges. But he had never seen a challenge with such heavy odds against success. Knowledge of the process was practically nil, and the fantastic requirements were not realistic; they had no precedent in industry.

When Keith refused the assignment, his former MIT professor W. K. Lewis took him aside and gave him a long talk. "You have to take the job!" he said. "We all know what the chances are. But look at Lawrence and his ridiculous method! Look at Du Pont taking the plutonium job — a metal no one has seen! Believe me, they are worse off! If you don't do it, there's no one else who can or will. You *must* take the job."

When it came to constructing plants, the self-confident Keith looked up to few people in the world. Like many engineers who were creating fabulous technological expansion in the new oil industry, he was not used to taking lessons from others in his field. But W. K. Lewis was different. "He is the teacher of us all," Keith had often said. "He is certainly the greatest chemical engineer this country has ever produced."

He listened to the older man carefully, even respectfully, as the professor gave him chapter and verse of the reasons why he should accept the assignment. When Lewis finished, the usually expansive Texan remained silent for a minute. Then he simply said, "OK, Doc! But there's one condition: we have to build a pilot plant first."

Lewis shook his head. "There can't be a pilot plant — we haven't time." Hearing this, Keith remained reluctant.

The New York streets were almost empty at this cold, late hour. There were few passers-by to notice the general and the stocky, ebullient man beside him. Groves had come to New York to win Keith over. He also intended to ask him to drop his other activities at Kellogg and concentrate all his energy and time on the new job. Such an "impossible" job had no chance of success unless it was directed by a leader with exceptional devotion and drive. Groves had reason to be deeply worried about the gaseous-diffusion project. Some British experts estimated the chances for success at only one in a thousand. Professor Urey himself was skeptical, though Dunning remained enthusiastic. But the translation of laboratory experiments into large-scale industrial operation would be a huge task. In December of 1942, the imaginary plant seemed to belong more to the realm of Jules Verne than to engineering and technology.

The Manhattan District's assignment to the Kellogg Company consisted essentially of a single order: design and serve as engineers on the building of a gaseous-diffusion plant — and *fast!* How, what size, what shape — nobody knew. There was no equipment because the plant's components had not yet been invented. Nor could they be unless certain new materials were quickly discovered. New tools, new techniques, new metals, new instruments and the specialists trained to use them — all had to be created from scratch for what would be a gigantic industrial operation.

As the two men strolled on, Groves unexpectedly spoke about himself. "I understand your hesitation, Mr. Keith. But you know, I didn't want *my* job either. I was badly disappointed when they canceled my overseas assignment. For a regular officer, that's frustrating. But they told me, 'If you succeed, you can shorten the war.' What could I do but accept?"

The light changed and the two men crossed Fifty-seventh Street. Keith was fascinated by the sudden metamorphosis in the general's personality — the stiff, authoritarian officer had changed into a human, almost humble man, talking about his long service in the Army Engineers Corps, about West Point, about his chaplain father. Keith felt that he could trust this man. He was intrigued by the general's simple, unshakable philosophy of life and duty, the kind of wholesome and slightly old-fashioned ideas so often ridiculed by cynics.

Keith was not a man to refuse the greatest challenge his profession could offer. But before surrendering to the call of duty and the persuasion of the combined brass of the Manhattan District and the S-1 Committee, the Texan tried a last defensive weapon: "I can't work unless I have complete responsibility and no interference from anyone," he told Groves. "I have to do the job the way I want and with the people I choose."

He thought that no military man would ever sign such a carte blanche, especially for a project running into hundreds of millions of dollars. But Groves surprised him.

"Granted," Groves said without hesitation. "You're the boss. I promise I won't interfere, and neither will anyone else. But I shall expect you to put everything you've got into this! Then I'll back you all the way."

The two men shook hands. After they had parted, Keith wondered what had made him believe the verbal commitment of a man he had scarcely known before. Somehow, though, he knew the general would keep his word.

Since the construction of a gaseous-diffusion plant was of such a highly experimental nature, Kellogg could give no guarantee, in signing the contract, that the plant would be successfully built. It was obvious, too, that the project would be of such enormous scope that it could not be handled by a single division of the company. Keith was therefore called off his other duties and told to create a new, independent organization devoted entirely to the gaseous-diffusion project.

"Kellex" ("Kell" for Kellogg and "X" for secret) was formed in the first days of 1943, and was destined to become one of the most unusual corporations in the United States. What Keith managed to put together was an organization in which the captains of industry fought, so to speak, as simple soldiers: some of the most important men in major American corporations abandoned their executives' chairs to join Kellex and work merely as engineers under Keith. They were highly individualistic men not used to taking orders from anybody. Many had prima donna temperaments, but each was an authority in his field — valves, compressors, electric power plants, leakage control or seals. In peacetime, no corporation could afford to hire such an all-star team; the price would have been astronomical. Yet they came to New York, some leaving their families behind, and sat in front of the drafting boards at Kellex, earning only the modest salaries strictly fixed by the Manhattan Project.

Keith's first recruits were the people of Kellogg's own "X" Division, which was already working on gaseous-diffusion engineering in the Jersey City laboratory. John Arnold became director of research and development (Keith's executive assistant); Al Baker, chief engineer; Manson Benedict, head of the process development, and Clarence Johnson, in charge of experimental research. Around this nucleus, top talent was brought in from outside to solve specific problems; Kellex soon grew into a large corporation employing three thousand people, with headquarters located on three floors of the Woolworth Building in downtown Manhattan.

Keith, usually a domineering and impatient man, conducted his orchestra of soloists with rare skill and tact. In organizing Kellex, he at first thought that he faced the alternatives of creating a stiff hierarchy and bossing everybody, which he knew none of the stars would accept; or of establishing a committee ruling by majority vote, which was contrary to his temperament and management beliefs. Actually, he did not select either formula. Organizational theory was not among his worries; all he cared about was getting things done. So he shaped Kellex into a loose organization of warlords, each one remaining full master in his fief but with the comfortable feeling that Keith would back him up all the way. As leader, the Texan's role was to provide the inspiration, to keep a sense of urgency alive and to assume personal responsibility for any fault, criticism or failure.

Before long Dobie Keith became, in the eyes of all the engineers and scientists, the personification of Kellex, with both the good and the bad that this new word conveyed.

18

THE PERSONALITY and behavior of Leslie Groves appeared quite puzzling to some of the scientists with whom he had recently come in contact. Despite the tremendous burden of his responsibilities and despite the exhausting tempo of the effort, he seemed to be strangly immune to most of the doubts, emotions and feelings of insecurity normally experienced by men in such a position. It was obvious that, no matter how intricate the problems, the general knew exactly what he wanted and where his duty lay.

Some saw in his absolute, unhesitating way of judging "right" and "wrong" a naïve, oversimplified moral code, if not a lack of sensitivity. They became his bitter, frustrated critics. Others found it difficult to believe that in the world of the 1940s any intelligent and well-informed man could remain so candid and undoubting. They concluded that the general, too disciplined and proud to show hesitation or anxiety, was sometimes hiding his feelings. But if Groves had, like everybody else, his moments of weakness or doubt, no one ever saw them. Not even his wife. Grace Groves had first met her husband when she was a very young girl and her father, Colonel Richard H. Wilson, commanded the Fourteenth United States Infantry, stationed in Montana. The family of Chaplain Groves lived in quarters close by the commanding officer's house. Leslie was a tall, serious boy, always studying and helping his family. The Wilsons felt that Chaplain Groves was too hard on his sons, especially on Leslie (or Dick, as he was called), the youngest one, whom the colonel thought was the best of the three. "That boy will go very far," he used to say.

At the Groveses' no one went anywhere on Sunday, except to church or for a quiet walk in the afternoon — they observed the Sabbath strictly. The boys couldn't play ball — all the children had to sit in the house and read. There was no frivolity, no waste of time there. The chaplain's pay was small, and there were four children to bring up. But the Groves family believed in education, so all the children went to the best of colleges, although the strictest economy was required to make this possible.

In Colonel Wilson's home the atmosphere was somewhat different. In keeping with their well-to-do Southern background, the members of the family were brought up to enjoy beautiful things, music and good food. The colonel, a West Pointer, was a man with a broad education, who spoke fluent French, German, Italian and Spanish, and read Latin and Greek for pleasure. The sophisticated colonel and the austere chaplain had high respect for each other, still the elder Groves could never approve the colonel's holding target practice for the troops and baseball games on Sunday, or the Wilsons' dinner parties at which wine was always served. The chaplain was a strict teetotaler, disapproving very much of smoking and drinking. Young Leslie was to adhere to most of his father's beliefs throughout life, especially to his disdain for the use of profanity.

The chaplain's children were endlessly fascinated by tales of their father's service in exotic, faraway places like Cuba, China and the Philippines. They were thrilled by old newspaper clippings such as the article, written in 1899, which described the chaplain thus: "Coming home from Santiago on the *Concho*, we had the Chaplain of the 8th Regulars, Rev. L. R. Groves. Terribly emaciated by yellow fever, he was one of the most afflicted men on the entire ship of fever-stricken souls. With disease withering him and death looking him in the face, he would stagger out on the deck and do the military honors above dead heroes 'ere we committed them to the sea."

Then too there were the battles of El Caney and San Juan in Cuba, of Imperial City in China . . . the names sounded so romantic to the Groves children. The family treasured an old letter sent by General A. S. Daggett in 1906 to the Secretary of War in Washington, D.C.: ". . . I want to recommend Chaplain Leslie R. Groves for promotion. It is difficult for me to see how there could be a more deserving chaplain. He has served in all the wars we have had since his appointment.

"During the campaign in China, where so many men were prostrated by heat, the Chaplain was constantly helping them in any possible way. . . . How a chaplain could put more conscience into his work, I know not. . . . Among the several good Chaplains I have served with, Chaplain Groves is easily the best and most efficient of them all."

He was a Presbyterian minister in Albany when Leslie was born on August 17, 1896. The father, descendant of French Huguenot settlers who came to America about 1640 from the Isle of Jersey, had been brought up on a farm outside of Utica, New York, and, as a farm boy, was the first one in his family to be educated beyond preparatory school when he entered Hamilton College. After teaching school for one year, he studied law in Utica and was admitted to the bar. A few years later he entered Auburn Theological Seminary and became a minister. Four months after the birth of Leslie, Jr., the father became an Army chaplain, and the family moved to Vancouver, Washington, where the Fourteenth Infantry was stationed.

For the first five years of his life, the child did not see very much of his father. Chaplain Groves went to Cuba in 1898 with the Eighth Infantry, where he had serious bouts with yellow fever and malaria. Soon afterwards he followed the Fourteenth Infantry to the Philippines, rejoining them and remaining there until 1901. During this time he went with the regiment on the Boxer Expedition to China.

During these years his wife and three sons and later a little daughter remained at Vancouver barracks in one of the officers' houses lining the huge parade ground. The chaplain's wife was a brave strong woman whose life with four children was not easy, especially after her husband contracted tuberculosis and had to be sent to an Army hospital in New Mexico. When their daughter developed spinal trouble, Mrs. Groves packed up and took the children to Pasadena, where the chaplain met them from time to time on sick leave from New Mexico.

For two years they all lived in California, until the chaplain was allowed, in 1908, to leave the hospital. Still convalescing, he was stationed at Fort Apache, Arizona, where the climate was favorable to his condition. Young Leslie spent six months of 1908 with his father in Arizona. He went to the local post school, which was taught by a corporal in a single room. The corporal had completed less than two years of high school, yet was a good instructor who could teach all grammar school subjects. But when maneuvers began, the troops left Fort Apache and the corporal went along with them. Leslie was sent home to Pasadena to finish seventh grade. It was just one more change in his peripatetic school career. For his first-grade schooling, he had been taught at home by his aunt; the second and third had been spent in a one-room school at Sandy Hook, New Jersey; the fourth was in Vancouver, and the fifth and sixth grades were in Pasadena.

Though the chaplain's health remained very poor, and he could come home on leave for only one month a year, his influence strongly marked the children. His discussions at the table were always instructive, and there was much reading and studying and work going on in the home. The day always began with the morning prayers, said by all the family members together. The boys read the *World Almanac* avidly; at an early age they could easily rattle off the names of the one hundred largest cities in the United States, together with their populations, and also the names, in order, of the entire succession of all the Presidents and Vice-Presidents, not to mention all major-league batting averages.

After the family moved to California, the Groves boys worked in the summertime from the time Leslie was eleven. The first job he had was picking walnuts; his schoolmates remembered that his hands were always stained a deep brown from walnut juice. His next job was picking fruit — prunes, peaches, apricots and grapes — which earned him about a dollar a day. During the entire year the boy worked on the family's acre and a half.

The father's authority was never questioned — it was inconceivable for the children even to think that anything their parents said or did could be wrong. Most of the things Leslie Groves learned in his boyhood came from his parents, not from schoolteachers. The chaplain was extremely well educated, and the mother, too, was well read, and very musical. Family evenings were spent in reading and conversation about history, geography or the American government. The mother would play the piano, and if the boys ever spent too much time reading the sports pages of the newspaper, the chaplain would chide them with a smile and say, "Isn't there something better to occupy your time?" But he would let them continue, though he preferred them to read history or biographies of great men.

Although Leslie's mother was a gentle woman, she was also firm in maintaining discipline in the family during her husband's long absences from home. She was an excellent bridge player and taught her sons to play very well, which did not make the chaplain particularly happy: to him, cards, like dancing, was a waste of time. But Mrs. Groves managed to present the bridge lessons as good training in "a will to win" as well as amusement, and the boys grew up with a love of all forms of competition. To play games for money, however, would never have entered the mind of any member of the Groves family.

As Leslie Groves grew up on Army posts, he had only one ambition — to go to West Point and become an officer himself. His father would have preferred some other career for him, but he realized that there was no use trying to talk the boy out of this idea. He set about doing what he could to get him an appointment to the United States Military Academy. In the meantime, Leslie entered the University of Washington at Seattle, where his father was stationed that year, then went on to MIT for the next year and a half, working hard and living on the very small allowance he received from home. Finally he entered West Point, at nineteen years of age.

The years at the Military Academy only confirmed and developed the clear-cut values he brought with him from Chaplain Groves's home.

People were often impressed by his self-confidence and his abiding sense of security. But he never quite understood why this should be so unusual. After all, he seemed to wonder, what's so complicated about knowing right from wrong, knowing about duty and honor? Wasn't it all spelled out very clearly?

WESTFIELD MEMORIAL LIBRARY
WESTFIELD, N. J.

19

FEW DEVICES could seem duller to any nontechnical person than the pump. There are some objects to which a certain glamour is attached — a sword, a microscope, a jet engine. But pumps are simply taken for granted, as though they always existed and no one ever had to invent them. But for the Manhattan Project a suitable pump had now become, after the barriers, the major headache in the gaseous-diffusion project.

At the beginning of 1943, after the Ingersoll-Rand Company had given up trying to design a suitable pump, Dobie Keith found himself with no one to tackle the problem. He approached Allis-Chalmers of Milwaukee, which was already under contract to build big magnets for the Manhattan Project. They were not very enthusiastic about the assignment but agreed to produce the pumps *if* given the model. This was where the real problem lay. No satisfactory pump design existed, although Dr. Henry Boorse's group at Columbia had made some progress.

Keith remembered General Groves's promise that he could bring any men to Kellex he needed. He thought of a friend in the oil industry, an experienced engineer who was particularly good at solving mechanical problems in new, imaginative ways: George Watts, chief engineer of Standard Oil of Indiana. Unfortunately, when Keith first called on Standard Oil president Edward Seubert, he was told that Watts was too valuable to the company. "We have too many other war projects," Seubert had said. "We can't spare our best engineer."

Dobie Keith, however, was determined to get Watts and mentioned the problem to General Groves, who promised his help. A short time later, Groves called on the Standard Oil president. After listening to him attentively, Seubert summoned Watts to his office and introduced him to General Groves. Then, with little explanation, the chief engineer was informed that he was to move to New York and work in a new company, named Kellex, on a very important war project. Watts, who had never heard of Kellex or the Manhattan Project, was greatly surprised. "Who are these people at Kellex?" he asked.

"Dobie Keith is the boss," answered Seubert.

George Watts, delighted to work with his old friend, accepted immediately. To him, Keith was the best recommendation for this mysterious Kellex company. In the ten years he had known the colorful Texan, he had formed a high opinion of him. Neither Watts nor Keith ever learned what Groves had said to Seubert to make him change his mind about giving up his chief engineer. But Groves often used the same approach to get his way. He believed that few top industrialists would say no to a general who had taken the time and trouble to come especially from Washington to see them in person, rather than simply writing a letter or sending an emissary.

George Watts received his first briefing on the gaseous-diffusion project in Keith's comfortable suburban home in New Jersey the evening of his arrival in February 1943. The Kellex boss emphasized the important problem of the compressors, or pumps. "These pumps have got to be radically different from anything we have today," Keith said. "They're going to have to compress a heavy, poisonous and highly corrosive gas that reacts violently on any contact with air. This gas corrodes most metals and materials. The pumps must operate at supersonic speed and in a vacuum far below atmospheric pressure. There must be no leakage whatsoever either. We expect to produce only a few pounds of end product a day, so if there is even an infinitesimal leakage in the thousands of pumps we're going to need, then the aggregate effect will be to 'eat up' our product before the end of the process.

"We have just managed to find a manufacturer — Allis-Chalmers," Keith went on. "The Army negotiated a contract with them and gave them priorities for construction of a new plant near Milwaukee. But we still don't have the model. That's why we called you in, George. You must organize a team and take charge of the pump design."

Pioneering was not new to George Watts. He was one of those engineers who had grown up with the modern oil industry in the United States. At the outset of his career, oil technology was still in its infancy. Engineers had to solve problems as they came. They had to invent and to improvise. There were no books, no manuals in which they could find the answers; there were no precedents. In such an unexplored field, all they could utilize were empirical methods and their native ingenuity.

George Watts had learned everything the hard way. He grew up in Missouri, the son of a locomotive engineer, a British immigrant, a man of good native intelligence but with only a grammar school education. Young George's dream was to become a mathematician, but when his father died early, the youngster had to support his mother. Mathematics not being a lucrative profession at that time, he was forced to take up a more practical field of study — mechanical engineering — at the University of Illinois.

For George Watts, however, study did not stop with a university degree. When he took his first job in the oil industry, he realized how little he knew about the latest scientific developments; how inadequate his mathematics were; how skimpy his knowledge of physics and chemistry. So, for fifteen long years, the studious young engineer took evening courses. Those courses proved extremely useful to an engineer in the pioneering days of the oil industry. No one knew much, for example, about things like the characteristics and behavior of metal under stress or high temperatures. There were few measuring instruments and no sure ways of detecting leaks; oil engineers had to improvise and invent. Keith, believing that this was the best possible schooling for men involved in a daring project like gaseous diffusion, recruited many bold inventive engineers like George Watts from the petroleum field.

But even a pioneer like Watts was shocked when Keith told him the facts about the pump that had still to be built. "We don't know about the requirements yet," he told Watts. "We haven't got final specifications for the pumps because these depend on the cascade design. But that cannot be definite before we invent the barriers. And that's the root of the trouble: we have no barrier yet. So we can't be sure of the number, size, or speed of the pumps we require."

"But, Dobie, how do you expect to make pumps if you don't even know their characteristics?"

"We have no choice, no time to waste. The Germans are working on the same thing, they're probably way ahead of us. This is an emergency. We're forced to build the pump factories before we have the design. We can only hope that in the meantime, somehow, we'll solve the other problems. We'll have to work in the dark — build before research, produce before having pilot plants, design without basic knowledge."

Watts went to work the very next day.

Keith realized that in the seal for the pump he faced his major problem. All existing pump models had been closely studied and many new ideas explored. But the building of a completely leak-proof seal, operating at supersonic speed and without a lubricant, still seemed highly improbable.

Looking for possible people to help, Keith thought of a fellow Texan, Judson Swearingen, a brilliant chemical engineer of thirty-six. A professor of chemical engineering at the University of Texas, Swearingen and a partner had earlier built a petroleum thermal-cracking plant in south Texas and operated it successfully. Like George Watts and Dobie Keith, he had lived under the pressure of constant improvisation and decisive action that was the order of the day in the oil industry during the thirties.

Kellogg had been working with the Elliott Company on the development of portable oxygen plants for submarines and needed a turbine specialist. Keith learned about Swearingen after he had built an unusual turboexpander that earned him some note in the oil industry. Keith went to see him in Texas and persuaded him to work on the submarine oxygen turboexpander.

During the summer of 1942, in the course of regular contacts between Elliott and Kellogg engineers, the question of the feasibility of a perfectly tight seal came up often in informal conversation. Swearingen and his superior, Ron B. Smith, head of Elliott's research, grew keenly interested in the problem without knowing anything about the secret use destined for the proposed seal. When Keith finally did brief Swearingen on uranium gaseous diffusion, the young engineer listened carefully to the long list of requirements — then unheard of in industrial technology — and gave his frank opinion: the pump itself might not be impossible to build; it was the seal that would present an almost insurmountable problem.

In the weeks that followed, however, Swearingen and Smith became fascinated by the challenge. Working in their free time, they devised several possible solutions and built a half-dozen models of the seals. None worked, but each threw more light on the central problem. Swearingen, growing more and more enthusiastic, felt that he was getting nearer, with each model, to the solution. For weeks he worked on the seal without pay, just as a personal service to Dobie Keith. When the pump problem reached a total impasse early in 1943, Keith asked Swearingen to come and join Kellex. The younger Texan had developed such friendship and admiration for Keith that he quit Elliott without hesitation and moved to New York.

Judson Swearingen was a friendly, alert man with a quiet manner, but he could become difficult and stubborn if he felt that people wanted to obstruct him. He had grown up in southern Texas, where his father had a ranch in an area where the influence and constant sense of urgency of the oil industry was omnipresent. After chemical engineering studies at the University of Texas, it was only natural for him to go into the petroleum business. When Swearingen joined Kellex's Pump Division, the compressor's impeller and case had already been designed and some preliminary tests carried out. Allis-Chalmers was about to start construction of a brand-new pump plant in a corner of one of its factories outside Milwaukee. Started in April, it was completed and ready for production in only fifty-seven days.

The feat was all the more remarkable considering the reluctance with which Allis-Chalmers had accepted the assignment. The company president, Walter Geist, believed that Allis-Chalmers already had enough to do with the Manhattan Project in manufacturing the giant magnets to be built under the direction of Lawrence; besides, there were all the company's other war contracts. It had taken all of Groves's persuasive ability to get Geist to accept the job, especially after having described the unusual requirements for the nonexistent compressor. When Geist explained that his company had neither space nor facilities for producing several thousand compressors, Groves promised that the Government would build a special new plant and give Allis-Chalmers top priorities for all materials and equipment.

From the moment that Walter Geist said yes to Groves and Keith, Allis-Chalmers was subjected to heavy pressure both from the Army and from Kellex. The company was not given time to breathe before construction of the plant began. Although the two Chalmers men who directed the work, James M. White and Joseph J. Rosecky, were very efficient and broke all records for fast construction of a plant, they were continually goaded by emissaries from New York who felt that the Allis-Chalmers people did not really have their hearts in the job.

The exasperation felt by Allis-Chalmers engineers was more than slightly justified. The Kellex company had been formed only a few months before and already numbered more than one thousand engineers and other experts. They were highly competent men, but they had not yet had time to become well acquainted with one another, nor did they understand the overall objective. Consequently, in their dealings with Allis-Chalmers, they often made engineering presentations that lacked uniformity. The Allis-Chalmers people thus did not know really what was expected of them, nor whether there was even a remote probability of ultimate success in building the radically new type of pump.

All this time Columbia and Kellex groups were working frantically on the design for a seal. The collaboration was good, due especially to the pleasant attitude of Columbia's Dr. Boorse, a man who never felt jealous of other people's ideas. By the spring of 1943, all efforts were concentrated on his design for a seal.

Models were built with the greatest care. New properties of the seal were discovered — but also a host of new requirements and limitations. After further study, preliminary tests seemed to indicate that it would work. But first Kellex had to build a pilot plant containing several stages of the gaseous-diffusion cascade in order to simulate conditions in the future plant. Batteries of special instruments had to be installed to test each component.

Finally, in the summer of 1943, the day came when the pilot plant was completed; the pumps, fitted with the Boorse seal, were turned on. They were operated for a few minutes, then shut off so that engineers could check on their performance. Inspection showed that every seal in the pilot plant had failed completely. It was a black day for the Kellex people.

The new Allis-Chalmers plant, with its complex machinery, engineers, security guards and skilled workers, waited vainly, ready for production that could not begin.

20

A VITAL DECISION had to be made, and someone had to make it, one way or another. The gaseous-diffusion plant, which had been given the code designation of K–25, was still very much in the planning stage, but the Kellex team realized that when and if K–25 were ever built, it would demand an extraordinary amount of electric power. Rough calculations showed that the process would use more electricity than a city the size of Boston.

No solutions for the barriers, the pumps, valves and pipes were even remotely foreseeable in the spring of 1943. How many months, or years, would these require? Was it even possible to build such a fantastic plant at Oak Ridge? No one was sure. Time was running short, every week counted. The Project could not afford to wait until the plant was constructed to start thinking about the electric power to run it: huge power plants take about two years to build.

There was, of course, electric power from Tennessee Valley Authority in the eastern part of the state. But neither Groves nor Keith were willing to count on it. They insisted that the gaseous-diffusion plant be independent, especially in case of a power failure. The scientists had figured out that any stoppage, even momentary, would be calamitous — long months would be required to restart the process. While Groves did not think that the risk was that big, he did not want to take any unnecessary chances, and ruled that any possible interruption of power must be prevented.

To Dobie Keith there seemed to be only one possible course of action: build a power plant immediately so that it would be ready when K–25 was finally constructed. But this would entail great risk — mobilizing thousands of workers, requisitioning tons of badly needed war materials, spending tens of millions of dollars. What if K–25 were never built?

When he took the job, Keith had demanded and gotten entire responsibility for the gaseous-diffusion project as far as his company's role was concerned. Now he stood alone facing the dilemma, with everyone watching to see what he would do. Throughout his career he had had to make bold, far-reaching decisions. But this was the hardest one he had ever faced; never before had so much depended on a single decision.

Keith called his principal colleagues to a meeting in his office on the eleventh floor of the Woolworth Building. Briefly, he stated the pros and cons of the gamble, then gravely announced that the steam-electric plant was to be built immediately. It would be the largest power plant ever constructed in a single operation. "From now on," he said, "there will be no retreat; we'll advance full speed ahead — to complete success or disaster." Those who were listening to him knew all that was involved. Keith gave them a last chance. "It's like crossing the Rubicon," he said. "This will be our point of no return; there won't be any way back. So if any of you are hesitant, you should leave now. I want you to be completely frank and honest now. Tomorrow will be too late!"

There was a brief silence, then someone asked, "When do we start?"

Keith smiled with relief to see that all his specialists were backing him up. He turned to Ludwig Skog, a large, Norwegian-born engineer of fifty-four who had just joined Kellex. "Ludwig, when do you think you can have a rough design ready?"

"Well," Skog said slowly, with his Scandinavian accent, "I am trying for days to find out what kind of electricity you need exactly — what frequency?"

It was a legitimate question coming from an engineer who had just been asked to design the biggest power plant in the world. And yet Skog's question made everyone ill at ease.

"Tell him, Manson!" said Keith.

Benedict turned helplessly to George Watts, who could only shrug, and then said, "I wouldn't know. It depends on the pumps. What kind of pumps, what speed, how many of them. When we have the pumps, then . . ."

But the pumps had not yet been invented. "I wish somebody could tell *me* what those pumps will look like!" moaned Watts. "If we ever make them!" added Owen C. Brewster, Watts's assistant in the pump group.

Thus the big decision to go ahead with the construction of K–25 and its power plant had been made long before the principal components were developed. The barrier work seemed to have reached an impasse, and a high-speed pump, which would be hermetically sealed and use no lubricant, was not yet designed. But the builders of the power plant had to know what type of pump would be used because the electric current would be different for different types of pumps. At this time the pump problem was extremely critical: Allis-Chalmers was not yet in the production picture, and Ingersoll-Rand, the only company that had accepted the challenge of trying to manufacture the pump, had suddenly withdrawn. Realizing the enormous difficulties involved, the company had admitted honestly that it had neither the personnel nor the facilities for manufacturing thousands of yet-to-be-invented compressors. Dobie Keith had again rushed around to all the pump manufacturers, urging them to help. But he could hardly blame them for not wanting to give a promise to produce a compressor that no one had yet successfully designed. It would be tragic if the whole K–25 project were to fail for lack of a pump. But, tragic or not, the fact remained that gaseous diffusion was inconceivable without one.

All this could hardly help Ludwig Skog. How could he design a power plant without knowing the frequency of the electricity? Some turbogenerators operate at 60 cycles and turn at 3600 revolutions per minute. Others work at 120 cycles and turn twice as fast. But if you use 240 cycles, then the speed of the turbine is 720 rpm. Different cycles give completely different speeds, and yet no one could predict the speed of the still undeveloped pump.

Skog had had great experience with electric plants. He was the second partner in the Chicago engineering firm of Sargent and Lundy, one of the largest builders of steam-electric power plants in the country. Skog's career read like an immigrant's success story. Born in a small Norwegian fishing village north of the Arctic Circle, he graduated from the Technical Institute in Trondheim. In 1909, with starry eyes and one hundred dollars in his pocket, he sailed for New York with a friend who had an uncle in Chicago. His first sight of New York harbor was on Labor Day, and ever after he was to remember it as "the most beautiful evening of my life." In Chicago he found a five-dollar-a-week room with board and began looking for a job. His search ended when he saw a want ad that said: "Sargent and Lundy: Mechanical Draftsman Wanted, $15 a week."

Now, thirty-three years later, Ludwig Skog was a very important engineer, partner in a distinguished firm and the designer of the modernized power plants for the Navy's destroyers. He was so occupied with war contracts that it took a lot of nerve for Al Baker to ask him to drop everything and join Kellex as a simple engineer. Al Baker, Kellex's chief engineer, had known Skog for a long time, from the period when they both had worked at Sargent and Lundy. During the Depression the company had gone through difficult times; many employees were laid off, and engineers and draftsmen, having no work to do, sometimes even played ping-pong on the design tables. In 1934 Morris Kellogg, president of M. W. Kellogg Company, called Sargent and Lundy to say how badly he needed a chief engineer in New York. Asked to send their best man, the Chicago firm first proposed Skog. Since he could not accept the job, Skog in turn suggested Al Baker, who was hired and went to New York.

When, eight years later, the problem came up of building an unusual power plant for the K–25 project, Baker immediately thought of his old colleague. "If anybody can build a power plant like that," Baker told Keith, "it's Skog."

Baker took the train to Chicago and appeared at Sargent and Lundy's one morning at ten o'clock. "Ludwig, I want you to come to New York. I'm in charge of construction of an extremely important plant for the Government. I can't tell you much about it because it's top secret; but I can assure you, it's a vital matter."

Skog shook his head. "Al, you know I'm running the whole company here, and I'm also working on Navy destroyers with Gibbs and Cox."

"Yes, I know it. But this project is even more important. Listen, Ludwig, I'll tell you this much: If we can design this plant and operate it successfully for fifty days, then we cannot lose the war."

Skog's broad, friendly face grew serious. "Let me think it over."

"I'll be back at noon, Ludwig, and you have to give me your answer then."

It was an important decision, Skog felt, for the executive partner to quit his company and embark on an undisclosed assignment. But he, a former Norwegian immigrant, was now the father of two young American boys, both servicemen — one in the Navy, one in the Air Corps — and both headed for overseas battlefronts. That changed a lot.

Skog telephoned his wife and described his conversation with Al Baker. "He really said that it might win the war?" she asked. She was also Norwegian with many relatives in the Nazi-occupied country.

When Baker reappeared two hours later, Ludwig shook his hand. "I'll come with you, Al. But please don't tell me more — I'll be worried that I might talk too much. But before going to New York, my wife and I want to spend a few days visiting our son. He's an ensign, you know, and leaving soon for sea duty. . . ."

Now, at the conference in Keith's office, over a month after his arrival in New York, Ludwig Skog still knew nothing about the atomic bomb project. All he knew was that he had to design the biggest steam-electric plant in the world according to some unheard-of specifications given to him by Keith, Baker and Dr. Benedict.

"Until we design the damn K–25 plant, we won't know what frequency current we need," Keith told him. "But we can't wait. Say, Ludwig, I have an idea. If we can't choose *one* frequency, what about building a power plant with *all* of them, with four or five different cycles? Would that be possible?"

Skog opened his eyes in amazement. It was like asking a shoemaker to make a pair of shoes fitting all sizes of feet! "I've never heard of that, it certainly never has been done," Skog said. But the unexpected challenge stimulated him. "Different cycles in the same plant!" he exclaimed. "Sounds sort of peculiar, but after all . . . it shouldn't be impossible."

He made a few rapid calculations in his head. "But, gentlemen, I hope you realize what will be involved — the equipment, the money . . . ?"

Keith interrupted him. "As long as you get this plant running, you can do anything you want to. Tell him, Colonel, isn't that right?"

Lieutenant Colonel James C. Stowers, the Manhattan District officer assigned to Kellex, instantly agreed. "You can get any boiler, any turbine, anything you need. We'll arrange top priority with the War Production Board. And don't worry about the money!"

Ludwig Skog really did have full power to act as he wished. He made the design with Sargent and Lundy and organized a small team there of engineers. He worked during the week at the Woolworth Building in New York, weekends in Chicago. From all over the country, he picked out turbines and equipment ordered by other war projects. Everything was made immediately available to him, as he needed it, through the Manhattan District. He thus acquired a couple of Allis-Chalmers turbines, a few from General Electric, others from Westinghouse — all of them under construction for other companies. General Groves saw to it that nothing necessary for the plant was refused.

On May 31, 1943, the first surveyors for the power plant arrived at Oak Ridge, where in other areas work had already started on the future town and on the electromagnetic installations. They were followed two days later by engineers of the J. A. Jones Construction Company. Building started in an isolated area on the Clinch River, seven miles from a railroad and only accessible over two narrow gravel roads. One access road was confined to the carrying capacity — two passenger cars of a hand-propelled ferry. The other road had a single-lane bridge with only an eight-ton load limit. No electricity or telephones were available.

Soon the labor force rose to 5600 men, most of them working on ten-hour day shifts. The foundation for supporting the boilers presented serious problems due to the topography of the site — and also the hectic building pace. The final solution was to sink forty concrete-filled caissons thirty feet deep in the red clay. With extraordinary speed and round-the-clock effort, the Jones Company erected the brick-and-steel building by that fall.

On March 1, 1944, only nine months after construction had started, the first steam rose from one boiler; this even beat the unrealistically short deadline of March 17 set by Groves. Six weeks later, three boilers, each producing 750,000 pounds per hour of high-pressure steam at a 950°

temperature, were feeding turbogenerators ranging in size from 1500 to 35,000 kilowatts. The generating equipment had a capacity of 238,000 K.S., which was enormous for that time.

Not only was the plant a complete success, but it was designed and constructed in record time, at a cost of $34 million. Cautious about the possibility of sabotage, Ludwig Skog insisted that all cables be laid underground between the power station and the site of the future plant. He was proud of the achievement: the first power plant that could produce current for five different frequencies. There was now electric power for a gaseous-diffusion plant to produce fissionable material for an atomic bomb. But there was still no certainty at all that the problem-ridden K–25 plant could ever be built.

21

Mrs. Elky Shazkin, a young physicist, came to Columbia on a Saturday in March 1943 to inform Dr. Francis Slack that, unfortunately, she could not take the job he had offered her. Her husband was about to be drafted; she wanted to be free to be with him whenever possible. Since Dr. Slack wanted her for some very secret work involving long hours, she had decided to turn down the offer.

The quiet-spoken professor was disappointed but understood her reasons. "What does your husband do?" he asked.

"He's with the magazine *House Beautiful.*"

"A writer, I see."

"Not exactly. My husband is their production manager. He's a printing expert. He majored in printing, and — "

"Printing! Did you say *printing?*" Slack had literally jumped from his chair.

Much surprised, the young woman nodded. "Why, yes. He got his B.S. in printing at Carnegie Tech while I was studying physics there."

Now Slack was really excited. "Where is your husband now?" he asked.

"Right here, waiting for me in the corridor."

"Please call him in!" said the scientist, then shouted through the door to the next laboratory, "Ed, come here. We have a printing specialist here!"

Edward Adler, a shock of black hair hanging over his forehead, came into the room, wiping his stained hands. This might give him some leads on a new barrier idea. Mrs. Shazkin introduced her youthful husband to them. He was hard put to understand why he had suddenly become the subject of such intense interest.

"Tell us more about your work in printing, Mr. Shazkin," said Dr. Slack. "What kind of press, for instance, do you use for your magazine?"

It was only the first of a barrage of technical questions about printing that the two scientists fired at Shazkin during the next half hour.

Born in Poland, Leonard Shazkin had come to the United States at the age of one, had grown up in New York City and had studied at City College and then at Carnegie Tech. He was quite bewildered when Slack and Adler asked him to work with them, even insisted that he start immediately. When he answered that he was about to be drafted, Shazkin was even more bewildered to hear them say, "Don't you worry! We'll take care of that! Your job with us is vital to the war effort."

A printer's work vital to the war? The Shazkins could not understand at all. Their amazement was compounded when they were told that, owing to security regulations, the Columbia laboratory, as a top-secret group, could not employ both husband and wife — and the printer would be chosen over the physicist, without any hesitation.

Three days later, still thoroughly baffled by the turn of events, Leonard Shazkin reported for work at Pupin Hall. His draft board had been outraged to see unnamed but obviously important powers intervening on behalf of a young and healthy printer whose place ought to be in the service. Four times the draft board appealed Shazkin's exemption; four times it was overruled. The orders were coming from the highest places. The disgusted draft board finally dropped the case.

To say that the American Chicle Company, makers of chewing gum (Chiclets), did not play a vital role in the war effort is not to detract from its standing as a good, respectable company. Its management, accustomed to the pleasant duties of catering to the chewing habits of the nation, was astonished when, out of the blue, it received several telephone calls from some Army colonels who, in a mysterious and authoritarian tone, announced the imminent visit of a Dr. Edward Adler, a Columbia scientist.

Soon after the call, Adler, accompanied by an Army captain, arrived at the five-story American Chicle Building in Long Island City, just across the East River from Manhattan. He did not have to be a chemist, Adler thought, to identify the strong aroma of tutti-frutti, spearmint and other gum flavors that permeated the whole neighborhood.

"What can I do for you, gentlemen?" asked the company's president, Philip Becker, as the visitors were ushered into his office. Becker had only the vaguest idea about the purpose of the visit. His business manager had merely received a phone call from some colonel who wanted to use — God only knew why — one of Chicle's printing presses, a French-manufactured one bought in 1936 to print five-color display packages.

"We need your Chambord press," Adler said bluntly.

"Now just a minute," Becker said. "Just who are you? And what's this for?"

The Army captain intervened. "The Manhattan Engineering District — a top-priority war project. I'm sorry, but we can't tell you anything about its functions. It's top secret."

Becker protested that the company just could not spare the press. He showed them its schedule — the machine was busy almost without interruption. But the fiery, intense Adler cut him short. "You'll have to rearrange your schedules. We need the machine."

Becker was more than slightly irritated. They could at least tell him *why* they wanted the press! People just couldn't walk into a factory and requisition a machine. What kind of free society was that!

"And suppose we refuse?"

The captain stiffened and became grim. "In that case, we'll arrive tomorrow morning with military trucks to dismantle the press and take it away!" He pulled a sheaf of letters and credentials from his pocket and handed them across the desk to Becker. "May I please use your telephone, Mr. Becker?"

"Yes, of course."

On reading the letters, the president of American Chicle had to change his mind. Still, he did not understand at all how a chewing-gum company's printing press could be *that* important in the war effort to President Roosevelt and Secretary of War Stimson. After the captain's phone call to Washington, Becker was no wiser but definitely convinced that he should cooperate. He called in "Doc" Smith, his production manager, and told him that his decision was now reversed. "They can use the machine. And get Charles in here!"

Reginald E. Charles, superintendent of American Chicle's box division, appeared and was informed that the Chambord press would no longer print display containers; it would be used, instead, by the Government for an unspecified purpose — and for an unspecified time. Charles, a puzzled man in a spotless white smock, went with the visitors to see the machine.

On the fourth floor, they emerged into the wilting heat of the plant's refining section. Passing huge vats used in the refining of chewing gum, they reached the "cool-flavor" vault — and were almost overwhelmed by pungent, spicy odors. In the next room, white-jacketed technicians were concocting formulas for chewing gum. A long passage led to the printing and packaging section, where giant presses ground out an endless stream of printed wrappers. At the very end of the box-and-carton section stood the Chambord press.

For the next four or five months, this corner of a redolent gum factory was the center of some bizarre activity. Every couple of days, Adler and his assistant, Leonard Shazkin, telephoned to say that they were coming: Would the pressmen please start the machine? They would arrive from Columbia University in a New York taxicab with their material and go to the special Chambord press, where two of Chicle's printers operated the machine under the direction of Reginald Charles. The printers did what Adler asked them to do, without asking questions. They were given different types of inks to try; tests were made with various ingredients in the ink, at different temperatures and speeds.

Adler, who obviously knew nothing about printing, and Shazkin, who seemed to know too much, would sit there for hours, watching the operation impatiently as their business suits became spattered with ink. They were not at all interested in color. All they wanted was to print some dots of a very special shape — which seemed impossible. They would examine samples under a microscope, and often changed the process accordingly. After several more hours of watching, they would cut off samples of the printed material, leave the plant and hail a taxi to take them back across the East River to the Columbia lab.

The supervisor Reginald Charles had to be cleared by security before he started helping, but he never understood why it was so important to perfect the printing of this unusual ink dot. All he was told was that the nature of the work could not be disclosed, but that the result would have a "profound influence" on the outcome of the war. Even Shazkin, when he had first started working at Pupin Hall, had been told only: "We have to print a certain pattern. . . ."

American Chicle's press had been chosen after a long survey of all printing machines available in the New York area. It was the only one that fitted the requirements. Some other presses had been tried in complete secrecy but with poor results. The Chicle Company's press seemed to offer better possibilities, but for months no satisfactory results could be achieved. Finally some success was attained, and the new barrier moved one step farther toward reality. But several other steps, all of them complicated and as yet untested, remained to be taken before a workable barrier could be fabricated. The Chambord press at American Chicle Company had served, however, a worthy purpose. As soon as the Columbia scientists left the Long Island City plant, a detachment of MP's swarmed over the place, cleaned and carefully dusted the press and removed every bit of evidence of the atomic energy work.

It was not until long after the war that the chewing-gum makers at the American Chicle Company learned that, for five months in 1943, an interesting technique in making the atomic bomb had been studied next to their kettles of spearmint. Meantime, Adler worked day and night on his barrier, constantly prodding his assistants, rushing around the lab and getting emotional, looking like a mad genius with his thick, unruly black hair almost standing on end. He never calmed down and never turned to another approach until all possibilities were exhausted.

22

IT WAS ALREADY ten o'clock at night when the train arrived in Washington, but General Groves's instructions had been clear and urgent. "Call me as soon as you return, no matter what time it is," he had told Lieutenant Colonel Franklin T. Matthias the day before when he sent him to Wilmington. It had been a vague assignment — Groves had simply asked Matthias to attend a meeting at Du Pont, to listen carefully and to report back to him, but he had not said what the meeting would be about.

A reserve officer on active duty, Matthias had spent the whole day of December 14, 1942, in conference rooms, just listening to strange and complicated talk by Chicago scientists and Du Pont engineers. He understood little of what was said; the subjects were over his head — plutonium, neutrons, reactors — words he had never even heard before. But he did understand that the men were trying to establish a list of requirements for a plant: such things as water, power, highways, railroads and distance from cities.

Matthias stepped into a phone booth in the station and called Groves. The general was still in his office. "Stay at the station!" he commanded. "I'll come right down and pick you up."

Rather unusual, thought Matthias, for the general to drive all the way to meet a younger officer. Well, the few dealings he had had with Groves were all unusual.

Some months before, during some work Matthias had been doing on the new Pentagon Building, the general had asked him to make a physical description of what a gaseous-diffusion plant would look like, based on a mysterious scientific report that did not mention the end product. Groves had told him the description was needed by the Air Force, which was looking for such a plant in Germany. Later he asked Matthias to review a site-selection report of a place called Los Alamos, again failing to mention what it was all about. Both times, Groves had appeared pleased by the work, though it was not his habit to voice praise.

Matthias was an energetic man in his thirties who had grown up on a Wisconsin farm, then worked his way through college to get his degree in hydraulic engineering. His friends called him Fritz, a nickname his uncle had given him as a small boy during World War I. That had been a bad name in those days and used to make him so angry the name stuck.

The general picked Fritz Matthias up at the station. "Tell me what happened," he asked as they drove off.

"Colonel Nichols was there, and a delegation of scientists headed by Arthur Compton, and some top Du Pont people. But as to what they said — well, maybe if I read some Buck Rogers stories, sir! . . ." Matthias described the meeting as best he could and enumerated the site requirements.

Groves spoke thoughtfully. "Well, tomorrow morning get hold of Gilbert Church and Al Hall — those two Du Pont engineers you met today — and make arrangements to find a place to build this plant."

"Tomorrow?"

"Yes, tomorrow morning! Go talk to General Robins and our electric power specialists. Find a spot where there is power, water and isolation in the United States. Personally, I think you'll find it in the Far West, near the Columbia River."

The car pulled up to the curb in front of Matthias's home, and there in the cold December night, Groves told him for the first time about the secret project.

The next day, Lieutenant Colonel F. T. Matthias was transferred to the Manhattan District. The following evening Church and Hall, the Du Pont engineers, left by plane for Spokane, Washington; Matthias was to follow later. It was bad flying weather and instead of landing in Spokane, where Division Engineer Richard Park had arranged for an officer to meet them, the plane went on to Seattle, and they had to take a train back to Spokane that night.

Groves had instructed all district engineers to help, although he did not tell them why a plant site was so urgently needed. Captain George Hopkins of the Army Engineers, who met Church and Hall, was a man who knew the area by heart; for two weeks he showed them all the most promising sites. These had been suggested by the Corps of Engineers in areas as far apart as Oregon, California and Washington. Everywhere they went, the Du Pont men were introduced as civilian employees of the Army.

Matthias's first glimpse of the village of Hanford, Washington, was from an Army plane flying in from the south. Church and Hall saw it as they were driving in from Yakima; it was the third site on their list. When all three later met at Pasco Air Base, they agreed immediately: Hanford was exactly what they wanted.

A small village of thirty or forty houses, with a church and a school, Hanford was situated on the west bank of the Columbia River, in the

WESTFIELD MEMORIAL LIBRARY
WESTFIELD, N. J.

midst of a vast, desert-like area of sagebrush and sand, some twenty miles
north of Richland. It was near enough to such good power sources as the
Bonneville and Grand Coulee dam systems. The weather was perfect —
rain fell rarely in this part of Washington state, yet the abundant
Columbia River water was cool and looked clear. Very few people lived
in the valley, just a few farmers along the river; most of them were
veterans and their families settled there after World War I by the state,
poor people who were struggling for a living from irrigated orchards.

Matthias, Church and Hall drove into Portland the same night to call
General Groves in Washington, D.C. Matthias was excited. "We've found
it!" he announced to Groves enthusiastically. "There's not much point in
seeing any other places."

But Groves insisted that they inspect the rest of the sites on their list.
"You should at least see them," he said, "so we won't have people yapping
at us later. Some scientists want to put the plant up on Lake Superior,
where the water would be very cold. But the trouble is, you couldn't do
construction work up there in the winter. The average scientist, you
know, is not always practical outside of his field."

The three-man team continued its inspection, then returned to Washington, D.C. Its final report, presented to Groves on January 1, 1943, was
unequivocal: Hanford, Washington, was by far the best site. A few days
later, it was approved, subject to inspection on the ground, and less than
two weeks later Groves inspected it himself. He liked the place but
noticed a handicap: its rail facilities consisted of only one, light-gauge,
seldom-used rail spur off the Chicago, Milwaukee and St. Paul Railroad.

As his car approached a rail crossing, he heard a train coming. "Better
slow up and wait," Groves warned his officer guide. "We don't want to be
hit by that thing — I can't think of anything more disgraceful than being
run over by a train that operates only twice a week in this desert!"

From the area, Groves telephoned Washington to initiate the real estate
operations necessary to obtain the land. Back in Washington, he summoned Matthias to his office. "Now we'll start construction," he said
briskly. "We've got to find someone to run this job for us in the district.
The Chief of Engineers has promised me any officer I want. I'd like you
to look them over and make some recommendations." As Matthias was
leaving the office, the general stopped him. "If you can't find anybody,
you'll have to do it yourself."

Matthias turned around at once. "General," he said, "there's no one I
can recommend."

Groves's reply was just as prompt. "Then the job is yours!"

The same day Lieutenant Colonel Franklin T. Matthias became Area
Engineer for the Hanford project. When someone asked why Matthias

had been chosen for the job, Groves replied without hesitation, "Why Matthias? It's very simple. If we have a catastrophe — which I pray the good Lord we won't — there's a guy that nothing will disturb. If anybody can get them evacuated, Matthias can do it."

Matthias thought Groves had hardly noticed him before; he had never suspected that the general had been watching him for months, closely studying his reactions to different situations. Only years after the war did he learn indirectly in what high esteem the general had held him.

When the order went out for the construction of the Hanford plant, the design of atomic reactors was only in its initial phase. The success of Fermi's small pile in Chicago had confirmed the scientific theory; but building huge reactors with industrial capacity was another matter. Many scientific questions still remained unanswered: Would the neutrons in the reactor, for example, continue to multiply, or would they decrease until the reaction died? In their experiments, the scientists had done the best they could, but their equipment and the number of neutrons available to them at the time were inadequate for a complete study. The physicists were therefore going along pretty much on faith, with the hope that "everything would turn out right."

But tremendous new problems had to be solved, unsuspected difficulties had to be surmounted. The Chicago scientists, after swallowing their first resentment over Du Pont's taking over the construction and operation of the plutonium project, began to realize that the role of industrial engineers was going to be, of necessity, at least as important as theirs. The strain between Chicago and Wilmington disappeared, and a close collaboration began between the Ph.D.'s of Arthur Compton's Metallurgical Laboratory and Du Pont's "TNX Division," headed by Roger Williams.

In Chicago, the work on reactor design was done mainly under the direction of Fermi and Wigner. The key person in the study of separation methods was Glenn Seaborg, the discoverer of plutonium. Leo Szilard, always bursting with new ideas, worked independently as a free-lancer, he was a kind of scientific gadfly, restlessly touring all the laboratories, asking questions, interrupting work, offering brilliant suggestions.

In Wilmington, Roger Williams put R. M. (Monty) Evans at the head of the manufacturing organization for the Project, with Crawford Greene-walt, formerly a member of the Reviewing Committee, and George Graves jointly in charge of the Technical Division. Another member of the Reviewing Committee, the flamboyant, self-made engineer Tom Gary, assigned to Fred Pardee a whole new department in his Design Division, devoted entirely to atomic works design.

Half of the thirteenth floor of the Nemours Building in Wilmington was isolated by security guards and put under strict secrecy regulations. The Design Division used the principles and specifications given by Wigner's group, then applied them to industrial proportions. With the increasing difficulties and problems, Pardee's division soon grew to four hundred engineers and designers. They did not know the exact ultimate purpose of their work (though some had suspicions), nor were they inclined to discuss the matter among themselves. Each one knew only his part in the design. The department head, Fred Pardee, a thirty-six-year-old chemical engineer, knew the plutonium project story, but was never told anything about work that would be carried out at either Oak Ridge or Los Alamos.

"No Admittance" signs were posted on the doors of all drafting rooms. The rumor circulated among Du Pont workers that a new type of nylon, the Du Pont product which had just been launched on the market, was being developed in the restricted area on the thirteenth floor.

"I want the security measures to be applied to everybody — without exception," Groves instructed Tom Gary.

"General, I was taught all of that in 1917, while you were still at West Point Military Academy!" Gary retorted impatiently. "You don't have to tell me what security is!"

Groves smiled and dropped the subject. Several months later, though, he stormed into Gary's office one day, obviously disturbed. "They won't let me into your drafting room!" he complained.

"Don't you have your pass?" asked Gary mischievously.

"No, I forgot and left it in my other uniform."

"Well, then you can't get in, General. Your orders were not to let anyone in without a pass."

Groves scowled for a moment, then laughed heartily. He always got along with the Du Pont engineer, a man as blunt and outspoken as Groves himself.

All contacts between Du Pont's Atomic Works Design Department and the Chicago scientists were handled by one executive: Crawford Greenewalt. Fermi and Wigner visited Wilmington only a few times but constantly exchanged information with Du Pont's engineers, always through Greenewalt, who acted as the liaison man with Chicago. His job was to take information from the scientists and translate it into usable terms for Du Pont's engineers, who would have to design and build a plant. He also participated in all decisions made by Du Pont. Though continuing to live in Wilmington, Greenewalt spent half of each week in Chicago.

The scientists found it hard to understand some of Du Pont's decisions. One case was when the company decided that, without even the testing benefits of building a pilot plant, they would use one separation method instead of several other possible ones. But Du Pont, from long industrial experience, was convinced that there was simply no time to work out three or four alternative methods, then decide which one was best. An immediate choice had to be made. So Du Pont's engineers picked the most likely, workable method, poured all their efforts into it, to the exclusion of any other method, and could only hope that the decision was right. It was an example of the calculated-risk approach to a problem.

The classic scientific approach, from its very nature, was radically different. "But you're doing all this the wrong way!" Fermi told Greenewalt one day. "You should go out there and build a reactor. If it doesn't work, you can find out why it doesn't work, and *then* you'll find a way to build a second reactor that *will* work!"

"Enrico, we haven't time for all that!" Greenewalt replied. "The first reactor has got to work — if it's humanly possible to make it work. On this large scale, when you have millions of dollars tied up and time is short, you can't make endless experiments."

Most of the difficulties stemmed from the scientists' complete lack of industrial experience; but the urbane, diplomatic Greenewalt always managed to smooth ruffled feathers. Groves did not interfere; he had given Du Pont carte blanche and was ready to back the company all the way. He had reconciled himself to the idea that no normal, cut-and-dried procedures could be followed in such a situation; he agreed with Du Pont that the important thing was to go ahead as fast as possible, even though the work would have to be based on very scanty laboratory data.

The pressing matter was to decide quickly on the cooling method. The reactor would generate enormous amounts of heat, and no large one could be designed until the problem of heat disposal was solved. Most scientists recommended helium as the coolant. Wigner's group was working on a water-cooling system, but the trouble there was that water — a strong neutron absorber — would slow down or might even completely shut down the reactor.

The choice was made even more difficult because more engineering would have to be done in order to find out which method had the greater feasibility. Leo Szilard proposed cooling the reactor with bismuth, a molten metal, but the idea never found sufficient support among his colleagues. Still another proposal was an air-cooling system, which was chosen for the pilot reactor to be built at Oak Ridge.

In February 1943, construction was begun in Oak Ridge on a graphite pile, which had been given the code name X–10. Though X–10 was under the jurisdiction of the University of Chicago, the staff was made up largely of Du Pont people. Everything connected with the project was kept secret; all classified materials were referred to by code name only.

The English code name for uranium was "tuballoy" and some local wag suggested "Myrna Loy" for thorium. Uranium–233, –235 and –238 were referred to respectively as "23," "25" and "28." Plutonium–239 became "49." Some confusion occurred when, by a freak coincidence, the three power-line crossings near the construction were marked by clearance signs (for the protection of mobile cranes) with the numbers 23, 28 and 49 feet, with a posted speed limit of 25!

The X–10 pile was still under construction when Du Pont suddenly decided to switch to the water-cooling method and develop the model conceived by Dr. Eugene Wigner and his group. This was a major decision, announced by Crawford Greenewalt only after the company's careful study of the different methods. Work on helium cooling was abandoned, and the efforts of Du Pont's Design Division were concentrated exclusively on Wigner's model.

Thus the plutonium project followed a peculiar pattern: design and development were carried out at the same time as the construction of the real plant and the building of the pilot plant. X–10 was completed in November, and although it could not serve as pilot for Hanford reactors, it produced small amounts of plutonium invaluable to the Los Alamos scientists as a research tool.

At the beginning of 1943, Daniel D. Friel, a twenty-three-year-old chemical engineer recently graduated from Johns Hopkins, was on the point of getting married when he received an order to go to Chicago the following day. He had been working in Du Pont's Explosives Department for only a few months.

"Well, Friel, I understand you want to get married?" said Charles M. Cooper on the train to Chicago. Cooper was the resident Du Pont man working with the Chicago scientists.

"Yes, in a few days. I plan to take off two weeks for a honeymoon."

Cooper shook his head. "Sorry, you're going to work with me in Chicago now," he said. "But you can have the weekend off to get married."

Friel was too young to contradict his new boss. When they arrived in Chicago, Cooper took him into his office. "We need an optics expert," he said in a confidential voice. He paused for a moment, then added, "You're a good chemical engineer, so . . . so we're going to remake you into an optics expert."

Friel failed to grasp the logic of such reasoning, but he listened attentively while Cooper explained the problem. Some way had to be found to enable the operators of the reactor to see through the thick concrete walls that protected them from dangerous radioactivity. The operators needed to be able to manipulate things on the other side of the walls: turn a valve, lift an object, pick up a radioactive slug that might have spilled onto the floor. It was also necessary at all times to see how the plutonium was behaving in containers and pipelines.

"We must develop devices for seeing through walls into the rear end of the reactors, so you can see slugs ejected after processing," Cooper explained. "What we're going to need are devices for looking at the separation equipment when the plutonium is removed from the other materials in the nuclear reaction. We need devices which will enable us to look inside tubes, to see through the walls of big tanks filled with water."

"But I know nothing about optics!" Friel protested.

"Neither do we," said Cooper. "But there is a Dr. George Monk here who will teach you — he's an optics expert."

Friel got married in Baltimore, went on a two-day honeymoon, then moved to Chicago to take a crash course in optics. For several months he worked intensively with Dr. Monk and attended courses on reactor theory given by Fermi, Wigner, Szilard and Alvin Weinberg. Monk and Friel had to revamp existing optical tools and parts to make new instruments. The optical companies were completely involved in war production; they had no time to develop whole new systems from scratch. So Monk and Friel were forced to invent new devices and develop new methods. When the great hour finally arrived for trying out their new optical apparatus in a reactor, something happened that no one had expected: the glass turned black. The fiasco was not the fault of either Friel or Monk. No optical expert had ever worked with high radioactivity before; they could not have known that radiation blackens glass.

The most serious obstacle to Wigner's water-cooled reactor proved to be the canning of the uranium slugs. Thousands of these slugs, which were embedded in long, cylindrical holes in the graphite, had to be cooled continuously. Water had to be forced into the very narrow space left between the slugs and the walls of the graphite holes, but the water should not come in contact with the uranium. The slugs therefore had to be placed inside of aluminum tubes so thin and tight that heat from the uranium would flow easily out through the aluminum jacket to the water.

If the slug fitted too loosely in its graphite socket, there would be an air gap, which would act as an insulator; this would prevent, or at least decrease, the cooling process. What was needed, therefore, was a perfect "metallurgical bond" — a solid metal union between the uranium and the aluminum, with aluminum solder filling the space in between. The other problem was to have the aluminum jacket so perfectly manufactured that there would be not even a pinhole in it.

The major difficulties in finding a perfect canning method began to cast doubts on the feasibility of a water-cooled reactor. Pure uranium metal was almost nonexistent, and very little was known about its properties. Metallurgists did not know how to work with it, did not even know its density.* Uranium was now needed, not only in tons, but also in definite shapes molded with near-perfect precision.

Several techniques were tried, all without success. The best way to achieve perfection of bonding seemed to be to pour about an inch of solder into the bottom of the aluminum can, then force the uranium slug into it. The solder then filled the space between, and sometimes it would force out all the air; but other times it did not, and then air would be trapped inside, which meant poor canning and an inadequate bond.

Meantime, most of the other technical obstacles had been hurdled, and the building of the plutonium city was progressing rapidly at Hanford. But even when the Du Pont operational people started to move to the site, the knotty problem of how to can thousands of uranium slugs was still unsolved. It was typical of the Manhattan Project, though, that other work went ahead full speed in the hope that someday, somehow, someone would find the answer.

---

*In fact, the density they estimated then was later proved incorrect.

23

"Scotty" Weir, a wind-burned, sixty-year-old farmer, was waiting for the light to turn at a street corner in the small town of Richland, Washington, when a stranger suddenly came up to him and asked if he were looking for a job.

"Matter of fact, I am," Weir said bitterly. That morning he had received an official letter informing him that his land was necessary to the war effort. He was given thirty days to vacate the premises.

"If you want a job at a dollar an hour with overtime, go to the Gray Building," the man told him.

At the Gray Building, Weir saw the Du Pont sign for the first time. "So you people are going to do the job that the Army is kicking us out of our homes for," he said after a physical examination. Weir was offered a job — and grudgingly accepted it — but he felt guilty: he was afraid the people at home would consider him a turncoat. "You know," he told a Du Pont personnel man, "if any responsible representative of the Government — including the President — came to Richland now, he would be shot on sight."

Weir was simply expressing the feelings of the fifteen hundred indignant residents of the Richland, Hanford and White Bluffs areas, people who had also received the order to evacuate their land. At first they refused to believe that in democratic United States, peaceful, law-abiding citizens could be chased from their homes. But very quickly they came to realize that opposition was useless; the Government was determined to acquire some six hundred square miles of land. A court order, dated March 9, 1943, and initiated by the Department of Justice, established the area as "necessary to the public interest" and made it subject to expropriation.

The worst part was that the Manhattan Project could not possibly explain to the landowners the reason for the expropriation. But Groves, knowing that the outcome of the war could depend on plutonium production, did not feel too bad about the local reaction. Most of the area was uncultivated sagebrush land, practically a desert, with a population of 2.2 persons per square mile. Except for a few irrigated orchards, yielding good crops of cherries, plums and apricots, the rest of the area was sandy, poor land. The older homesteaders were hardly making a living, but Mormons were beginning to settle in the area and to improve the agricultural yields in the valley.

The fruit crop that spring was magnificent, and, because the land was not yet needed, and because of the wartime need for food, the Manhattan Project allowed the farmers to stay and harvest. This gesture was generous from the human viewpoint, but proved to be extremely costly: crops being the best in years, prices soared up and served later as the basis for evaluating the price the Government would pay for the expropriated land.

Another of Groves's appeasing measures had nearly as disastrous an effect. The Government demanded full ownership of only part of the area — here no one was permitted to live. But in other parts of the Government property, residents were allowed to stay temporarily. The general's order read: "No increase in the population of any of these individual farms will be permitted." People were shocked. "How dare he!" they protested. "Who is this general to interfere with our family life?"

Groves hurriedly straightened out the misunderstanding. "I didn't mean the normal increase," he explained. "Having babies is all right, but taking in boarders is not!"

While they were still under fire from angry residents, Groves and Matthias discovered that other people before them had had their eye on the Hanford site. The Army and the Navy Air Force had just reached a joint agreement for using it as a bombing and gunnery training area. Matthias immediately requested that flights over Hanford be stopped. But the Office of the Under Secretary of War answered that the allocation had already been made; it was too late to change it.

Much alarmed, Matthias appealed directly to the field commanders, General Edward T. Williams in Spokane and Admiral Frank D. Wagner in Seattle, to give up their plans. But the secrecy of the Project was such that Matthias could not divulge the nature of the Hanford Engineering Works; the two top commanders were told to take his word that it was the most important war project of them all. At the same time, Groves was intervening in Washington, D.C., but without disclosing the purpose of the site. Finally, both the Army and the Navy agreed to cancel their arrangements; henceforth their commands in the area cooperated completely with Matthias, without asking questions.

As soon as Matthias moved to Hanford, Groves ordered him to visit the newspaper editors in the area, as well as the governor, state officials and the Office of Censorship. Matthias called on editors in Pasco, Walla Walla, Yakima, Prosser, Spokane and Seattle, asking them to print nothing about the Project without discussing it with him first. "I'm unable to tell you what it's all about," he explained, "but it's extremely important to our war effort." After some discussion, all newspapers agreed to check with him on any information before they published it. Matthias got the same cooperation from Governor Arthur Langlie and Congressman Halbert Holmes.

Du Pont assigned as project manager Gilbert P. Church, the thirty-three-year-old civil engineer who had selected the Hanford site with Matthias and Hall. Church moved to Hanford in March 1943 and found bachelor's quarters in Pasco. Although he directed the whole construction work, he was never told about the secret. Church was not even to hear the word "plutonium" until more than a year later.

Church was directly responsible to a formidable character, Du Pont's assistant chief engineer Granville M. Read, an unusually large, outspoken man of fifty who looked like Churchill — and sometimes behaved like him. "Slim" Read had managed to combine in his youth a technical education at Virginia Polytechnic Institute with art study at the Beaux-Arts Academy in Paris. He had known General Groves from the time Du Pont began building ammunition plants, and the two men had great respect for each other. Read had contributed considerably to Groves's favorable opinion of Du Pont. Extremely self-confident, inclined to be gruff and hard-boiled, the cigar-chomping engineer had some of the same characteristics as the general. Slim Read never avoided responsibility and was known for his insistence on detail and precision. A colorful, hard-hitting individualist with no inhibitions, he cursed and shouted when mad, and despised formal meetings. "Jesus Christ!" he would comment when jobs were to be done by committee decisions. "I don't understand how people get anything done this way!"

Read was directing the construction work from Wilmington but periodically visited Hanford, where Gil Church was stationed full time. "Listen to me, you guys!" he would tell his men. "The major problem in building these plants here is that we only have one chance. It's got to be right the *first* time. A reactor is not like an automobile — if a car doesn't work, you take it apart and fix it. But here, you won't get a second chance!"

The engineers in charge of building the mammoth plant never suspected one of their problems would be the welfare of salmon. From the moment the Hanford site was selected, Groves was preoccupied by the fate of the Columbia River salmon. How would the atomic plants affect their life? Would the water become contaminated by radiation, or become overheated, and kill the fish?

Leslie Groves had been fascinated as a boy by his father's tales about the strange behavior of salmon, how the extraordinary instinct of this salt-water fish urged them to return to the river of their birth in order to lay their eggs. Groves had reason to be afraid that the plant's discharge of radioactive material into the Columbia River might have a deadly affect on the fish. Enormous amounts of water would have to be used for cooling the reactors; nobody knew if this water, when discharged into the river, would be contaminated.

"Don't forget that the salmon catch is terribly important to this area," General Groves reminded his aides. "If we destroy the salmon in the river, we'll be subjected to terrific — and justifiable — criticism. The whole population will turn against us. And if the word spreads, we'll scare the country to death!"

Groves discussed the problem with Dr. Stafford L. Warren, chief of Manhattan District's Medical Section, who in turn contacted the University of Washington, in Seattle, which had one of the best schools of fishery in the country. Dr. Lauren R. Donaldson, a big, quiet-spoken man of forty, who not only taught science but was also a football coach, was assigned by Warren to study the effect of radiation on aquatic organisms, specifically fish. Warren did not tell Donaldson the reason for the study; he only said that there would be problems involving high levels of radioactivity along the Columbia River. Donaldson was warned not to talk about his research program and not to identify it with the Columbia River — his studies had to be conducted in the normal research setting at the university, and no explanation should be given the school's authorities.

Donaldson was inclined to think the whole idea was silly. He had once taught physics and knew that there wasn't enough radium in the world to make radiation a problem. But since he had been told that the study was of great importance to the Government, Donaldson plunged into the work, fully aware that he would have to draw some final conclusions based on near-zero information.

Groves knew that the value of Donaldson's research might prove questionable as far as the Hanford operations were concerned because of two factors. First, the Seattle laboratory had to use X rays, since Hanford's reactors were not yet built and their radioactive products were therefore not yet available. Second, any thorough research program would require years of observation of successive generations of fish. The salmon, a migratory fish born in fresh water, spends from two to four years in the ocean before returning to the place of its birth to spawn and die. The eggs obtained from adult salmon in 1943 would produce fish that would not return until sometime between 1945 and 1947.

Fortunately, Donaldson's first studies led to the conclusion that radiation, as far as it was possible to determine at the time, did *not* harm the salmon. Any danger from a higher water temperature, or from salmon swimming up into the pipes, really did not exist, the scientist concluded.

Groves and the Du Pont people were greatly relieved to hear this; work on the Hanford plant could go ahead with one less worry for the builders. But just to be on the safe side, Groves instructed Dr. Donaldson to continue his salmon studies indefinitely, and soon after asked him to establish a fish laboratory on the Columbia River at Hanford itself.

To recruit a labor force of forty-five thousand construction workers at a time when every war industry was begging for manpower was an extraordinary performance. Du Pont created a formidable organization, headed by Howard Miller, with offices in Pasco and branches in almost every state, which sent one hundred skilled employment recruiters roving around the country. With fierce competition from other industries, the job would have been impossible without the help of the War Manpower Commission. It instructed all its local branches to give preference, by direction of the President himself, to the Hanford Engineering Works, and if necessary, to draft workers from the aircraft industry.

Hiring in the Hanford area began in March 1943, but nationwide recruitment was not launched until May. The state of Washington supplied the largest part of the manpower — 29,762 people — but Du Pont's recruiters constantly toured United States Employment Offices in over five hundred cities. In some towns, even clergymen were asked to publicize job openings from the pulpit. Recruiting pamphlets contained no details about the nature of the work but gave some blunt advice: "The most essential thing to bring with you is a padlock. The next important things are towels, coat hangers and a thermos bottle. Don't bring cameras or guns."

The recruiters hit a different town practically every day. They were puzzled by one strict order that instructed them to avoid New Mexico and Tennessee and also not to hire people from those states. The reason: the Army was worried that if some laborers were recruited from Tennessee or New Mexico, they might see some connection between Hanford and the installations at Oak Ridge or Los Alamos. Once a week, recruiting men would receive, from the central office in Pasco, Washington, a telegram that would run something like this: NEEDED FOR FOLLOWING WEEK: CAR-PENTERS, 200; LABORERS, 600; MILLWRIGHTS, 50; CRANE OILERS, 25; TRUCK DRIVERS, 25; TELEPHONE OPERATORS, 18. Before leaving a town, a recruiter would send back a telegram stating how many people he had interviewed and how many were hired.

Because of the manpower shortage, the standards of examinations were not high. If a man said he was a mechanic or welder, the recruiter had to take his word for it; there was no time to check. This practice led Colonel Matthias to ask one of the chief recruiters, Phil Gardner, "Tell me, is it true that you people would hire a man as a carpenter if he could just identify a hammer?" Gardner laughed. "No, we're not quite that tough. If the man can convince us that his *father* would have known what a hammer was, we take him!" If the man was not really a carpenter, he could be reassigned to any of the ten other different job categories. The workers, of course, never learned the purpose of the Hanford Works; in fact, the recruiters themselves did not have the slightest idea. High wages were mainly what attracted the workers. A dollar an hour for common labor was good pay at the time. Then, too, there was the added attraction of getting to travel across the States on a ticket provided by the employer. The recruiter gave a railroad ticket, plus a few dollars for food during the trip, to each newly hired worker the day of departure. The price of the ticket was later deducted from his pay, but this was reimbursed to workers who stayed with the job over four months. But the men had to leave their families at home — the housing problem in Hanford was too acute.

After the glowing promises of the recruiters, there were several cases of disappointment. "Where are the pine trees? Where are the mountains and the streams and the deer?" the men grumbled on arrival at the flat, dusty plant site. Many left in disgust immediately; others stayed on with the idea of making just enough money to buy a return ticket. To provide housing, food and transportation in a desert-like area for forty-five thousand men quickly assembled from all over the country, and to keep them on a job without telling them what they were doing — this was an experience that Du Pont had never encountered before. Some workers lived in Richland, twenty-five miles away. The main construction camp was located six miles from the nearest reactor, fifteen miles from the farthest. Men working on the transmission lines and the railroad had to travel up to thirty miles to reach their camp. An extraordinary transportation department had to be organized by Du Pont, with seven thousand pieces of equipment operated by forty-two hundred people. After great difficulty, nine hundred buses (an item on the critical supply list) were rounded up, but seventy-five of them were substandard, designed for only "stand-up" transportation.

The workers disliked these buses intensely and made many complaints to their unions. But the head of the transportation department, A. M. Schefferius, solved the problem in an ingenious way. He organized the bus line at the loading stations so that the doors of only the front bus were opened. The worst buses were last in line in the morning but first in line for the return trip after work. Thus the workers reporting for work last and quitting earliest rode on the worst buses. Complaints soon died down.

All sorts of people passed through Hanford, from practically every state in the Union. There were old, seasoned construction workers; inexperienced youngsters thrilled by their first trip west of the Mississippi; winos from California and rowdy characters with unsavory records from everywhere. Whatever their individual background, they were all staggered by the gigantic scope of the construction work underway at Hanford. They had never seen anything like it before.

A new city was emerging on the barren banks of the Columbia River, colossal plants were appearing among the sagebrush, railroad tracks and highways were rapidly spreading across the desert. Even veterans of many big public works — men who had helped construct huge dams and power plants — had never seen so many people working in the same place at the same time. Nobody knew what was being built so feverishly, but it was obvious that it must be something of tremendous importance. More than 11,000 pieces of major construction equipment were gathered at the job. That alone would be enough to stretch for 35 miles! Total earth excavation at Hanford was to reach the figure of 25 million cubic yards — the equivalent of building houses for a city with a population of 400,000! Railroad trackage stretched for 158 miles, and 386 miles of roads were constructed; 40,000 tons of structural steel, 780,000 cubic yards of concrete, and 160 million board feet of lumber went into the huge building program.

The construction camp was the biggest ever seen in the West — a sprawling complex of 1177 buildings, plus eight big mess halls. The trailer camp west of Richland, probably the largest in the world, started with 480 trailers and was increased to 639. Peak population reached forty-five thousand construction workers, plus six thousand wives and children.

Most problems were new, many situations without precedent. Cleanliness standards for workers in some critical areas were unheard of: they had to wear special uniforms, and even the laundering of these uniforms had to be done with special soap. Ordinary soap containing boron would have been harmful to the atomic process.

Among the first installations to be put into operation at Hanford was the water-study laboratory. In order to simulate the tremendous quantities of heat released by the reactors, five steam locomotives were set up on the banks of the Columbia River. Though stripped of wheels, they were manned by regular locomotive firemen and could generate enough

WESTFIELD MEMORIAL LIBRARY
WESTFIELD, N. J.

steam to simulate temperatures that the future reactors were expected to produce. It was a strange sight to see five steaming, roaring locomotives standing still on the desert plateau; but the forty-five thousand people working at the Hanford site were getting used to seeing peculiar things — and not asking questions.

24

"THIS IS the damnedest metal I've ever seen in my life!" moaned Dr. Frank G. Foote in despair. Gathered around him in the University of Chicago laboratory, other metallurgists looked equally puzzled and helpless. Uranium, they were learning, was a strange substance with properties never observed before in any other metal.

Organized in the spring of 1943, the metallurgy group, which was first headed by Edward C. Creutz and later by John Chipman, had been assigned the task of developing a method for making uranium slugs for the reactors. Trouble with the new metal started right at the outset. First of all, no one at that time knew anything about the metallurgy of uranium. To learn about its melting point, metallurgists had to look in the *ASM Metals Handbook* in the library. They found the figure of 1750° centigrade, which turned out to be quite erroneous. The actual melting point, they soon discovered, was 1130° — a tremendous difference. Unlike the chemists, who by then had learned something about the chemistry of uranium, the metallurgists were starting from scratch.

The rods they were asked to make for the Hanford plant had to be done with fantastic precision. Even a fraction of a millimeter would have made a difference in the tightly fitted aluminum can. Yet the rolling of uranium into rods proved to be an extremely difficult operation. The work was done on weekends when the metallurgists could use a mill that normally manufactured stainless steel. They found that the best way of rolling uranium so it would not oxidize too much was to use "black heat." But having no instruments to measure black heat, they were doing it "by feel," just the way someone would barbecue a steak; they would look at the metal and say, "Well, that looks done," or, "Let's roll it some more!"

In rolling a metal, the trick was to get it out of the furnace and push it through the mill just as fast as possible. Otherwise, it cooled off to a point where it was no longer manageable. That was exactly what the experienced crew did with the uranium. It was a complete failure, however. The metallurgists discovered that hot uranium, once in the rolling mill, started oxidizing and self-heating to a point where it became so hot that it would break up and melt. Finally they had to adopt the opposite technique: the hot bars were left on the steel floor until they cooled off enough to be put through the mill.

The most unusual phenomenon of uranium was something that both baffled and exasperated the metallurgists. One of them, Andrew Van Echo, had made the disturbing discovery. In heating a uranium rod, he had observed that the metal became a little longer, just a few millimeters. This was normal, but when Van Echo reheated the same rod, he expected to find the dimensions stabilized, as would be the case with other metals. He was surprised to find, instead, that the rod had lengthened still a little more. He repeated the experiment several times, and with each reheating the rod kept getting longer.

His colleagues, to whom Van Echo reported his upsetting observation, started heating and cooling the rods over and over again. The uranium kept on increasing in length; there was no stabilization. Intrigued by this unheard-of behavior, the Chicago scientists continued until the rod reached six times its original length. The original two-inch rod had become twelve inches long!

The rolling of uranium into rods where millimeter precision was required was now out of the question. The best metallurgists of 1943[*] could not find a way to stabilize this ornery metal. Another method had to be found to make the rods; the obvious choice was extruding — the squeezing of metal by pressure through a small opening. Since it was a more primitive and wasteful technique, the metallurgists adopted it with reluctance.

Development of the extruding technique for uranium was partly done in Detroit, where the senior metallurgist of Wolverine Tube Company, James F. Schumar, was recruited for the uranium project by Ed Creutz of the Chicago group. The workers at Wolverine never learned exactly what this peculiar metal that Schumar referred to only as "tuballoy" was. It sparked so beautifully, however, that machinists began taking pieces to make flints for their cigarette lighters. When the horrified Schumar discovered this, he immediately confiscated their highly radioactive flints.

The metallurgists did not know much more than the machinists. When Creutz first visited Wolverine, bringing a uranium billet to be extruded, nobody knew what pressure to use. After Creutz and Schumar had put the billet into the container, the press operator asked them, "You want me to give it five hundred pounds of pressure, or the full seven hundred and fifty tons?"

---

[*] Much later technology wiped out this problem: it was discovered that the capricious uranium could be stabilized simply by heating a rod to about 700° centigrade, then plunging it in water. The pioneering metallurgists in Chicago had heated the metal up to only 600° during their rolling process.

The two metallurgists hadn't the slightest idea. Creutz decided to go down into the pit beneath the extrusion press where he could observe what happened as the operator gave the uranium billet five hundred pounds of pressure. Nothing happened, so the operator turned on the full seven hundred and fifty tons of pressure, and suddenly sparks showered the whole area as the billet shattered into a million pieces. Creutz and a helper, their clothes smoking from the sparks, stumbled out of the pit. Creutz almost wept when he realized that the uranium, which had melted like butter, was lost beyond all recovery. "I've spent three weeks making that damned thing!" he moaned. "Now I'll have to cast another billet and come back again."

It took many more experiments before the metallurgists discovered that, for reasons they were unable to understand, the uranium billets became stabilized during the extrusion process. They were happy — but baffled — to see that the problem solved itself, mysteriously. What had happened, actually, was a rare stroke of luck: since extrusion could only be carried out under very high temperatures, the metallurgists were heating the billets well above 700° centigrade — the threshold for the stabilization of uranium. By using the extrusion method, which they thought was only second-best,* they had in effect been stabilizing the rods' dimensions — and without knowing it!

But it was only one more step on the long road toward eventual mass production of slugs for the Hanford reactors.

---

* Had the Chicago laboratory succeeded earlier with the rolling technique, as they wanted to so desperately, the rods would not have been stabilized, and a disaster might have resulted. Because of heating and radiation, the uranium rods would have lengthened and cracked all the aluminum jackets. After the war, however, when the properties of uranium were more fully understood, the rolling of rods finally did replace the extruding technique.

25

To THE EYE of an outsider, the activity in a small chemistry laboratory on the fourth floor of the Jones Building in Chicago would have been totally mystifying. Several men in white laboratory coats were playing — but in dead earnest — a sort of game that called to mind Hans Christian Andersen's fairy tale "The Emperor's New Clothes." They seemed to be handling and weighing something invisible, examining it and carrying it from one table to another, all the while being extraordinarily careful not to lose it somewhere in the room.

What Dr. Glenn T. Seaborg and his colleagues were doing in the early summer of 1942 went under the name of "tracer chemistry," and the invisible element they were working with was plutonium. In tracer chemistry the element under study cannot be seen; its presence is only detectable by counters and electronic instruments. Plutonium was contained in a liquid solution, usually nitric acid, which seemed exactly like any other nitric acid, except that it reacted to a counter.

Glenn Seaborg had found it difficult to recruit scientists for his section of the Chemistry Division in Chicago. Most chemists at that time were already involved in various war projects, and Seaborg was not allowed to tell them why they were needed more by Chicago's Metallurgical Laboratory than by the particular work they were doing. "Sorry, Glenn, but what I'm doing is important — a new antimalaria drug," one of them had answered. Another chemist came pretty close to guessing Seaborg's secret. "Look, friend," he said, "I've a funny feeling that you're working on atomic energy. We have no time for that now. Can't you wait until the war is over?"

In forming his team, Seaborg had to rely mostly on friends and former students from Berkeley. "You just come," he would write. "We're working on something that is more important than the discovery of electricity."

Though young (he arrived in Chicago on the day of his thirtieth birthday), Seaborg already had a fine reputation as a chemist and was counted among the few isotope experts in the country. A lanky six-footer, he was born in the little mining town of Ishpeming, Michigan, into a family of Swedish stock. At twenty-nine, he was already a full professor at

Berkeley when Arthur Compton asked him to join the Chicago Metallurgical Laboratory as chief of one of its chemistry sections.

When interviewing candidates for his staff, Seaborg would ask what they thought his section was working on. Naturally, no one had a clue, and the answers were as varied as they were amusing. But Seaborg and his close friend Isadore Perlman, who had come with him from Berkeley, exchanged smiles when one candidate replied with assurance, "I don't know what you're doing, but being chemists, you must be working with some of the ninety-two elements that God created, and that's all I care about!"

But he was wrong; it was exactly what Seaborg's group was *not* doing. And when the new chemists were signed up for the job and told its nature, they were wild-eyed with astonishment. For Glenn Seaborg was a young man with a secret, an extraordinary secret known to only a handful of scientists in the world. Since the beginning of time, the elements of which matter is composed had remained unchanged. As far as scientists knew, nature had ninety-two elements — no more, no less — and the heaviest element was uranium.

The impossibility of transforming one element into another was one of the principles on which the whole of modern chemistry was based. Then suddenly, in May 1940, an extraordinary event occurred. A young physicist, Edwin M. McMillan, and his associate Philip H. Abelson, bombarded uranium in Berkeley's cyclotron and produced a new, unstable element — a ninety-third element — which they called neptunium. At the end of 1940, with the same cyclotron, twenty-eight-year-old Glenn Seaborg, assisted by Joseph W. Kennedy and Arthur C. Wahl, discovered a ninety-fourth element. With this discovery, the wildest dream of ancient alchemists — the transmutation of elements — became a reality.

Because of self-imposed censorship among scientists, Seaborg's discovery was registered secretly and withheld from publication. Throughout 1941, "element 94" was referred to by the code name of "copper." But when copper had to be introduced into the experiments, the problem of distinguishing between the two was posed. For a while, plutonium was mentioned as "copper," and real copper as "honest-to-God copper." But this became cumbersome and confusing, and after considering the name "plutium," "plutonium" was finally chosen because it sounded better.

At the time Seaborg came to Chicago, plutonium had never been actually seen, and its properties were still unknown. The quantity produced in the Berkeley experiments was infinitesimal, invisible even through the most powerful microscopes. The new metal was simply a presence, detected by ultrasensitive tracers. But even so, there were indications that the unseen stuff would prove fissionable, like uranium–235. This hope was the raison d'etre for the giant Hanford reactors.

The Metallurgical Laboratory's task was unique: to find ways of raising the supply of plutonium from a few micrograms to *kilograms* — one billion times more plutonium than they had managed to produce to date! It would certainly be the greatest scale-up ever attempted by chemists. But would the same laws and characteristics be as valid for kilograms of plutonium as for micrograms? Could chemists learn about plutonium chemistry by studying just a few micrograms, especially since a microgram was the equivalent of only one 30-millionth of an ounce? Nobody knew, and yet if there was such a thing as a plutonium expert in the world, this should be the discoverer of the new element. All eyes turned accordingly to the gangling young chemist from Berkeley.

The truth, however, was that even Glenn Seaborg knew extremely little about the properties of the new metal he had brought into the world. When he first came to work in Chicago, there were about fifteen chemists crowded into Jones Laboratory. When the group increased, it moved to the New Chemistry Building on the edge of the campus, and then again to the "New New Chemistry Building." Seaborg soon had one hundred chemists under his direction.

The work with minute tracer amounts of plutonium was done by radio-chemistry, an art that had not been practiced very much in the United States. Most of the basic work in this field had been done in France, Germany and Russia, and there were virtually no radiochemists in America. Plutonium specialists had to be developed. Seaborg, an excellent organizer, took scientists who were familiar with the ultramicroscopic techniques. His assistant, Isadore Perlman, was a physiologist; Paul Kirk was a microchemist specializing in criminology; his student Burris Cunningham was interested in ultramicroscopy; Robert Patton, an entomologist, had done research on the digestive systems of cockroaches and other insects.

Seaborg displayed excellent qualities as a leader. He was one of those "scientist-administrators" who, unlike many of their colleagues, liked to work with people and knew how to get the best out of them. Beneath his manner of friendly politeness was great strength of purpose. If he was displeased with someone's work, he never bawled the man out; a few days later, however, somebody else would be doing exactly the same work across the corridor. Seaborg would purposely not stop at the first fellow's laboratory for several days — and soon the message got through.

Surrounded by many scientists who had their heads in the clouds, Seaborg, though still very young, always knew where he was going and how to get there. When he believed in some project, he was always ready to go ahead boldly and take the necessary risks. Despite widespread skepticism, he was convinced that microgram quantities of plutonium could be produced by cyclotron. After several months of bombarding hundreds of pounds of uranium in the cyclotrons at Berkeley and at Washington University in St. Louis, Seaborg at last had his first micrograms of plutonium. His assistants Burris Cunningham and Louis B. Werner then succeeded in weighing 2.77 micrograms of plutonium oxide — almost one-millionth of an ounce of the new element. It was an infinitesimal amount, but the scientists were enthusiastic: at last, methods of microchemistry could be applied to research.

Several visiting scientists, on learning that the new element was already visible, came to the laboratory to see it. Seaborg's men did not have enough plutonium to spare for exhibition, so they used a trick that later made them feel somewhat guilty: they colored some aluminum hydroxide with green ink and showed it to the delighted visitors with the equivocal explanation that, "This *represents* a sample of plutonium hydroxide." When General Groves came, however, a real sample was displayed with great pride. But disappointment followed: the general, after leaning over the microscope for a few moments, grumbled, "I don't see anything."

It was dangerous work and the Chicago chemists did not know enough about protection. With plutonium, the danger is not radiation but ingestion. A speck of dust as little as 0.6 of a microgram, inhaled by the lungs, would cause a bone tumor. The scientists used hoods, but their protective measures were primitive. Working with even microscopic amounts of plutonium was like being locked in a room with an invisible killer, not knowing when or where death would strike. Fortunately, luck played a great role: somehow, no one was hurt.

The greater part of the mammoth plutonium installations at Hanford was designed and constructed in a state of ignorance concerning the true properties of plutonium. The Project was really in luck; the complex element it was dealing with was not fully understood by anyone. Fortunately, the misconceptions about plutonium — and there were a number of them — did not seriously impair the boldly projected processes which had been developed, using only microscopic quantities of the new metal in the lab, onto the prodigious scale of Hanford.

After a long study of the ninety-fourth element, the usually reserved Dr. Seaborg said, "Plutonium is so unusual as to approach the unbelievable. Under some conditions," he continued, "plutonium can be nearly as hard and brittle as glass; under others, as soft and plastic as lead. It will burn and crumble quickly to powder when heated in air, or slowly disintegrate when kept at room temperature. It undergoes no less than five phase transitions between room temperature and its melting point.

Strangely enough, in two of its phases, plutonium actually *contracts* as it is being heated. It also has no less than four oxidation states. It is unique among all of the chemical elements. And it is fiendishly toxic, even in small amounts."

The specific task of Seaborg's section was to find a technique for separating plutonium that would leave the reactor embedded in the irradiated uranium. Plutonium is produced by exposing uranium to the reaction of an atomic pile: after remaining for several days in the reactor, part of the uranium in the slugs is transformed into plutonium. But the chemists then had to find a way of separating it from the rest of the uranium.

Various processes were developed, but Seaborg's team had to fight the paralyzing handicap of not really knowing the chemistry of the invisible metal. A working hypothesis had to be adopted, and the best available was that the chemistry of plutonium was similar, if not absolutely identical, to uranium's. It was a reasonable assumption to make, and by following it, some satisfactory results were obtained.* After several unsuccessful attempts, the breakthrough came unexpectedly when Seaborg and an assistant, Stanley Thompson, discovered that bismuth phosphate was an excellent plutonium carrier. This was another instance of plutonium's puzzling behavior. There were grave doubts that the bismuth process could possibly work — it did not seem to conform with all the theoretical expectations: the chemical format of bismuth was such that it should not carry plutonium!

The first tests were made on an ultramicroscopic scale with cyclotron-produced plutonium. Then, after larger amounts of the strange metal became available, a complete, mechanical test was carried out on a larger, near-industrial scale. Still, there were skeptics who thought the process, even if possible at the trace and microgram concentration, would never work out at the huge Hanford plant.

Nevertheless, a decision had to be made before the results were conclusive; Du Pont had to start building separation installations at Hanford. It

---

* But the paradox was that this assumption turned out to be incorrect. Only much later, when the bomb was already built, did the scientists realize that the properties of plutonium and uranium were, in fact, very different. But it was one of the few cases in science in which ignorance, perhaps, was bliss. Had Bush and Conant suspected the incredible complexities of plutonium, it is doubtful that they would have dared to recommend to President Roosevelt to go ahead so quickly. By extraordinary luck, the few properties of plutonium that counted in the separation technique happened to be similar to those of uranium; the guessing had turned out right. But the opposite *could* have happened. It was equally possible that these same properties might not have matched. In that case, the whole plutonium project would have been in serious trouble. Seen in retrospect, the assumption that the two metals would behave generally in a similar way was completely wrong.

was on June 1, 1943, that Crawford Greenewalt visited Seaborg's laboratory for a final review. After a very intense meeting that lasted the whole day, he was still not completely convinced, despite Seaborg's faith in the process. "Can you guarantee a yield of at least fifty percent by bismuth phosphate?" Greenewalt asked bluntly.

"Yes," answered Seaborg without hesitation.

Greenewalt thought hard for a moment. This would be another great risk, another great gamble — a calculated, well-informed one, but still a gamble.

"OK," he said finally, making the decision for Du Pont. "That's the way we'll do it."

26

WHEN THE green light was given for the building of the K–25, the gaseous-diffusion plant at Oak Ridge, an immediate question arose: what company should operate it? Kellex already had the assignment to design the plant and develop the components, but some large chemical company was needed to run it. Du Pont was already involved in the plutonium project; Groves knew that he had to find some other powerful industrial organization.

Dobie Keith had suggested Union Carbide to Groves at their first meeting in New York and the Du Pont engineers had made the same recommendation. The company had an excellent reputation and was already working on other war projects, including production of vitally important synthetic rubber. Moreover, some of Union Carbide's affiliate companies had already been collaborating for a long time with Colonel Marshall's District and with some of the Chicago and Columbia scientists. There were the National Carbon Division, supplying pure graphite for the Chicago atomic piles; Linde Air Products Division, which had been approached by Szilard and Fermi in their search for liquid oxygen for experiments, and the United States Vanadium Division, which already had a contract with the Government for the supply of uranium ore from mines in Colorado.

For several years, large amounts of uranium oxide had been piling up unused on the Colorado plateau. These were tailings from the operation of the Vanadium refinery there and, the company could find no use for the uranium oxide. Lyman Bliss, forty-two-year-old vice-president at Linde, was assigned to work on possible commercial uses of uranium. At the time, small amounts were being employed for only one purpose: to give a yellow color to ceramics. But Bliss's problem was how to dispose of tons of useless uranium oxide, possibly as an alloy in steel and a small pilot refinery was built at Tonawanda, New York, to try to make various uranium compounds.

When the Manhattan District was formed in 1942, Colonel Marshall and Lieutenant Colonel Nichols became extremely interested in Union Carbide's uranium oxide, and an order for eighty thousand pounds was signed in October. Colonel Marshall, and later General Groves, were accustomed to dealing with Lyman Bliss, and it was in Bliss's fifteenth-floor office, in the old Carbide Building on the corner of Madison Avenue and Forty-second Street, that Groves first came to discuss the corporation's participation in the K–25 project.

It was the first time that Lyman Bliss or anyone else at Union Carbide had heard of the gaseous-diffusion plant. Bliss happened to have a notion about the process because he had read, by chance, a fascinating article on John Dunning's work at Columbia which had appeared in the June 1940 issue of *Harper's* magazine under the signature John J. O'Neill. The issue containing the article had been withdrawn from circulation almost immediately after publication, but many of the aspects and possibilities of nuclear energy had been revealed. But Bliss thought the scientists were talking about some future, far remote time. He never expected that anyone would attempt to build a science-fiction type of separation plant right away. General Groves did not give any details, but even the principles that he revealed sounded impossible to the Carbide engineer. Lyman Bliss was more than startled. He was appalled.

"It's too big a decision for me. We'd better go and see Jim Rafferty," said Bliss.

In every company he dealt with, Groves had a general rule: always try to deal directly with the person who could issue an order that nobody else could countermand. And this did not necessarily mean the president or the chairman of the board. Every company was run in a different way, and often it took some inquiring to find out who was the driving spirit, the executive with the real power of authority in a large corporation.

However, at Union Carbide, even though it was a huge organization with several, nearly autonomous subsidiaries, Groves did not have to search very far. It was common knowledge at Union Carbide that one of the driving forces behind the company's spectacular growth was the executive vice-president, James A. Rafferty.

He was a sturdy Irishman of fifty-seven, a two-fisted man who would call a spade a spade, and probably because of it, had an extraordinary gift for handling men. After twenty-five years with the company, this capable, outspoken engineer had earned a reputation as an indefatigable dynamo who had left his mark on practically every division in the corporation. He had started at the Linde Air Products Division, advanced to general manager and vice-president of the Carbide and Carbon Chemicals Division, then climbed to the presidency of the Bakelite Division.

"In recognition of his being 'the workhorse of the Carbide backfield,' " read an article in *Chemical and Engineering News*, "Rafferty was made vice-president of Union Carbide and Carbon Corporation, the parent corporation of all Carbide units, in 1939. This did little to destroy the idea held by some, however, that over 100 men named James A. Rafferty worked for Union Carbide and its many units."

Born in Chicago, Rafferty was one of eight children in a poor Irish-American family. He started out to be a priest or a lawyer, and was well advanced in Latin and Greek when he switched to chemistry and engineering. He graduated from the Lewis Institute of Technology, worked nine years for a utility company, then joined the Linde Air Products Company in the same year it became a unit of Union Carbide and Carbon. An executive with drive and vision, Rafferty contributed tremendously to the birth and fantastic growth of a new industry in America: synthetics made from petroleum rather than from coal, as they had been formerly. In his field, Rafferty was hailed as one of the great "makers of the chemical industry." To him the word synthetic denoted something worthy: a material of uniform quality, designed for a particular purpose; a man-made product far superior to a natural material.

When Leslie Groves was ushered into Rafferty's oak-paneled office, the two men liked each other at sight. Groves realized immediately that he was talking to someone who loved action and efficiency, a man who would push things ahead. As for Rafferty, he was a firm believer in the American system of free enterprise and the importance of industry's participation in the war effort. It was not difficult for the general to convince Rafferty that his corporation should help the Manhattan Project. "The American chemical industry thus far has benefited tremendously from the stimulating atmosphere of American free enterprise," Rafferty used to say. "During several visits to Europe, I studied industries abroad and compared them with our own. I feel that the well-being and national security of a nation is in proportion to the success and extent of its industries." Rafferty was impressed by Groves's earnest persuasion; he promised to discuss the matter with the top people of those Carbide units that would be involved.

At a second meeting a few days later, Groves arrived with Colonels Marshall and Nichols. Rafferty was surrounded by the top men in Carbide, William Barrett, Fred Hagerson and Benjamin O'Shea, and two of his assistants, Lyman Bliss and George Felbeck. The Carbide brass listened attentively as the two Army engineers spoke; then they asked several technical questions. Groves was particularly emphatic that afternoon, and the tension in the room was extreme. As he spoke, the Carbide men began to realize that something tremendously important was in the making. As engineers, their normal judgment would definitely be against accepting the Manhattan Project task because at first sight it seemed to be impossible. At the same time, however, they were all too aware that their corporation could not refuse to help. Both Rafferty and Bliss had already recommended acceptance of the contract, despite the reluctance of some of the company's best technical experts. In less than an hour, Union Carbide agreed and signed a letter of contract to operate the gaseous-diffusion plant and help with the development of certain components. "I was amazed," Bliss admitted to Groves later. "I thought they'd kick you out; instead, they stood there with their mouths open and didn't even raise a question!"

The first full-scale briefing of Carbide's top men by Columbia scientists and Kellex leaders took place on March 1 in the stockholders' meeting room at Carbide's Madison Avenue offices. General Groves arrived with Marshall, Nichols and Stowers, the Manhattan District's representative for gaseous diffusion; Rafferty brought ten of his company's leading executives and experts.

The detailed description for building the giant diffusion plant at Oak Ridge was given mainly by Dunning, Urey, Keith and Benedict. It nearly frightened the Carbide engineers out of the contract. It was certainly the most unrealistic project that any of them had ever been asked to consider. When the speakers told them about the three thousand stages of the gaseous-diffusion cascade, many Carbide men thought that their first fears about the whole process had been more than legitimate. It was just not feasible.

In the meantime, however, Rafferty had gone ahead and organized the nucleus of a new Carbide operation. He had selected his colleague and good friend Lyman Bliss, who had considerable gifts as a negotiator as well as an adviser, to be his personal assistant on all matters concerning the project. Then he put Dr. George Felbeck, one of the company's hardest-driving engineers, in charge of the whole operation. From that moment on, Felbeck was to become one of the dominant figures in the development of the gaseous-diffusion plant.

George Felbeck had a brilliant mind and a strong, if sometimes temperamental, personality. His forte was ideas — he was less successful in handling people. Because of his Scandinavian reserve, it took time to know him well, but those who got close to him became fast, admiring friends. He was a big, forty-six-year-old Swede from Kansas, with a bachelor's degree in mechanical engineering from the University of Illinois. After working for fifteen years at Union Carbide, he suddenly decided, after a disagreement with a superior, to leave for California and get a doctorate in physical chemistry at Cal Tech. Already forty-five when he received his Ph.D., he started teaching in California. But Rafferty, who

WESTFIELD MEMORIAL LIBRARY.
WESTFIELD, N. J.

had esteemed his talents highly at Carbide earlier, wooed him back to the company, offering him a very good salary and position.

A combination of man of action and intellectual, Felbeck had all the necessary qualities to head up Union Carbide's operation within the Manhattan Project. Having put in long years of experience with gas-separation and high-pressure work, he was especially qualified now for work on gaseous diffusion. Not only did he possess the mind of a true inventor, but he was also a prodigious worker who used to take work home in the evening after a hard day and yet come back to the office at seven o'clock the next morning full of fresh ideas. His method was simply to get up and go — even if it meant going in the wrong direction. He hated long meetings and did not want reports; action alone was what he demanded, and he could be terribly impatient when results came slowly.

Felbeck often impressed people at first as just another high executive who could not speak the common language. He was always thinking, even in conversation with others. Whenever someone discussed a problem with him, Felbeck was already busy trying to solve it. But on closer acquaintance, people began to realize Felbeck was interested in them and what they had to say.

Lyman Bliss had been among Felbeck's closest friends for almost twenty years, and the complete confidence between the two men was soon to play an important role in Carbide's future operations. Since the two friends were close to the overall boss, Rafferty, all the company's activities for the Manhattan Project quickly came to be supervised by a triumvirate of brilliant engineers with different, but complementary, talents and temperaments.

The real day-to-day operation was directed by George Felbeck; he became for the Carbide team what Dobie Keith was for the Kellex team. Carbide's assignment was not only to run the plant when it was finished, but also to make sure, during the period of design and construction, that it *would* work. General Groves had made his directive crystal-clear: no one was to give excuses later for not having done the best possible job. He also encouraged Felbeck to look over the shoulders of the Columbia and Kellex men in order to help them find the best solutions to the multitude of problems facing them.

Because Carbide was going to be fully responsible for operating the future gaseous-diffusion plant, Felbeck's men were extremely careful not to accept any design or component that did not satisfy them completely. A Carbide man was assigned, full time, to each major development group at both Kellex and Columbia; he was to learn his future job and also help in improving each component of equipment. Every design and blueprint of Kellex had to be approved and signed by a Carbide man. George

Felbeck attended the weekly meetings at Dobie Keith's office in the Woolworth Building. Both strong leaders, they clashed frequently when disagreeing on crucial decisions; but personally they liked and respected one another. Carbide's collaboration with Kellex, as well as with the Columbia group, was highly satisfactory.

Of all the problems that faced the Manhattan Project, the critical barrier situation had become the gravest. General Groves began to show signs of impatience. Dr. Urey was frankly alarmed. Dobie Keith pushed Clarence Johnson and other Kellex colleagues to the limit of their strength. Only John Dunning, in his Columbia laboratory, remained an unperturbed optimist, but then, Dunning had been born hopeful — nothing could change him.

While the Norris-Adler team was struggling desperately with the difficulties of the development of its type of barrier, Foster Nix continued his experiments with his nickel powder at the Bell Telephone Laboratories. His barrier, contrary to the brittle Norris-Adler membrane, was structurally strong, but its separative qualities were still very poor. In addition, Nix had encountered another obstacle that made his barrier unusable for the time being: it could only be made in small specimens produced in Nix's laboratory. The Nix barriers were measured in terms of square inches. What was needed was a barrier to be projected into square *miles*. Various techniques were tried at Bell. None succeeded. The mass production of Nix's barrier seemed impossible.

When Carbide joined the project, George Felbeck assigned one of his young engineers, Alvan H. Tenney, to look into the barrier situation. Tenney first examined the Norris-Adler barrier — and found it very disappointing. In addition to its fragility and pinholes, the Norris-Adler barrier showed no uniform quality: when tested, each sample gave a different result. It was definitely unacceptable as such. Al Tenney then visited the Bell Laboratories in order to report to Felbeck the technique that Nix was using to produce his stronger barrier. Nix's work was obviously interesting, Tenney felt, although the techniques were limited only to laboratory scale. Felbeck decided to examine it in more detail.

In the spring of 1943, Felbeck brought a small Carbide team over to visit the Bell Laboratories. Foster Nix showed them samples of the barrier and demonstrated his techniques. He admitted that he had no way of producing it in large quantities; that he had had no experience in industrial production. The Carbide people did not know much about nickel, but Felbeck asked his Carbide team, "Couldn't some of you help in this?"

One of the members of the team was Leon K. ("Ken") Merrill, superintendent of Carbide's Bakelite plant in Bound Brook, New Jersey. In Bakelite's laboratory there was a sharp-witted expert on production techniques named Frazier Groff. Groff was told to go over and take a look at the work in the Bell Telephone Laboratories. He was not a scientist. A superior technical man, with a B.A. degree in chemistry, he had extraordinary skill in selecting and applying the proper technology to new processes. He was considered almost a genius — a temperamental genius, with immense willpower, an extremely conscientious and single-minded perfectionist who was very hard and exacting on the younger men working under him.

Groff, a sturdily built, gruff, forty-eight-year-old man of Scottish ancestry, was a complete individualist who needed few friends and got along well with few people. Strong-minded and opinionated, the husky, florid-faced chemist was very outspoken and easily excitable. He was dedicated to two things only: his career as a chemist and his family — his wife and two daughters. The Groffs lived in Plainfield, New Jersey, and their garden, in which Groff himself grew the vegetables, was the finest in town. But Groff's great joy was vacationing in New Hampshire, where the family was accustomed to renting a cottage on Lake Winnepesaukee. He loved to go fishing by himself there. People around the lake said he caught more black bass than anyone else. He liked to disappear for hours on end, and there, while dangling a line into the water, he would wait for a bite — and also solve a great many of his professional problems. Often, coming home after a day of fishing, he would telephone excitedly to his New Jersey office and give some new ideas or possible solutions to current problems. He was a man who was completely absorbed in his work at all times — weekends and vacations included.

Groff was capable of working eighteen hours at a stretch when necessary, and he was extremely single-minded about other things, too. When he decided to learn how to play golf, he bought a set of clubs and a few manuals and went straight to the golf course. After a few weeks of meticulous practice, he was already shooting in the eighties.

If not especially liked by others, Groff was nonetheless highly respected at Bakelite for his intuitive, creative mind. When he was dispatched to see the barrier developed by Foster Nix, he did not have the slightest idea about the Manhattan Project. He did not know much about metallurgy, and knew even less about barriers and uranium separation. All Groff realized, after a quick look at the Bell Laboratories, was that Foster Nix was totally unaware of the existence of some modern techniques of industrial production.

Groff returned to his New Jersey laboratory, explained his idea to Ken Merrill, his superior, then went directly to work. Several visits to the Bell Laboratories followed, and several times Foster Nix came to New Jersey to work with Frazier Groff at his Bound Brook laboratory. In spite of both being strong-minded and opinionated, the scientist and the industrial expert liked each other. More important still, their collaboration promised to be fruitful. What Groff was trying to do was to find a way to duplicate Nix's laboratory operations but on a big scale. Up until then, this was considered impossible. All the scientists and experts said the same thing: the existing barrier types could never be made in large, uniform quantities.

After carefully examining the processes involved in making the barrier material, Groff had an idea: "Look, why not try to do it the way we would in industry?"* The first results were encouraging, and Groff worked for months to improve his method. The first successful operation at the Bakelite laboratory was repeated with larger quantities by the International Nickel Company at Huntington, West Virginia.

The tests showed great improvement by October, but the separating qualities of the barrier Groff produced were still very unsatisfactory. The pores were just not fine enough to be considered for industrial production. Nevertheless, the new powder material might eventually solve the structural problems of the barrier. It was one example — one of many — of the "cross-fertilization of minds" between American scientists and experts in quite different fields, and it moved the Manhattan Project slightly nearer to its goal.

---

* The technical details of the process developed are still classified.

27

No ARCHITECT had ever received such an assignment. It was, in fact, an architect's dream. The specifications were vague but grandiose, wide-sweeping: Build a new town from scratch, a totally planned community on virgin land; then design the houses, gardens and streets according to your own taste. Everything will be provided — you don't have to worry about the established habits of a population, their traditions or tastes. As soon as you build the town, the Manhattan Project will supply the people. Make it comfortable for, say, thirteen thousand families to begin with; if we need a greater population, we'll let you know.

This, more or less, was what the firm of Skidmore, Owings and Merrill was asked to do by the Government in February 1943. For several years the company had been working with the John B. Pierce Foundation of New York on the development of low-cost prefabricated houses using panels made by the Celotex Corporation. Several hundred units had been constructed successfully at the Glenn Martin airplane plant outside Baltimore.

The Pierce Foundation, having heard rumors of a large housing project to be constructed by the little-known Manhattan District, was eager to propose its own house model. It was not easy, however, for Joseph F. O'Brien, executive director of the Pierce Foundation, to locate the Manhattan District. No such organization was listed in the telephone book; no one seemed to know anything about it. Finally, owing to a mix-up at the switchboard of the New York Engineering District, O'Brien did manage to get through to the right colonel; he warmly recommended the Pierce prefabricated house and also the architectural firm of Skidmore, Owings and Merrill. The seven-year-old firm had been struggling to survive in the face of a severe wartime scarcity of building materials. It was a fantastic opportunity — an entire city to be designed by just one architectural-engineering firm!

The partnership, started in 1936 by Indiana-born Louis Skidmore and his impetuous brother-in-law Nathaniel Owings, had done only a few sizable projects before 1942 — several H. J. Heinz Company warehouses, a Brooklyn housing project, a hospital in Michigan, a paper mill in

Wisconsin. But it was a dynamic firm, thanks to the personality of its founders, and a very versatile one, thanks to a top-flight staff of specialists in a wide variety of fields. In the 1930s the majority of American architects had limited themselves to domestic housing, leaving the large-scale projects — industrial plants and airfields — to the engineers. But "Skid" Skidmore and Nat Owings, along with their third partner, John O. Merrill, felt that "the architect should win back his historical role as the creator and coordinator of big projects."

Decentralization was another characteristic of the SOM partnership. The ebullient Nat Owings, a short, forceful man who had once been described as "looking amazingly like Smokey the Bear on a U.S. conservation poster," was in charge of the Chicago office, while the dignified and debonair Louis Skidmore set up an office in New York. "A couple of guys like the two of us," Skidmore often said, "can only feel comfortable if each has his own bailiwick."

Skidmore, who had studied at the Beaux-Arts Academy in Paris, had been chief designer of the 1933 Chicago Exposition, where he became familiar with the use of lightweight, mass-produced materials. When he asked his brother-in-law to join him in a partnership, the two architects, influenced by Le Corbusier, Walter Gropius and Mies van der Rohe, decided that they would build only in the contemporary style. As young talent was brought into the company, they were encouraged to discuss new ideas and look for bold, new applications of the ideas of modern architecture. "If two partners ever find themselves in *complete* agreement," Skidmore used to remark, "one of them should leave the firm."

Unfortunately, the dream contract of the Manhattan District had some catches. After receiving a free hand in designing the town — the network of houses, schools and hospitals, the shopping centers and the streets — it was natural for the architects to ask where the town was to be built. "We can't tell you yet," was the Army's reply. "It's a secret. You prepare the plans, and if we approve them, you'll be given the details." It was an unorthodox way of designing a whole new town, but people were getting used to not asking too many questions in wartime. "All right," the architects said, "we'll design it from the maps of the area."

But all that Skidmore, Owings and Merrill could get from the Army engineers was some aerial photographs and a few topographical maps — but with titles and names cut out. These showed a rugged area of hillside, which descended some five hundred feet from a wooded ridge on the north to a narrow valley about two miles to the south. Except for a few mountain trails, there was only one road extending east and west through the valley. The only signs of habitation were a few farmhouses and mountain cabins. They were good maps, but planning a town without seeing the site was no better than choosing a bride by mail order. The photos of the rolling country, which showed sharp ridges covered with scrub oak, reminded the architects of some places in the Carolinas and in Tennessee.

When the Army engineer said he wanted the preliminary site plan in three days' time, the partners thought it was just a military way of saying "very fast" or "urgent." But the Manhattan Project representative meant exactly what he said: a plan for approval had to be submitted within seventy-two hours.

In the firm's small offices on East Fifty-seventh Street in New York, architects, engineers and draftsmen began working around the clock at a feverish tempo that could never have been sustained on a routine job. William S. Brown, a thirty-four-year-old architect from Ohio, was put in charge of the special project in the New York office, with a staff of ten architects, whose number was soon to swell to four hundred.

The original plan was for a community of thirteen thousand families. Luckily, the firm of Skidmore, Owings and Merrill had had previous experience in rapid erection of prefabricated houses. They had developed prefabs made of "cemesto," using panel construction of cement-asbestos board. These were compact, one-story houses with picture windows, fireplaces and a blower system of air circulation. Though rigid restrictions had been put on the use of most building materials, cemesto and asbestos were fortunately not on the critical list.

None of the partners had any idea of how many supermarkets, hardware stores and barbershops would be needed for a population of thirty thousand. There was no textbook to give the rules for the best location of schools, drugstores, firehouses. But the SOM architects read almanacs and phoned experts, then did their best to make reasonable estimates.

Skidmore and Owings spent the final night before the deadline putting last-minute touches to the master plan. In the morning they carried it jubilantly out of the office — only to find that it was too big to fit into the elevator! They had to waste a humiliating hour trying to get it in; after much confusion, the master plan was finally sent down by placing it on top of the elevator car.

The Army approved the plan immediately. "Now, how soon can you send a team out to the site and go to work?" the architects were asked.

"Immediately — if we only knew where to go," came the reply.

Once again, though, the Manhattan District flatly refused to divulge the location of the site. A compromise was finally reached: six SOM architects, headed by John Merrill, were told to be at Pennsylvania Station at a precise time; there they would be given their tickets in sealed envelopes with the train number written on them. It was only after boarding the train that the architects opened the envelopes and learned their destination: Knoxville, Tennessee.

On arrival the next day, they were met by Colonel Nichols, who gave them the necessary instructions and sent them on to the Oak Ridge site. Stone and Webster's earth-moving machines and tractors were already at work scooping up sections of terrain. Merrill improvised a field office in the rear of a garage and started surveying the area on foot. His first job was to lay out the roads from the preliminary site plan made by Stone and Webster's survey crews. It was necessary to inspect all the road locations on foot, so as to adjust them in the case of unforeseen topographical obstacles.

The rigid security regulations enforced by the Manhattan Project created some communication problems for the first team of architects. They were told, for example, that they could not write directly to their families. Letters had to be put in a big manila envelope that the Army then sent to Skidmore's office in New York; there they were opened by a confidential secretary and forwarded, with a New York postmark, to the architects' families. More than one architect had to do a great deal of explaining later on to a suspicious wife.

The office for the architects was soon moved to a four-room farmhouse on the site. Working hours were from dawn to sunset, seven days a week — as they had to be on the biggest job of rapid town construction ever attempted in the United States. Individual house plans were prepared simultaneously in SOM's New York office, then house locations were staked out on the newly located roads. Each house location had to be individually inspected and adjusted to fit contours, thus avoiding time-consuming grading.

After a few weeks, the whole original planning staff of SOM — four hundred architects, engineers and draftsmen — moved out to Tennessee to work on the site. Conditions were highly primitive: cramped housing, no office space, no telephones. While Merrill was struggling on the site with roads, sewers and lighting, Skidmore and Brown spent their evenings in a room in the Andrew Johnson Hotel in Knoxville hunched over a huge roll of tracing paper spread out on the bed, sketching out their plans.

Despite constant improvisation, the outcome proved to be one of the most skillful jobs of town planning ever seen. The town itself was a narrow strip less than one mile wide and six miles long, following a major ridge and crisscrossed by small ridges. The original development was designed for three thousand cemesto-type, permanent homes. Later, thousands of prefabricated houses were added. They were shipped to Oak Ridge in prefabricated sections, complete with walls, floors, room partitions, interior wiring and plumbing. Even furniture was placed in the sections before shipping. Most of the houses were factory-built in Indiana, and by late 1943, the roads leading southward to Tennessee had become congested by a constant stream of trailer trucks, each carrying a piece of house which, with one side temporarily covered with canvas and some furniture already placed, resembled an oversized doll's house.

Since time was too short for conventional building, new methods had to be devised. Detroit's assembly-line techniques were adopted, and construction was divided into separate operations, each performed by a specialized crew of workmen. The system proved so efficient that workers were soon completing a house every two hours and turning them over for occupancy at the rate of thirty to forty a day.

Skidmore, Owings and Merrill did an outstanding job of town planning, considering the unprecedented rush, the difficult site and the extraordinary conditions imposed by the military. For the Manhattan District, though, the important thing was the industrial plants; the living quarters only needed to meet the most basic requirements. In military eyes the main factors were keeping down construction costs and using noncritical materials.

Despite this, Oak Ridge was not divided into a monotonous grid, with right-angle streets going in one direction from 1 to 100 and in the other from A to Z, but was designed to take advantage of the hills' contours. The streets followed the natural curves of the terrain without ever becoming too steep. Shopping centers and schools were designed within easy reach of residential areas; each neighborhood had ready access to all services and facilities.

The architects worked very closely with Army engineers on housing, roads, community services, sewers and transportation. No one at Skidmore, Owings and Merrill knew, however, the reason for the new town, except that there were some secret plants over behind the hills, making something for the military — probably explosives, since great quantities of chemicals were involved. It was not until much later that the architects learned what was going to be built in those plants.

Initially, the task of building a brand-new town for thousands of workers had been given to Stone and Webster, the Army's general contractors. The firm prepared the preliminary town layouts and blueprints in the summer of 1942 in its Boston offices. When Skidmore, Owings and Merrill was called in, six months later, to lighten the burden of Stone and Webster's multiple responsibilities, they inherited a well-prepared site, which had been cleared and graded for building. A sizable highway-construction program was already under way, and the main administration building — "the Castle," to which Colonel Nichols later transferred the Manhattan District's headquarters from New York* — was practically completed. Though Stone and Webster continued design work on all utilities — water, electric, transportation and sewerage systems — their main effort was now concentrated on building the electromagnetic production plants, in the so-called Y–12 area at Oak Ridge.

Before November 1942, Stone and Webster had been the only engineering company engaged by the Manhattan District, with overall responsibility for all construction. It had been selected by the Army because of its experience in building TNT and synthetic-rubber plants. As early as March 1942, Eger Murphree, a member of the S–1 Committee, had asked the Boston engineers to prepare preliminary design and estimates on a plant for centrifugal isotope separation. Stone and Webster had also participated in the selection of the Oak Ridge site, had designed the Argonne laboratory for the Chicago physicists, and was involved in the construction of a heavy-water production plant at Trail, British Columbia. At Los Alamos, Stone and Webster engineers were also engaged in the building of the first bomb laboratory. But none of the earlier jobs would compare with the enormous challenge of constructing the electromagnetic plants at Oak Ridge.

Engineering work for Lawrence's process began in July 1942 in Boston, after a few Stone and Webster engineers visited Berkeley to learn about electromagnetic isotope separation. Some of them took up residence in Berkeley and played an active part in final research on Lawrence's method and in the detailed design of the calutrons. They fed design information to their colleagues back in Boston, where a large organization was specially set up.

Although the new group duplicated most of the functions of the main Stone and Webster organization, it had to be organized wholly apart, for security reasons. It soon employed eight hundred engineers, draftsmen and clerical personnel working on thirteen floors in four separate buildings. Not more than a half-dozen Stone and Webster men were entrusted with complete information concerning the project and its objective. Each floor had an armed guard on duty. Burglar alarms were installed on all doors and windows. Everyone had two wastebaskets — one painted red, for classified material. Every evening these were taken downstairs and their contents incinerated in the presence of a security officer. Only American citizens were permitted to work on the project, and then only after being cleared by the War Department's intelligence services. Visitors had to fill out a slip and to tear off a stub of this slip: by doing so,

---

* In August 1943 Colonel Marshall, promoted to brigadier general, received an assignment overseas and Nichols succeeded him as District Engineers.

they left, without suspecting it, their fingerprints on the specially sensitized paper of the stub.

The word uranium was never used — a number of code names were used instead. Drawings were deposited in sealed filing cases or vaults. Even the manufacturers who developed equipment for Stone and Webster's secret project were subjected to the strictest secrecy regulations, and parts of their plants were placed under guard. Since work was done in four different Stone and Webster buildings, it became a common sight to see a messenger girl walking down the street with a roll of blueprints under her arm and followed by a big Brinks Company guard with a revolver at his hip.

The man Stone and Webster assigned to direct all its work for the Manhattan Project was an engineer with unusual drive and energy, August C. (Gus) Klein, who had been among the first top Boston engineers to visit Dr. Lawrence's Radiation Laboratory at Berkeley and learn about the electromagnetic method from its creator. Gus Klein was a short, ebullient man from New Jersey, an extrovert always on the go, grabbing naps at airports and railroad stations. He made friends everywhere he went, and it was largely through his acquaintances with Army engineers and scientists that Stone and Webster became so deeply, and so early, involved in the atomic bomb project.

In building the complex Y–12 installations for the still not completely developed electromagnetic process, Gus Klein and his colleagues were faced with problems of a nature and magnitude never before encountered. Magnets, electric power supplies, control devices and much of the auxiliary equipment were of radically new design. The pumping equipment had to be able to evacuate huge volumes and to produce a vacuum thirty million times greater than that commonly used in standard power plants. The entire vacuum system, including the equipment, was developed from Stone and Webster designs. A vacuum system of this magnitude had never before been attempted; it was necessary to develop entirely new devices for pressure measurement.

Design and production of the magnets — huge structures 250 feet long, and each containing thousands of tons of steel (*one hundred times* larger than the magnet of Lawrence's 184-inch cyclotron at Berkeley — the largest in the world) presented many problems. Their magnetic field was so strong that an ordinary wrench or a piece of pipe would be wrested from a workman's hand . . . or, if he held onto it, he would be drawn against the magnet-face and his knuckles skinned and brused. To prevent this happening, all movable equipment had to be built of nonferrous metals, or of nonmagnetic steel. It was impossible to use standard designs for any of this equipment. Large quantities of stainless

) 168

and other nonmagnetic steels had to be procured at a time when they were badly needed for other war programs. Workmen in many shops had to be trained in the welding of these materials, in heat-treating them and hardening them in many other ways. A complete set of small tools of beryllium copper also had to be designed and produced. Electrical control problems, too, were unprecedented and unique.

One important adjunct to the Y-12 plant at Oak Ridge was the extensive "chemical area." The reason: not all of the feed material was separated into the two component isotopes during the processing. Much went astray and had to be recovered from the walls of the containing vessels and from parts of the moving parts, for atoms tended to combine, physically or chemically, with the metals comprising the separating equipment. All parts of the operating mechanisms, therefore, had to be removed periodically, then cleaned and washed by steam, acid and electric stripping. The resulting acid solution of uranium compounds contained impurities like iron, nickel, copper and other metals.

Construction of the chemical plant was also particularly difficult since uranium chemistry was practically unknown; new processes had to be originated during the engineering period. One notable achievement thus developed: the extensive use of glass piping. An entirely new technique of field cutting and welding of glass pipe had to be perfected. The result: duplication, in glass, of all the advantages of steel-pipe welding. (So that matter would not collect on the ground, all floors were made of stainless steel and every joint was welded.) Still another very essential feature: the salvaging of every particle of enriched uranium. Ventilating air in the chemical area was treated so as to recover uranium-bearing dust, which would otherwise be carried out of the building and lost in the atmosphere.

28

On March 20, 1943, K. T. Keller, president of the Chrysler Corporation, received a phone call from Ed Garbisch, the son-in-law of the company's founder, Walter P. Chrysler. Garbisch, onetime West Point football star and now serving as a colonel in the Corps of Engineers, told Keller he was calling on behalf of Colonel Marshall of the Manhattan District. Keller had never heard of either Colonel Marshall or the Manhattan District.

"They want me to arrange a meeting with you in Detroit," Garbisch explained. "They have a very important matter to discuss with you. I'm not in a position to tell you what it is, but it's vital to the war effort."

"Is this about something they want us to make?" asked Keller. Chrysler was already deep in war-production contracts.

"Yes," Garbisch admitted. "If you take it on, it's going to involve making something." Then he added cryptically: "By the way, if you need to take advisers to the meeting, limit them to as few as possible."

The conference was fixed for April 2. K. T. Keller, surrounded by B. E. Hutchinson, Herman Weckler, Fred Zeder, Alan Loofbourrow and Nicholas Kelley, received the three visitors in the small, walnut-paneled library on the fifth floor of Chrysler's executive building. The guests introduced themselves: General Leslie Groves and Colonel Kenneth Nichols of the Army's Manhattan District, and P. C. Keith of Kellex.

After emphasizing the importance and the secret nature of the project, Groves explained that they were engaged in the construction of a mammoth gaseous-diffusion plant. Chrysler was needed for the key job of designing and manufacturing the large, metal diffusers — the containers in which the barriers would be placed. Groves said nothing about why the Army needed the plant. As he began to explain the technical details of what was wanted, the Chrysler executives grew more and more confused.

After listening for a while, Keller became impatient. "I'd like you to know," he told his visitors, "that everyone in this room is a loyal American citizen. If we can't find out what we're supposed to be making, we aren't going to be able to do a very good job for you."

Groves, Keith and Nichols exchanged glances, then excused themselves and withdrew for a moment into a small adjoining room. When they returned to the library, the head of the Manhattan Project revealed the secret of the fantastic weapon the Army wanted to build, then explained the principle of the separation of uranium isotopes by gaseous diffusion. He emphasized, above all else, the urgent need for building the diffusers as quickly as possible. Groves was not exaggerating. Although no satisfactory barrier had yet been invented, the Manhattan Project could no longer delay construction of the diffusers, an undertaking that would be beset with enormous, unforeseeable difficulties and probably require at least a year or two of work. It was a task that only a large industrial organization could possibly undertake; both Groves and Dobie Keith realized that what the job needed most was a hard-driving leader of the caliber of Detroit's famous K. T. Keller.

"K.T." was a celebrity in the automobile capital. His fabulous, rags-to-riches career was a part of local folklore. In the eight years since he had become president of the company, Chrysler's success had filled the industry with admiration and envy; everybody in Detroit was talking about the aggressive leadership of the hard-boiled, self-made man who looked like a stout, barrel-chested, bull-necked James Cagney. For years the late Walter Chrysler, founder of the company, had said admiringly, "When Keller gives the go-ahead, the job is as good as done." There was a story circulating about how Chrysler had taken on the production of M–3 tanks for the Army. In June of 1940, William Knudsen of the Office of Production Management telephoned Keller from Washington and asked point-blank, "Will you make tanks for us?"

Keller's reply was immediate: "Yes. Where can I see one?"

The Army arranged a visit to the Rock Island Arsenal in Illinois, where Keller examined the vehicle in silence, touched every part and finally said, "So that's a tank." Then, with 186 pounds of blueprints drawn up by the Army, he returned to Detroit and promptly organized mass production of the M–3's.

Tough, courageous, practical, his feet securely on the ground, Keller knew every bolt and screw in his plants better than the mechanics themselves. He was a man of extraordinary physical and mental ability, who believed, above all, in his work. In 1926, when Walter Chrysler had asked him to come and work with him, Keller's only question was, "Are you yourself going to devote your life to the Chrysler Corporation?" And when Chrysler replied emphatically, "You bet I am!" Keller accepted with enthusiasm.

Chrysler was already doing a full-time job of building tanks, military vehicles and other equipment for the Army. Groves, Nichols and Keith were very eager, even so, to persuade Keller to take on still another war contract. But they ran into serious complications when they explained that the diffusers had to use uranium hexafluoride, a highly corrosive gas, and therefore must be made out of solid nickel.

The Chrysler men immediately saw the difficulty. "You'll need several thousand of these diffusers?" asked Keller. "And they'll be very large — something like an anchor buoy? Where do you find that much nickel?" Obviously, with nickel in short supply, the job did not seem possible. Everybody in the room was thinking hard; finally Keller came up with a suggestion.

"I have it!" he exclaimed. "Why don't we make the diffusers out of steel, then electroplate nickel onto the surfaces? A thin layer of nickel. That way we'll use only a thousandth as much."

"We've already thought of that," Groves replied. "We've tried different methods of electroplating and spent one hundred thousand dollars on it — and we've gotten nowhere."

The scientists had confirmed that no plating could resist hexafluoride gas. Any kind of nickel-plating would peel off, and the gas would then devour the steel. Nickel-plating was very difficult because of the nature of the metal; a perfect layer had never been achieved. When examined under a microscope, it always showed some small pores, which would make the plating process ineffective for the diffusers.

Keller did not know anything about uranium hexafluoride, but he had had wide experience with plating and did not like to take no for an answer. "Could we try it?" he asked.

"Well, do you want to spend your own money? . . ."

K. T. Keller thought it over for a few moments. It would have to be his decision; he was not going to ask Chrysler's board of directors — it was not his way of running the corporation. He always kept them informed about all important matters, but felt that decisions were his job — and only his.

He glanced once more at his visitors. He liked them; they seemed to be dynamic, dedicated men who knew their business. From the moment he met Groves, Keller had confidence in him. They spoke the same language, and Chrysler's president was sure of his own ability to recognize a leader when he met one. Colonel Nichols did not say much, but the few things he did say revealed great technical competence. Though Keller did not understand what the exact relationship was between the Army and Percival Keith, it was obvious that the Kellex boss was also a top-flight engineer.

K.T. turned to his men. "I think we'd better make the effort and try to get this thing going," he said briskly. His engineers nodded approvingly.

Thus the Chrysler Corporation, with its vast resources and engineering talent, joined in the effort to separate fissionable material by gaseous diffusion. It was an act of faith; no one knew what future problems might complicate existing ones; nor what the outcome would be. But having gained a powerful new ally, Groves and his aides left Detroit both relieved and happy.

The man who took the responsibility for involving the huge automobile company in a $75-million gamble did not know exactly how the nickel problem could be solved, but he was fully confident that a solution could eventually be found. K. T. Keller, a born fighter, was only stimulated by new difficulties.

Chrysler's president had started life with the considerable handicap of having been christened Kaufman Thume Keller. A certain Mr. Kaufman Deutsch was the rich man of the small town of Mount Joy, seventy-five miles from Philadelphia, and when the boy was born there in 1885, his father, a poor horse dealer, sold Mr. Deutsch four horses in order to meet the cost of the birth. "Do me a favor," said his benefactor, "give the boy my first name." So Kaufman the child became. (Thume was the Austrian family name of the boy's mother.)

A very poor boy, K.T.'s father had been indentured to a Mennonite preacher who raised him. He learned to read and write only later in life, when his own children were in school. However, he did know a lot about horses, and young K.T. started helping around the stables when still so small that he had to stand on a chair to brush the horses' manes. At thirteen, during a summer vacation, he had his first factory job — making handkerchiefs with a sewing machine. The next job he found was assembling kitchen hardware; then he ran a drill press. By the time he finished high school at sixteen, Keller had learned a good deal about machinery. To earn additional money to go to a business college in nearby Lancaster, he also raised pigeons in his father's barn and sold the squabs.

The big chance in the country boy's life came when he fell in love, or thought he did, at seventeen. Since he was nearly on the point of accepting a job in his girl's home town, with the idea of getting married, his worried family took the drastic step of sending him abroad to see the world. For fifty dollars they bought him a second-class round-trip ticket to England and gave him another fifty dollars to spend on a couple of weeks abroad. "If the girl loves you, she'll wait for you," said his mother, shedding some farewell tears.

K.T. had never left home before except once to go with his father to Philadelphia. Now he was on his way to Europe alone, with the huge sum of fifty dollars in his pocket! On the boat he met a temperance worker, an evangelist of the American Baptist Church named John Quincy Adams Henry, who was going on a lecture tour to England. The Reverend Henry needed a secretary and offered the boy $7.50 a week plus all living expenses. Keller jumped at the chance: he figured he could work for a month, then return to America and still have his fifty dollars to get married on.

The evangelist considered England "a pretty drunken place," and had a busy schedule of meetings at which he tried to get people to sign a pledge to stop drinking. Keller had been contributing to the salvation of British souls for six weeks when a letter arrived from his mother: his girl had married someone else. Keller stayed with the temperance preacher for three years at $7.50 a week, traveling through the British Isles and meeting all kinds of people, from lord mayors of major cities to humble village blacksmiths. One summer Reverend Henry put him up with Dr. Thomas J. Barnardo, the famous philanthropist of London's East End, who gathered homeless children and taught them trades; the next summer he worked as a counselor at a children's camp in northern Wales.

After three years of such wholesome living, K. T. Keller came back to America with his fifty dollars intact and took the day train to Pittsburgh. On the way to a cheap hotel that the stationmaster had recommended, the young man passed a Westinghouse plant. It was the biggest industrial enterprise he had ever seen. That, he thought admiringly, was where he should go. The next morning he applied and was hired for a job in a Westinghouse office for sixty-five dollars a month — good pay at that time. But after a few months he went to the manager and asked to be sent to the factory as an apprentice, even though the pay there was only twenty cents an hour. In Keller's career, it was the first of several voluntary switches to jobs that paid a much lower wage which he made in order to broaden his experience.

After Keller had become an expert mechanic, Westinghouse sent him as assistant general foreman to Detroit, where the company was building engines for Chalmers Motor Company. There he became chief inspector in an axle plant at $150 a month, then moved over to the Metzger Motor Car Company. By 1910 Detroit had become the nation's unchallenged automotive capital, and K. T. Keller was out to learn the maximum at each job. "This Keller is the best man we've ever had!" the Metzger plant boss said. But Keller was always ambitious, too eager to advance quickly, and one day he was fired.

Then followed three months of hunger and anxiety as a jobless young man in Detroit, but it didn't break his spirit in the least. He had to start all over again from the bottom, on a messy manual job at the Hudson Motor Car Company at forty cents an hour, before he found an opening in Tarrytown, New York, as a chief inspector at the Maxwell Company.

Keller was making $220 a month when General Motors offered him a job in Detroit for $150. But by 1912, General Motors was becoming a big organization; Keller again switched to a lower-salaried job without hesitation. It proved to be the right decision: K.T. grew up with the company and filled some of its top executive posts until 1926, when he left and went to work with Walter Chrysler.

But even as chief executive of a great automobile company, he was occasionally encumbered by his unusual name. Keller enjoyed recounting an experience he had when he applied for membership in one of Detroit's most exclusive clubs. Despite his important position, he had some inexplicable delay being admitted, until, after being on the waiting list for several years, he met by chance some of the members of the admissions committee in the shower room. They took a good look at him, and the next day he was invited to join the club.

As president of Chrysler, Keller kept continuously in touch with the daily mechanical work in the plants. "They all know I can run any damn machine in the place," he would say. And he was right: one day when a plant had trouble with a new type of compressor, he interrupted a business luncheon with five of the plant's executives. "Come along with me," he said abruptly. "I want to go down and see this!" The factory was an hour and a half's drive from the restaurant. Keller looked at the compressor, asked for a wrench and hammer, dismantled the parts and examined them carefully. The mechanics still could not see what was wrong with the machine. "Give me a six-inch file!" ordered Keller. Half an hour later the parts were reassembled. "Start it up!" he said. The mysterious vibration had disappeared. "Now let's go back to lunch!" said K.T. matter-of-factly.

Excellent mechanic though he had always been, K. T. Keller knew very little about the electroplating of nickel for gaseous diffusers. But he had great confidence in Chrysler's plating laboratory, and in its director Dr. Carl Heussner. As soon as he accepted the Manhattan District assignment, Keller instructed Fred Zeder, vice-president in charge of engineering, to do his utmost to solve the nickel-plating problem. A few days later, Dr. Heussner came to see Keller in his office on the fifth floor of Chrysler's executive building. Heussner was a full-faced, chunky man of German descent in his late forties, with unruly hair and a pleasant smile. Many people considered him one of the best experts on plating in the United States. In spite of his complete intolerance of ineptitude and his harsh reaction to any mistake, Carl Heussner was much admired and liked in his laboratory.

"Mr. Zeder wants me to tell you that he is afraid the company has stuck its neck out too far, sir," Heussner began. "I have looked into the problem. The other day we went to Columbia to see what they were doing." Heussner paused, then added, "I don't believe, Mr. Keller, that we can nickel-plate steel to stand up against uranium hexafluoride gas."

Keller's spirits sank. But suddenly he remembered that Heussner had just received a doctor's degree, and that everybody at Chrysler's had congratulated him about it. "Doctor," he said, emphasizing the title, "I know I did stick my neck out. But let me tell you why I did it. It was only because of my confidence in you. I know you're the only man who can do it. Will you try?"

Heussner blushed. He was flattered by the confidence that the company president was putting in him; it was as if the whole future of the Manhattan Project now lay in his hands. Like any scientist, Heussner had his secret dream of inventing a new technique one day. "I'll try," he said after a pause, "but what I have in mind will cost a lot of money — and only just to try! There is no guarantee . . ."

"Well, Doctor, how much do you think it would cost?" Keller asked bluntly.

"Perhaps forty-five thousand dollars."

"I'm making seventy-five thousand dollars available to you now," Keller told the scientist.

Heussner locked himself in his laboratory for several days of intensive experiments. Soon a small building was specially erected inside the press plant, where there was a large crane. After a huge tank had been brought in and hooked onto a big generator, which had formerly been used for making axles, Heussner started testing his new electroplating process in earnest. A few weeks later, he reported that his process appeared to be successful. There was, of course, no uranium hexafluoride gas in Detroit with which to try the plated samples; Heussner, however, felt he had obtained the perfect surface, with no porosity in the layer of nickel. Columbia University remained more than skeptical but agreed to test Heussner's plating samples in their gas chamber.

When Keller went down, on the spur of the moment, to see the new plating tank, he found Heussner in the process of draining the chemicals from the tank and recharging it for the next step. The German-born scientist was wearing a raincoat and a fireman's hat. Water was gushing and flooding everywhere. Some of the water lines had broken, and Heussner was completely drenched from head to toe in spite of his raincoat. Impulsively, Keller took a hundred dollar bill out of his wallet and handed it to him: "Get yourself a new suit — you deserve it!"

With water pouring off his face, Heussner looked untidier than ever, but he was smiling broadly. "It worked, Mr. Keller, we did it!" he shouted happily as he showed some of the ten-inch-long square steel bars he had nickel-plated. "We're sending samples to Columbia for testing. They still don't believe it can be done, but . . . !"

K.T. did not have too much respect for the opinions of scientists he considered "highbrow" — too intellectual. "These scientists are sometimes not so good about technical things," he used to say, and often told a story to illustrate his point, about a camping experience in the redwood country of California. "I used to have a lot of respect for Ph.D.'s until that time," he said, "but then I went out there with some California friends on a camping trip. There were acetylene lamps in the tents there. One of these Ph.D.'s who was along wanted to go to bed, but he didn't know how to turn off the light. So what does he do but hang a towel over it! And pretty soon, of course, the towel's on fire, the tent's on fire, and the woods are, too. We had three fire departments up there! Now you tell me what you think of that!"

As the opinions of Carl Heussner were lined up against those of Columbia's Ph.D.'s, there was no question about which side Keller was on. Heussner was confident his plating would not absorb any hexafluoride gas at all. "That's good enough for me, Doctor!" K.T. said, with a beaming smile. "Now I want you to do a full-scale test. Get all the help and material you need!"

Heussner first sent samples of his electroplating to New York, together with bars of pure solid nickel of high purity for comparison. Then, without waiting for Columbia's findings, he launched a full-scale experiment at Chrysler's Highland Park plant. It was done with makeshift equipment. A pit was dug for a plating bath; then a steel sheet of old boiler plate was brought in, cleaned and welded into a cylinder that equaled the size of the future big diffusers. Heussner covered it with a thin coating of nickel — and matched the success achieved with his earlier samples.

An excited Keller telephoned Washington, and Groves arrived with Dobie Keith to see for himself. In the meantime the verdict of the Columbia tests had come in: not only did Heussner's nickel-plating completely resist the corrosive effects of UF-6 gas, but the absorption was even less than with pure, solid-nickel samples, which in fact contained small amounts of impurities.

Groves and Keith were highly impressed. "Cut out a hundred pieces of that in two-by-four-inch size!" they said. Samples from the full-size cylinder were then sent to several other laboratories for testing. A few days later, Keller received word from them: "Further experiments unnecessary. Go ahead and nickel-plate!" It had taken only six weeks from the time of Groves's first visit to Detroit for Chrysler to lick the formidable problem of nickel-plating.

But a tremendous manufacturing operation had still to be organized at Chrysler before there could be any mass production of diffusers. Keller himself had noticed, in Detroit's downtown section, a vacant department store at 1525 Woodward Avenue, where the United States War Bond Drive had temporary headquarters on the first floor. K.T. immediately rented the upper floors but kept the bond drive office below as a convenient camouflage for the top-secret Chrysler operation, which was given the code name X–100. All designing and experimental work on the diffusers was done there, right in the center of Detroit and unknown to thousands of passers-by in the busy neighborhood.

For the manufacturing of the diffusers, Chrysler converted its Lynch Road factory, and moved the production of tank transmissions and truck parts to another plant. In order to get the necessary headroom in the low building, which had originally been built in World War I to make recoil mechanisms for howitzers, the floor was ripped up and a long trench dug. All the walls, beams and columns in the plant had to be carefully washed and painted white. Because of the inflammable character of hexafluoride gas whenever it came in contact with any kind of grease or other organic substance, the regulations to ensure cleanliness were even more stringent than in a health clinic. Not even microscopic bits of lint or ordinary shop dirt could be tolerated. In the area where barrier tubes were going to be installed, the air had to be completely filtered by electrostatic filters. Each cylinder and its parts had to be washed chemically.

Lieutenant Colonel James Stowers, the Manhattan District's representative for gaseous diffusion, brought some of his key men to the Chrysler plant. Keller appointed one of his engineers, J. M. Hartgering, to head the whole project and tool up for an efficient assembly line. Without waiting for a final solution of the barrier problem, Chrysler went ahead full speed with research, development and manufacturing of the other component parts of the diffusers.

Now everyone was waiting for the day the barrier tubes would start arriving from the Houdaille-Hershey plant, in Decatur, Illinois. Chrysler engineers were optimistic. They did not know about the barrier problems that still lay ahead.

29

IF AN AIR of impending disaster was sensed by only a few leaders of the gaseous-diffusion project, it was due to the compartmentalized security regulations rigorously imposed by General Groves. Most engineers and scientists were not allowed to know anything outside their specific fields; thus, only a handful of men at the very top suspected that a dramatic failure was about to wreck the most crucial element of the gaseous-diffusion project: the barrier.

But by the summer of 1943, the tremendous gamble was already too far advanced; there was no way to back out. The world's largest electric power plant was already under construction at Oak Ridge; the huge K–25 plant was about to be built at a cost of hundreds of millions of dollars. Kellex, Union Carbide, Allis-Chalmers, Chrysler and dozens of other industrial firms had already mobilized thousands of people in a joint effort. The whole gigantic project was going full speed ahead — and on the assumption that the barrier existed. Yet the truth was that there was still no barrier.

Like a poker player betting everything on one card, Kellex's Dobie Keith desperately needed the barrier to avoid disaster. In making their decisions, Groves and Keith had never cringed at the enormous risks involved, but they had not committed their country to a reckless adventure. There simply was no other way to play the game — time dominated all other considerations, and it would have been foolhardy to stop the rest of the Project while waiting for the barrier.

Even the building of the barrier plant itself could not be postponed. In the hope that the Norris-Adler material would somehow be improved, steps were taken to erect a special plant for large-scale production. To construct a plant before the end product had even been invented, let alone tested, was highly unorthodox; but then, so was nearly everything else connected with the Manhattan Project.

The directors of the Houdaille-Hershey Corporation with headquarters in Detroit were not told any details when the Manhattan District first contacted them in April 1943. The company had been selected for the job because the only available barrier that seemed to approximate what was

WESTFIELD MEMORIAL LIBRARY
WESTFIELD, N. J.

desired was the Norris-Adler barrier, made from nickel, and Houdaille-Hershey was the largest user of finished nickel, which they employed primarily in plating automobile bumpers.

On April 21 representatives of the Houdaille-Hershey Corporation met at the Woolworth Building with the top Kellex people and the Manhattan District staff. They were told, in general terms, that the Army needed large quantities of a newly invented material which had already been made in experimental quantities. But the Houdaille-Hershey people were not informed of the material's ultimate purpose, other than the fact that it was of the utmost importance to the war effort and was needed ten times faster than normal production time would allow.

The same evening, Houdaille-Hershey accepted the challenge and signed a contract. Lieutenant Colonel Stowers established an area office of the Manhattan Engineering District at Decatur, Illinois, where a new plant was to be built, at an estimated cost of several millions. When Houdaille-Hershey joined the Project, the instructions from Kellex and the Manhattan District were straightforward: construct and equip a plant to produce a certain amount of square feet of barrier per day. The company assumed that the research work in progress at Columbia would be completely successful; that the preparation of the Norris-Adler barrier would follow a step-by-step procedure described by the Columbia scientists.

Soon after the contract was signed, however, company engineers began to have serious doubts about this "step-by-step" procedure. They realized that the Columbia scientists, though brainy theoreticians and lab men, did not have an industrial viewpoint. The process envisaged by the scientists involved more than a dozen steps, but it took the Houdaille engineers very little time to discover that not one of the steps was clearly enough defined to enable them to set up an operating plant.

The company went ahead, as instructed, with plant design and the ordering of equipment. But the Houdaille engineers began to look with mounting skepticism at certain aspects of the Columbia research program. Two months after getting into the project, Houdaille requested authorization so that its own research facilities could operate independently, to a large degree, of the Columbia group. This private research group reached the disturbing conclusion that the Norris-Adler barrier would probably never be practical to manufacture.

Meanwhile, outside Decatur, in the midst of a big Illinois cornfield, construction of the barrier-production plant by Houdaille-Hershey went steadily ahead. Columbia and Kellex, at the same time, launched a final, all-out effort to solve the barrier problem. In July a pilot plant was set up in a Columbia lab for the Norris-Adler material. Running around the

Argonne National Laboratory

eo Szilard and Norman Hilberry stand be-
le the site where the world's first nuclear
reactor was built

Argonne National Laboratory

Dr. Enrico Fermi

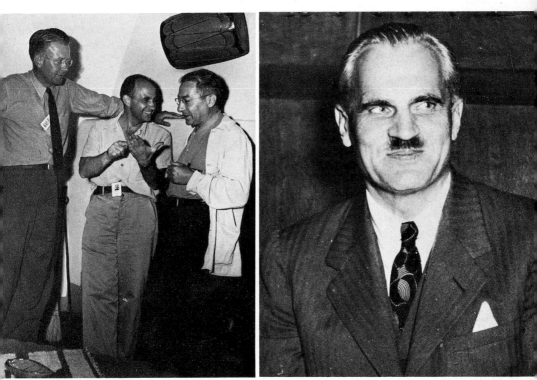

Los Alamos Photo Laboratory

rs. Ernest O. Lawrence, Enrico Fermi and
Isidor I. Rabi

Argonne National Laboratory

Dr. Arthur H. Compton,
photographed in 1946

Dr. George T. Felbeck

Dr. Judson S. Swearingen

Donald Nelson, chairman of the War Production Board, and K. T. Keller, president of Chrysler Corporation

Dr. Manson Benedict

Dr. Foster C. Nix   J. C. Hobbs

eft) In the basement of Columbia University's Pupin Physics Laboratories, Dr. John R. Dunning (left)
1 Dr. Eugene T. Booth at the control panel of a cyclotron. (*Right*) Dr. Clarence A. Johnson

Wide World Photos

(*Left*) Drs. Enrico Fermi and Walter H. Zinn look over a nuclear instrument during a reunion Chicago on the fourth anniversary of the famous Chicago pile experiment. (*Right*) Colonel Kenn D. Nichols

(*Left*) Alexander Sachs talks with General Groves. (*Right*) Ernest O. Lawrence and J. Robert Oppenheimer examine diffusion pumps for creating an almost perfect vacuum in an accelerating cham between poles of the new 184-inch cyclotron

D. Cooksey

The S–1 Committee photographed at the Bohemian Grove, California, in 1942. Left to right: J. Robert Oppenheimer, Harold C. Urey, Ernest O. Lawrence, James B. Conant, Lyman J. Briggs, Eger V. Murphree, Arthur H. Compton, Robert L. Thornton, Colonel Kenneth D. Nichols

Hanford visitors: **Dr. Vannevar Bush, Dr. James B. Conant, General Leslie R. Groves and Colonel Franklin T. Matthias**

E. I. du Pont de Nemours and Company

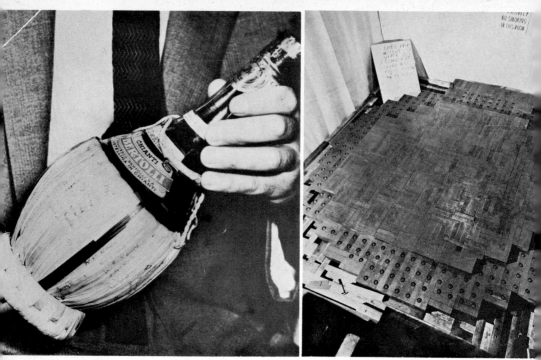

Argonne National Laboratory

Argonne National Labo

(*Left*) The famous Chianti bottle presented by Eugene Wigner to Enrico Fermi with signatures many of the scientists participating in the first successful Chicago experiment. (*Right*) Photograph tak from above during the addition of the nineteenth layer of graphite as part of the assembly of the fi nuclear reactor in the racquets court at Stagg Field, University of Chicago

Argonne National Laboratory

Racquets court under West Stands, Stagg Field, University of Chicago. Photograph of an original painting by Gary Sheehan of the scene in which the scientists witnessed the first nuclear reactor as it became self-sustaining

Argonne National Laboratory

he Chicago group. **Front row:** Enrico Fermi, Walter Zinn, Albert Wattenberg, Herbert Anderson.
iddle row: Harold Agnew, William Sturm, Harold Lichtenberger, Leona Marshall, Leo Szilard. Top
w: Norman Hilberry, Samuel Allison, Thomas Brill, Robert Nobles, Warren Nyer, Marvin Wilkening

Dr. Alfred O. Nier   Percival (Dobie) C. Keith   Edward O. Norris

George Watts   Dr. Edward Adler

E. I. du Pont de Nemours and Company

...lter Carpenter, president of Du Pont, as he talks with Generals Levin H. Campbell, Everett Hughes ...d Charles T. Harris of the Ordnance Department during World War II

Wide World Photos

...ve key scientists inspect the huge pole faces of the four-thousand-ton cyclotron at the University of ...lifornia. Donald Cooksey, Ernest O. Lawrence, Robert L. Thornton, J. Robert Oppenheimer and ...lliam Brobeck

Oak Ridge: "cubicles" in the electromagnetic plants; Alpha One control room

Oak Ridge: "race track" for the electromagnetic process

E. I. du Pont de Nemours and Company

Housing at Hanford Engineering Works

Oak Ridge: K–25 under construction

LABORERS
CARPENTERS
WAMPERS

3-1201.
3-651.
3-1600
3-1200

3-2051.
3-1601.
4-801.
4-451.
4-100.
3-2600
3-2050

1-251.
4-800.
4-450.

1-1700.
4-1250.

PAY WAGON

Wes
BAD
I
PLA
VI

E. I. du Pont de Nemours and

Some attractive Du Pont paymasters who traveled from one area to another over the $350,000
Hanford plant

Midway in construction of the Hanford Engineering Works

E. I. du Pont de Nemours and

clock, it managed to produce enough barrier for testing purposes. But the tests showed complete failure. Just as before, the material turned out to be fragile.

At the same time, at Bell Telephone and Bakelite, Union Carbide teams were working twenty-four hours a day on other barriers based on the nickel-powder material developed by Foster Nix and Frazier Groff. But time was running out; all other developments in the gaseous-diffusion program had reached a stage where the barrier was indispensable.

As the situation grew increasingly critical, doubt and skepticism arose in the minds of the few people who had been let in on the full secret of the gaseous-diffusion project. Could a barrier be built at all? Was the whole process unfeasible? With every successive lab failure, the number of believers dwindled. Common sense and the very facts of the problem could hardly justify Dobie Keith's determination and John Dunning's optimism.

Very few people knew the private opinion of Professor Harold Urey, the nominal leader of the gaseous-diffusion project. Had the thoughts of this eminent Nobel laureate been made known, the worries of the industrialists and engineers would have turned into downright consternation. For, paradoxically, the ranking scientist in charge of gaseous diffusion had lost his faith in the process. Urey, an emotional man, had become unhappy and frustrated, torn between his duty as leader of the project and his growing conviction that the project was doomed. A man with an extremely keen sense of integrity, Harold Urey found himself in an unbearable position.

Few chemists or physicists in America had been confronted before with responsibility for failure in their scientific work. From a scientific viewpoint, the failure of a laboratory experiment often has as much value as its success. The proof that a method does *not* work, or a chemical does *not* react in a certain way, could be as interesting to science as if it did. But in the Manhattan Project, purely academic scientists were given fantastic amounts of money for their laboratories, unlimited supplies of material and personnel, then were told to succeed at any cost. They had never had such responsibilities before. Negative results were not acceptable; even when they offered great theoretical value, they could not be taken into consideration. The scientists had done a marvelous job in predicting the feasibility of isotope separation by gaseous diffusion. But when it came to actually doing it on an industrial scale, they found themselves helpless in the face of insurmountable technical obstacles.

If there was a pure scientist in the group, it was Harold Urey. His remarkable academic career, his avid intellectual curiosity, even his appearance and manner of the "absent-minded professor," fitted him perfectly for the role. Throughout his career as a chemist, he had known all the excitement of laboratory work, some experiments ending in positive results and others with only negative results. But now he suddenly found himself directing a new kind of experiment, involving incredible amounts of money, people, plants, laboratories. After trying every method and material that anybody in America or England could think of, they made a thorough assessment of the situation. His conclusions plunged him into deep despair: to the best of his judgment, the process did not seem feasible, at least for the time being, because of the lack of an adequate barrier.

In laboratory terms, this would be a rather disappointing but nevertheless interesting conclusion, one worth communicating to a scientific journal. In industrial terms, however, with the nation at war, failure could take on catastrophic proportions. Urey was not a man who wanted or was prepared for this kind of responsibility.

Harold Urey, administrative head of the scientists working on gaseous diffusion, hated all administration. Restless, absent-minded and disorganized, he had no interest or talent for it whatsoever. Red tape made him suffer; giving orders was a thing he could never learn; and any financial balance sheet puzzled him no less than his own formula for heavy hydrogen would puzzle a layman.

Urey had not asked for the job. On the contrary, he accepted it reluctantly when his colleagues on the S-1 Committee insisted that he was the only man that could direct the gaseous-diffusion project. Later he suspected that he had been used, that his name was being employed to give prestige to the risky undertaking and to attract the younger scientists that the Manhattan Project needed so badly.

In the beginning, he did not mind; he felt that it was for a worthy cause. But as tension grew and frustrations piled up, Urey felt that the Manhattan Project might be using him as a potential scapegoat: in case of failure, the leaders could not be accused of not having consulted and won the approval of the best scientific authorities in the country — men like Nobel Prize winner Harold Urey. And in the meantime his name was helping to recruit top-drawer scientists for the project. They joined with confidence in the belief that Urey considered the process workable since he, after all, headed the project.

Beset with doubt and resentful, Urey even suggested to Colonel Nichols that he be relieved of his post. But it was too late. Things had gone too far, he was told, and whether he liked it or not, the project was already linked for good with his name.

Harold Urey had another reason for disliking his position. He was the nominal leader of the Columbia project, but from the beginning, its driving force had been John Dunning, a much younger man, and there was no love lost between them. The project was Dunning's baby, and he had no desire to let anybody else run it. Yet he was too young and still too unknown to sit on the committee with Nobel laureates like Lawrence, Arthur Compton and Fermi. On the high scientific, governmental and Army levels, Dunning and his project were represented by Urey, a man with whom he felt no affinity. Impetuous and enthusiastic about his work, Dunning could not understand — or forgive — Urey's doubts and hesitations concerning the project.

The lack of sympathy was mutual. The older professor thought Dunning was an overeager, ambitious young man in too great a hurry to succeed — and also afraid that his seniors might steal the show. Their temperaments were completely different, and while Dunning was the doer and promoter type, Urey felt at home only among his books and in his laboratory. With Dunning taking over the effective leadership, Urey became more and more what he called bitterly "a glorified personnel manager."

Urey's interest in isotope separation had begun with the discovery of heavy hydrogen, made at Columbia in 1931. When the war broke out and the problem of isotope separation arose, he was the natural choice for the job. But he had never worked on diffusion separation of uranium isotopes and was rather appalled by the immense difficulty of the job. He was particularly worried about the enormous corrosion problem caused by uranium hexafluoride. The whole process demanded a large-scale industrial operation that he knew little about. Nevertheless he accepted, after some persuasion, the job of representing the Columbia University group.

When the Army took over in 1942, and the gaseous-diffusion project went ahead full speed, results of the preliminary experiments discouraged Urey. He was particularly disturbed when British scientists asked Columbia to supply them with some barrier material. No one could produce even a square inch of it! Urey concluded, in all sincerity, that the diffusion idea was impractical.

Nor was he the only one to be discouraged. His British colleagues, whose opinions Urey had learned to value and respect, were equally skeptical. His friend Franz E. Simon shared his view that under existing conditions, diffusion separation was not possible.

When Urey lost faith in the program, he felt it his duty to put a stop to it. At the same time, he was torn by his duty as its leader to make the program succeed. The strain of the conflict began to show, and Urey became tense and highly nervous. His relation with the drivers of the project — Groves, Keith and Dunning — went from bad to worse.

WESTFIELD MEMORIAL LIBRARY
WESTFIELD, N. J.

Urey's pessimism, and the persistently bad news from those working on barrier development, began to affect the morale of the Manhattan Project. Leaders of other programs in the Project, especially Lawrence and Marcus Oliphant, the British representative in his laboratory, tried to get most of the Columbia group's credits and priorities switched away from Urey and transferred to them. "Why, Urey, the man in charge of it, says it won't work!" General Groves was told. There was fear that the Army would grow impatient and even begin considering the reduction, if not the abandonment, of the diffusion project in order to limit the catastrophic effects of failure. But then, on June 19, 1943, something happened that gave Keith new hope — and reassured Leslie Groves.

It began prosaically. Dr. Clarence Johnson, a short, bespectacled chemist of twenty-nine, had called his wife in Westfield, New Jersey, that evening and told her that he couldn't take his usual train home from Kellex's Jersey City laboratory. He was going to have to work late.

Johnson was in charge of a huge laboratory staffed by two hundred men and goaded incessantly by an impatient Dobie Keith, who wanted his barrier at any price. Clarence Johnson, buried under administrative duties, could find time for his own experiments only after his office work had been cleared away.

The son of Swedish immigrants, Clarence Johnson had been raised on a farm in Alberta, in western Canada. Life was hard for the family, and Clarence, though lame in one leg, began doing chores around the farm at an early age. The nearest school — a one-room building for all eight grades — was five miles away, in the small town of Minburn (population: 200). With his three older brothers and sisters, the boy drove to school in a horse and buggy in fine weather and, when winter came, in a sleigh they hitched up for the hour-long trip. In winter the temperature often fell to forty degrees below zero, but the children still went to school. It was only when it fell to fifty below — or more — or when there was a heavy blizzard raging, that the parents gave their children permission to stay home.

Johnson was determined to get a higher education and become an engineer. While still in high school, he trapped wild animals and sold the skins in order to save up money for a college education. He managed to go to the University of Alberta, where he majored in chemical engineering. Then he won a grant, for work on natural gas, from the Research Council of Canada while he was getting his master's degree. His work was so outstanding (he was always first in his class) that he came to the attention of authorities at MIT, who offered him a scholarship while he studied for a Ph.D. and, after he received his degree, a post on the faculty.

It was while studying in Cambridge that Johnson met Manson Benedict. When Benedict mentioned to him that Kellogg Company desperately needed top-flight engineers for its war contracts, Johnson decided to leave teaching and apply for a job with the company. After writing for an interview, Johnson arrived at the Transportation Building in New York on the appointed day. Unfortunately, the elevator operators' union had gone on strike, and Kellogg's offices were on the twenty-third floor. Johnson trudged up twenty-three flights of stairs, despite his lame leg, and arrived on time for his interview.

The interviewer glanced at Johnson's lame leg, then asked him incredulously: "Do you mean that you climbed *twenty-three* floors in order to get here for this interview?"

Johnson shrugged. "Well, yes. I was brought up on a farm and —"

"Just a minute," the interviewer interrupted, "I have to speak to Mr. Keith about something."

The interviewer told Keith about Clarence Johnson's academic record, with which the Kellogg executive was already acquainted, and the young man's determined effort to reach his interview on time even though it meant climbing twenty-three floors with a lame leg.

Dobie Keith's reaction was in character: "You hire Clarence Johnson immediately! That's the kind of man we want."

Leading up to that night of June 19, Johnson had felt very stimulated. He had been talking to Frazier Groff, whose new industrial technique threw further light on Johnson's own experiments, which had been carried out for months in Jersey City on variations of the Norris-Adler material. He had not had much success; the barrier — or the "lace curtain" as Dobie Keith used to call it — was still too fragile for use in a plant.

It was about 8 P.M. when Clarence Johnson and his young assistant Tony Suleski entered their small laboratory to conduct some more experiments. For several days running, Johnson had been excited and obsessed by a new idea: Was there some way to combine the best features of the existing barrier types? He had already tried different techniques without success. At least five times in recent experiments he had produced some kind of barrier; but something had always failed — the piece would break, or the porosity would be insufficient, or the holes would be too large. But now they were going to try again.

That June evening Johnson switched to another of the various techniques he was trying methodically. When he picked up the newly produced sample, he noticed that the material seemed flexible. The two men stood tense and silent as Johnson, squeezing one corner of the piece between his fingers, tried to bend it. The material did not break. Slowly he tried a little harder, then as hard as he could. The piece resisted.

A broad smile lit Tony Suleski's face. "Say, it looks like . . ." But before he could finish, Johnson, who was greatly excited, raised his hand and said, "Wait! There's just one more test! Let's find out about its porosity!"

Did the material have the right number of pores — the billions of holes per square inch? To find out, they performed tests which lasted for two hours. It was 10:30 P.M. when Johnson and Suleski scrutinized the last measurements. No doubt about it: the new barrier had successfully passed all tests!

A tremendous feeling of relief and joy swept over the two men. The "impossible" problem of the barrier, which had paralyzed the whole gaseous-diffusion project, now seemed solved. Clarence Johnson went to bed exhausted — and happier than he'd ever been in his life. Early the next morning, he phoned Manson Benedict so early that he woke him up. "Manson, I think we have it!" he said without any elaboration. Then he rushed to the lab, called Keith and also told him about the successful experiment of the night before.

"Do you think you can reproduce it?" Dobie Keith asked gruffly, trying hard to hide his excitement. "Come and see me immediately!"

Clarence Johnson was sure he could duplicate the success. But his enthusiasm was soon dampened. After turning out two more efficient barriers, he produced several others that were obviously unacceptable. Johnson and Suleski puzzled over the failures, then suddenly realized the cause: in their excitement, they had omitted one of the necessary steps of the process. The next time, using extreme care, they found them wholly satisfactory. After over a year of agonizing failure, Kellex now seemed to have a workable barrier. If it could be produced industrially on a huge scale, it would remove, at last, the major obstacle on the road to the key process of gaseous diffusion.

30

AN INCREDIBLE labyrinth of pipes, hundreds of miles of them, with thousands of valves, joints and weldings meticulously made and assembled — acres of intricate plumbing that would have to function with a fantastic, clockwork precision never conceived before in engineering history: such was the bold vision of the men designing the gigantic gaseous-diffusion plant that would produce fissionable material at Oak Ridge, Tennessee. Then, somewhere along the miles of the intricate piping system, a small leak appears. It is invisible, just the size of a pinhole, but slowly, inexorably, the leakage grows; air penetrates the closed system, corrosion eats into the metal. The whole process is ruined, the miraculous apparatus ceases to function. The $500-million gadget becomes useless.

This peculiar nightmare, in different versions, haunted the sleep of many a member of the Dunning and Keith teams in 1942 and 1943. Special groups were directed to work on methods of leak prevention so that any perforation could be immediately repaired. But all studies proved fruitless. The reason: how could leaks be immediately detected when they were only the size of a minute pinhole? There was no technique sensitive enough to do the job. No such instrument existed, for the simple reason that industry had never needed such a fantastic degree of tightness before. But now the engineers realized that when the scientists of the gaseous-diffusion project talked about leakage, they were not even considering pinholes; they were worried about the much smaller microscopic pores that exist sometimes as imperfections in the metal itself, or as a result of defects in the welding. There was no way of detecting such leaks over several miles of complex pipelines.

It was not the first time scientists had been faced with a seemingly impossible detection problem. The ingenuity with which most scientific precision instruments are conceived and built is hardly believable. The scientists of the gaseous-diffusion project had seen so many examples of it that they felt confident that somehow, someday, this difficulty would be solved, too.

In the spring and summer of 1942, when study of the feasibility of the process by Columbia and the Kellogg Company was going full speed, the problem of leak detection became increasingly a main topic of discussion. "That will be a tough one," Dunning admitted at Pupin Hall. "We'd better call Nier." At the same time engineers at the Jersey City laboratory were just coming out of the bewilderment caused by the unheard-of tightness requirements. "Any idea how we could detect the leaks?" asked Dobie Keith. Many techniques were suggested and quickly discarded. "Some new instrument has to be built specially for the process," concluded Manson Benedict. "Why don't we ask Nier?"

They were not the only ones to call on Dr. Alfred O. Nier in the busy summer of 1942. Though only thirty-two, this young professor at the University of Minnesota had a long-established reputation as a wizard in precision-measuring techniques. He had already been asked by Vannevar Bush and Harold Urey to build a special instrument for uranium-isotope determination. With another of his instruments, Nier was also busy making analyses for the heavy-water project directed by Urey and Princeton's Professor Hugh Taylor.* At the same time, he was evaluating samples of enriched uranium coming from the first small cascade model that Dunning and Booth had built at Columbia.

Al Nier had his fingers in nearly every pie at the Manhattan Project. Besides all the analyses and measurements, he was attempting isotope separation by the so-far-unsuccessful thermal-diffusion method; in his free moments he was also making trips to Berkeley to help Lawrence with his electromagnetic process. Indeed, Lawrence's entire separation method and his calutrons had used as their model the rather primitive-looking instrument for which Nier was famous in scientific circles all over the country: the "mass spectrometer."

The mass spectrometer was an electromagnetic device that separated dissimilar molecules of a gas into separate beams, according to their different weights. When it came to building ultrasensitive mass spectrometers and applying them to various analytical techniques, Nier was a true virtuoso. He had the feeling of the instruments in his fingertips, as other people have a feeling for molding clay or transforming stubborn wood or stone into intricate carving.

Prior to the formation of Kellex, Columbia and the Kellogg Company decided to ask Nier to develop a leak-detecting instrument. The University of Minnesota scientist was already busy with his work for Dunning

---

* The development of a nuclear reactor using heavy water instead of graphite as moderator for slowing down the neutrons was progressing simultaneously with the other programs during the war. The British, French and Canadian scientists played a particularly important role in the heavy-water project. After the success of the first Fermi pile, however, the major effort of the Manhattan Project (conducted by the Chicago group and by Du Pont) was concentrated on the graphite reactor.

and Booth. As usual, the enriched uranium produced at Columbia had been sent from New York by railway express, and the janitor had taken it down to the basement of the physics department building, to door No. 62, marked in gold letters, Ionization Laboratory No. 1.

A short, cheerful man in a gray laboratory coat, Nier, who looked as young as any postgraduate student, received the package with boyish eagerness, then emptied the thin, foot-long tubes (originally manufactured as standard parts for home refrigerators) in which the samples had been sent. The small cement-floored room, lighted from the inside by two little windows high on the wall, looked more like the untidy workshop of some amateur dabbler than the laboratory of a gifted scientist. Pushing his way through the clutter of tools, wires and pipes, Nier made room for the newly arrived tubes.

Nier's famous mass spectrometer, which measured the enrichment of the samples, was a big magnet, about three and one-half feet tall, with its coils turned up. A semicircular glass tube, one yard long, was placed between the coils. The most unprepossessing, unscientific-looking tube imaginable, it was completely blackened from a multitude of previous experiments. Al Nier had made it himself, and it certainly looked it: the quality of the thick, rough, unpolished glass suggested a marmalade jar more than a scientific precision instrument. Yet, despite its appearance, the mass spectrometer was probably the most sensitive measuring device that any physicist had seen in America. It was the only instrument that could tell Dunning and Booth whether the diffusion through their Norris-Adler type of barrier had produced any enrichment in the processed uranium.

Nier had put the samples of separated uranium through his mass spectrometer and examined the results. There was no doubt: the sensitive instrument recorded that the small experimental barrier had worked. A few hours later Dunning and Booth received a cryptic telegram that filled them with elation: SUCCESS SAMPLE A 1212 ONE-HALF PERCENT, SAMPLE B 1322 SIX OVER SEVEN, NIER. It did not mean that a workable barrier was invented yet, a barrier efficient enough and strong enough to be produced by the acre and resist corrosion, pressure and stress. But it was an encouraging step forward.

Alfred Nier had extraordinary talent for inventing ingenious measuring devices of incredible precision; he had a special, personal touch that made him a kind of Stradivarius of scientific instruments. He made his clumsy-looking masterpieces with his own hands in the University of Minnesota workshop, with the help of a few young students and the shop's veteran glassblower, Edward Grienke, the only craftsman whose work satisfied Nier completely.

For his age, Alfred Nier's record was impressive. He had first become interested in atomic physics when, as a student, he was looking for a subject for a thesis and decided to concentrate on rare isotopes. He was still only a graduate student when he discovered potassium–40, then a very rare isotope. This led him to the use of radioactive potassium in determining the age of minerals, a field in which he was soon acknowledged as a pioneer. Then he switched to uranium isotopes and became the first scientist to determine the U–235 content in natural uranium: only one part in 139. Nier was then a postdoctoral fellow at Harvard and only twenty-six. When he returned to Minneapolis as an assistant professor in 1938, Nier continued his work on lead and uranium isotopes, using a mass spectrometer as an atom-weighing instrument.

But Nier's most spectacular contribution was the first separation of small amounts of U–235 in 1940. Nobody had ever seen U–235 before. A few years earlier Professor Arthur J. Dempster in Chicago had proved the existence of this isotope on a photographic plate where black marks had been caused by U–238 and U–235. But the amount was so small that no more than a few grains developed, much in the same way that light develops the grains on a photographic plate. Nier was the first to separate large enough amounts to permit nuclear measurements. True, they comprised only several micrograms; they were barely visible, appearing like a small decoloration on little strips of platinum where the uranium had been deposited. But these discolored spots were to play an enormous role in the future development of nuclear physics.

In 1939 scientists all over the world had been greatly excited by the news of the first splitting of the uranium atom, but no one knew which isotope of the metal had been responsible for the fission, the abundant U–238 or the rare U–235 — or both. Some people, like John Dunning at Columbia, physicist of intuition, suspected that U–235 was the only fissionable isotope. The great Niels Bohr thought the same. But Enrico Fermi felt, without being certain, that it might be the U–238. The question was of capital importance; but there was no way of proving either hypothesis.

Dunning, who was only thirty-two at the time, and his colleague, Eugene Booth, conceived the idea of bombarding samples of U–235 and U–238 with neutrons, but separately, so as to see which isotope would split and which would not. This, though, introduced another problem: how could the separated uranium isotope be found?

In April 1939, Nier received a three-page letter from Dunning. The Columbia scientist explained his work on uranium fission and spoke of his hopes for achieving a chain reaction. "There is one line of attack that deserves strong effort," the letter said, "and that is where we need your cooperation. . . . It is of utmost importance to get some uranium isotopes separated in enough quantities for a real test. If you could separate effectively even tiny amounts of the two main isotopes, there is a good chance that Booth and I could demonstrate, by bombarding them with the cyclotron, which isotope is responsible. There is no other way to settle this business. If we could all cooperate and you aid us by separating some samples, then we could, by combining forces, settle the whole matter."

Al Nier became fascinated by the proposed experiment. At a meeting of the American Physical Society in Washington later in the year, he discussed it with Dunning and Fermi, then went right to work on his return home on adapting his mass spectrometer to uranium isotope separation. In the beginning he tried with uranium hexafluoride gas, which was sent from Columbia by Dr. Aristid V. Grosse, the chemist in Dunning's group. Unfortunately, this gas did not work and Nier switched to tetrachloride and tetrabromide. Edward Grienke blew a special glass tube, and Nier made the necessary metal parts himself. On February 27, 1940, Nier started the separation and two days later it was completed: microscopic deposits of U–235 and U–238 were obtained on nickel collectors about a centimeter long and only a few millimeters wide.

Nier fastened the samples to a card with a piece of tape, added a letter written in longhand and took it down to the Minneapolis post office, where he sent it airmail special delivery. Dunning received the samples the next afternoon and worked feverishly with them all through the night.

Early the next morning — a Sunday — Nier was awakened by a long-distance telephone call from Dunning, who was jubilant. The two samples had been bombarded with neutrons from Columbia's cyclotron, and the fission fragments came from the sample Nier had labeled "235." From that day on, it was clear that no uranium bomb could be built if a way were not found to separate, in quantity, the fissionable U–235 isotope from the abundant but useless U–238. Nier, the superb physicist-technician, had played a key role in Dunning's discovery.

A few years later, Nier was again called on to find a method of detecting the smallest leakage that might occur in the gaseous-diffusion plant. He accepted the assignment in the same matter-of-fact way that he had accepted all the other war jobs on which he was also working in 1942. There was a war to win and he, as an expert whose advice and help were badly needed, did not hesitate to shoulder a heavier work load. And whenever there was a concrete job to be done, Al Nier always did it to the best of his ability.

The son of poor, uneducated German immigrants, Nier was born in St.

Paul, Minnesota. His father was a hard-working machinist, his mother came from a family of cabinetmakers. They wanted their son to enter a profession when he grew up. It soon became obvious that engineering or science was the indicated career for young Alfred; he was a studious boy, particularly good in physics, chemistry and mathematics, and not very interested in other subjects. He easily skipped a year and a half in grade school.

At fourteen he started delivering newspapers, earning up to forty dollars a month, which he saved toward a college education. By the time he finished high school two years later, he had savings of almost four hundred dollars, which enabled him to enter the University of Minnesota and study electrical engineering. He graduated in 1931, in the midst of the Depression, when jobs were very difficult to get. Luckily, since he had been a top student, he was given a teaching post so that he could continue studying for his Ph.D. in physics. After earning his degree, Nier, who was already a skillful researcher, received one of the coveted National Research Council fellowships and studied at Harvard for two years before returning to accept a post at the University of Minnesota.

Alfred Nier found a way of detecting leakage in the gaseous-diffusion system by developing a special mass spectrometer tuned permanently to helium. The helium content in the atmosphere is only one part in 200,000, but the instrument was sensitive enough to detect it. The pipe on the tank to be tested was first connected to a pump that emptied the air from inside; then it was attached to the mass spectrometer. The whole pipe was wrapped in a plastic bag, and helium was sprayed on the exterior walls of the pipe. If there were the slightest leak, some helium would penetrate the vacuum inside the pipe, and its presence would show on the spectrometer.

The instrument, called "helium leak-detector," was incredibly sensitive — every invisible pinhole or pore, no matter how small, was easily detected. But how would the engineers be able to test, one by one, the fantastic number of pipes, weldings, pumps and diffusers in a giant plant? Nier came up with an ingenious idea: he simply built a portable leak-detector and put it on wheels. It was a square steel device that looked like two file cabinets placed side by side with one side sloping. The detector, four feet tall and weighing five hundred pounds, contained the glass spectrometer tube, pumps to make the vacuum and an electronic control circuit. The instrument could be rolled to any place where an electric cord and a water connection for cooling the pumps were available.

Nier made the first models himself at his laboratory in Minneapolis with the help of a few of his students. They still had many weaknesses —

for instance, the glass parts made them too fragile — but the principle was right. While Nier was still working on improvements, Kellex was formed in New York and, in the summer of 1943, he was invited to join the new corporation, which was in sore need of his skills. It was a difficult decision for Nier to make; he had also been invited to work at the laboratories in Chicago, Los Alamos and Columbia. All the jobs seemed equally important and urgent, but Manson Benedict, a friend from Harvard days, succeeded in convincing him that nowhere was his help so critically needed as at Kellex.

In July, Nier arrived in New York with his wife and started working in the Woolworth Building. Put in George Watts's department, he worked closely with Tom Abbott, a former General Electric plant manager. Abbott's background was useful, because Nier's instruments were pro- duced at G.E., and both men were soon taking the train regularly to G.E.'s Schenectady plant.

The leak-detector with the mass spectrometer tube made of glass was good for laboratory tests; but it would be impractical for industrial use. For several months Nier tried to build an instrument with all parts made of metal. Finally, with the help of Charles Stevens, the all-metal detector was built and General Electric started production.

Nier was still working on leak-detectors when Kellex came to him with another, even bigger problem. If the giant K–25 plant could be built and operated, there was the absolute necessity of being able, at any moment, to observe and check at any point in the cascade the composition of the process gas. Once the plant started running, it could easily be shut down and even destroyed if it developed a leak so that the air could get in. It was important to monitor the plant at many points and at regular inter- vals, to keep a constant eye on the composition of the processed gas stream.

This presented extraordinary difficulties in view of the gigantic size of the future plant and the complicated construction of the cascade with its thousands of stages. What instruments could make continuous, highly precise recordings in a hermetically closed process? No such instrument existed and, in the opinion of many engineers, could ever be made. But Dobie Keith and the other Kellex leaders were so blasé by this time, encountering seemingly insurmountable obstacles nearly every day, that they were accustomed to accepting impossible targets as a sort of routine; only the possible tasks had become the exception. At weekly conferences in Keith's office in the Woolworth Building, Kellex engineers were no longer even discussing whether the overall gaseous-diffusion project was possible. It was completely beside the point; the only valid questions now were: "How?" and "How fast?"

Since the new question contained the words "recording instruments," the answer was the usual one: "Let's ask Al Nier." Nier spent much of his time in the library, reading and thinking about what he could do to lick the problem. His first idea was to adapt and use some special kind of mass spectrometer. But then he felt that this technique would be much too complicated, and started trying new methods. There was so little time — the plant itself was already being designed; no one could help him with details and specifications — the designers themselves did not know.

Nier found it impossible to develop new techniques without having more precise data at hand about the plant. Then one day, while Nier was struggling with the problem, Albert L. Baker, chief engineer of Kellex came over to him and said, "Listen, Al. We hired you because you're supposed to know something about mass spectrometers. Why don't you just go ahead and build one?"

Nier did. He developed a small recording mass spectrometer that was given the code name of "line-recorder." It was tuned to the composition of the gas at any specific point of the cascade; it could even pick out, automatically, certain components in the stream whose presence might be caused by a leak. The data was recorded on panels in a central control room that regulated the entire plant.

It was the first time that mass spectrometers had ever been scattered throughout a huge plant but with their readings recorded in a single control room. Nier built the first half-dozen line-recorders himself; later they were copied and produced in quantity by General Electric. Al Nier had invented yet another device without which the Manhattan Project could never have become a reality.

31

ONE DAY in early March 1943, Dorothy McKibbin, an attractive, blue-eyed widow in her forties, received a visit at her Santa Fe home from a former local resident named Joe Stevenson and a stranger who was introduced to her as Duane Muncy.

"We're wondering," Stevenson said, "whether you would like a job as secretary for a housing project?"

"A housing project? Just what do you mean?"

"It's called Project Y, and I'm the project manager. But I'm not at liberty to divulge any further information about it. It *is* important, however."

Dororthy McKibbin studied her visitors for a moment. Stevenson, she knew, had recently gone out to Berkeley, California, for some kind of training course; and the man named Muncy, from the look of him, could also be from California, she thought: he was wearing a gabardine suit that one did not see often around Santa Fe. Was it possible that some California outfit was involved in this mysterious Project Y?

"Can't you tell me something about what I'll be doing?" she asked. "You see, I'm on the point of accepting a job with a bank. I don't much care for figure work, but at least I know what I'd be doing in that job."

Stevenson shook his head. "Sorry, Dorothy, I just can't give you any details. But tell me — what will you be paid at the bank?"

"One hundred twenty dollars a month."

The two men rose to leave. "We'll pay you one hundred fifty dollars, but you must give us a definite answer within twenty-four hours. Let's meet in the lobby of the La Fonda Hotel tomorrow about noon."

Dorothy McKibbin was more than a little nonplussed by the offer. She was not a good typist, not good at figures, and she had barely managed to pass the employment test for the bank job. Indeed, the only thing she did know well — and loved deeply — was the countryside around Santa Fe.

The daughter of a well-to-do Kansas City lawyer, she had been educated at Smith, then traveled a good deal abroad with her father. She had first come to New Mexico because of tuberculosis, and was eventually cured in the dry, clear climate. A woman of artistic temperament, she was much taken by the beauty of the landscape. A few years later, she married and moved to St. Paul, Minnesota. Then, when her husband died she decided to return, with her ten-month-old son, to Santa Fe, where she built an attractive, adobe-type house, tastefully furnished with Spanish Colonial furniture and Indian rugs.

When she arrived at the La Fonda Hotel the next day, Dorothy McKibbin had still not made up her mind. She found Stevenson and Muncy standing by the newsstand. "Have you made up your mind?" they asked.

Before she could answer, a frail-looking man wearing a trench coat and a porkpie hat approached them. He greeted Stevenson and Muncy, who in turn introduced him to Dorothy McKibbin. She didn't catch the name but gathered that he was somehow connected with Project Y, too. Though he said only a few words before leaving them, she was struck by the intensity of his blue eyes, his quiet assurance of manner. She felt strongly, and for no logical reason, that this unusual-looking man was involved in something momentous.

She turned to Joe Stevenson. "Has this project anything to do with the war effort?"

"Yes, it does."

"All right," Dorothy McKibbin said quietly. "I'll take the job. When do I start?"

She started immediately. Dozens of scientists were already arriving in Santa Fe en route to Los Alamos; Dorothy McKibbin's job was to receive them and act as guide. The administrative offices of Project Y, located at 109 East Palace Street in five rooms opening onto a patio, were guarded day and night by the Army. The rooms were rented by a "Mr. Bradley" — the assumed name of J. Robert Oppenheimer, overall head of the Los Alamos project.

Since very little housing was ready at Los Alamos, only a few scientists had gone up to live on "the Hill." The rest were sent to several dude ranches and private homes between Santa Fe and Los Alamos. Dorothy McKibbin, notified in advance by telephone, would issue them a pass, find a room and provide transportation.

During the spring and summer, the people of Santa Fe became used to the sight of strangers who dressed differently and often spoke with heavy foreign accents; they arrived one day and disappeared the next. Though a great amount of curiosity was aroused, the word quickly spread among local residents that "one shouldn't ask questions." Mrs. McKibbin's telephone rang continuously. "Dorothy, there's a strange-looking man here and he's lost." "Send him over!" she would answer, with no further comment. More and more ranches had to be rented in the sparsely populated area. In moments of acute shortage, many scientists' families spent nights in Mrs. McKibbin's house at 1099 Old Pecos Road.*

Most of the recruitment of the first Los Alamos team was done by Oppenheimer personally. He traveled from university to university — Princeton, Berkeley, Chicago, MIT, Cornell — and contacted promising scientists, primarily those who were already engaged in some form of nuclear research. Nearly all accepted the invitation to embark on a new and uncertain adventure and live in the wilderness of New Mexico's mountains. The crash programs to develop radar and the proximity fuse — two top-priority war projects that had previously drained the nation's supply of first-rate scientists — were completed by 1943, and Oppenheimer was able to recruit some stellar scientific talent — men like Edwin McMillan, Luis W. Alvarez, Kenneth T. Bainbridge, Robert F. Bacher and others.

Because of the purpose and the secrecy of the Los Alamos laboratory, the original idea was to make it a military installation and put all the scientists in uniform. Conant approved of the idea; having served with the Army's chemical warfare unit during World War I, he was in favor of a military laboratory. Oppenheimer himself was not against the idea, and plans were discussed of making him a lieutenant colonel and giving the heads of the laboratory's various divisions the rank of major.

But strong opposition came from many scientists, especially from Bacher and Isidor I. Rabi, who were winding up work then on radar at MIT before heading west for Los Alamos. Oppenheimer wanted these two top physicists, but they refused categorically to work in uniform. They insisted that a scientific group organized along military lines would be too rigid and inefficient for laboratory work; rank would be an annoyance and a serious impediment. Facing the danger of losing other talented scientists loyal to Bacher and Rabi, the Project's leaders abandoned the idea; Los Alamos would be organized as a civilian laboratory. Most people who did not know Groves well expected him to raise the roof; as it turned out, however, he did nothing to impose the militarization. He only chuckled, privately, when imagining how some professors would look in uniform — and trying to salute at that!

The first men to arrive at Los Alamos were Robert Wilson from Princeton, Robert Serber, McMillan and Joseph Kennedy from Berkeley, John H. Williams from Minnesota, and John H. Manley, a nuclear physicist who had worked at Columbia before joining Chicago's Metallurgical Laboratory. Manley had been used earlier to help organize the

---

* Her home became such a haven for scientists passing through that thirteen weddings were celebrated there during the war.

new laboratory. He had been sent, by Oppenheimer, to Minnesota, Wisconsin, Purdue and other universities to persuade scientists to come to Los Alamos. Manley's big handicap in recruiting was that he was not allowed to reveal the exact purpose or location of the laboratory. Nevertheless practically all of the scientists accepted. Manley also went to Boston to discuss the design of the Los Alamos buildings, which were to be constructed by Stone and Webster.

Oppenheimer arrived in Santa Fe on March 15, 1943, and the offices were moved to Los Alamos in the middle of April. Working and living conditions at that time were extremely inadequate, even primitive by big-city standards. Housing construction was slow, the road was bad and telephone conversations with Santa Fe were possible only over a Forest Service line.

While waiting for the construction of Los Alamos, the scientists who had already left their homes grew impatient and decided to go up to the Hill even before their living quarters were ready. They drove their cars up the dirt road to the mesa and started helping construction workers by counting the cement loads, checking trucks in and out, even redesigning the piping and electrical lines for more efficient functioning, often only to add to the confusion. Oppenheimer had had no experience in organizing a large laboratory, and had not shown any particular predisposition for teamwork before. His appointment had therefore been met with some surprise and criticism by many colleagues. But very soon he amazed everybody by his rapid transformation from academic professor to competent administrator. The initial plan, drafted by Oppenheimer, McMillan and Manley, provided for a scientific staff of about one hundred. Four divisions were formed, each one including different groups with specific assignments.

Hans Bethe, a brilliant, forty-year-old German refugee and former Cornell professor, became the head of the Theoretical Division, in which physicists of the caliber of Teller, Serber and Victor F. Weisskopf were among the group leaders. Bacher, who had also taught at Cornell earlier, became leader of the Experimental Physics Division with Emilio Segré, Manley, Wilson, Williams and Darol K. Froman heading the various groups. Both Bethe and Bacher had been working on radar at MIT when Oppenheimer came to recruit them. Joe Kennedy, only twenty-six but already one of Glenn Seaborg's outstanding students, was put in charge of the Chemical Division. Captain William S. Parsons, a studious, efficient Regular Navy officer who had been for a certain period Vannevar Bush's assistant on the combat use of the proximity fuse, became the leader of the Ordnance Division.

Most of the specialized equipment was brought or sent out to Los

Alamos by the scientists who were going to use it. The University of Wisconsin group, for example, arrived with two Van de Graaff machines for accelerating atomic particles; Manley's team from the University of Illinois bought a Cockcroft-Walton accelerator; the Berkeley scientists provided highly specialized physics apparatus.

The largest item, a cyclotron, was "borrowed" from Harvard by Robert Wilson's Princeton group — but not without some difficulty. When Wilson first asked for it, he did not mention what kind of project it would be used for. "We need it for some medical research," he merely said. But when the Harvard scientists refused to part with so precious a research tool, Wilson had to admit, "OK, it's not for medical research. I'm not allowed to tell you exactly what, but it's going to be used for very important things. You can trust us!" Then Conant dropped a few words to one of his assistants at Harvard and no further questions were asked; the cyclotron was taken apart and put on rail flatcars for the long journey west to Sante Fe.

The newly arrived scientists were first briefed by Serber, who gave them some necessary background information. Then, at the end of April, a series of conferences was organized under Rabi of MIT and Fermi and Allison of Chicago, who had been asked out as consultants.

At the time, knowledge of the behavior of fast neutrons, which had to be used in the future weapon, was meager, indeed. The problems that lay ahead were tremendous. How many neutrons, for example, came from uranium, and how far did they go before they caused fission? How much fissionable material was needed to make the explosion? What was the best way to arrange it in order to get the biggest explosion for a given amount of material? All these questions remained to be answered in 1943. The Chicago scientists had learned a great deal about the chain reaction with neutrons in the pile, purposely slowed down by a moderator; but no information was yet available about fission caused by *fast* neutrons.*

Explosion would occur when uranium or plutonium reached a critical mass, but no one knew just how much uranium this meant. And how to assemble it quickly enough so that it would not explode prematurely? The problem of timing seemed insoluble: the assembly had to be performed, incredibly enough, in *millionths* of a second.

The scientists also had to find out what were the chances of fission being produced by a neutron. What if the neutron merely entered the uranium and got caught in the nucleus without producing any fission?

---

* Fast neutrons: The bomb's explosion is caused by the action of fast neutrons, resulting from fission of the nucleus. In a pile (or reactor), on the contrary, their initial high speeds are slowed down and controlled by moderators (graphite or heavy-water).

Did the neutron have to travel a long way into uranium before it triggered a fission, or only a short way? These and dozens of similar questions had to be answered before a weapon could be designed. The whole Project — how much fissionable material had to be produced and how long it would take, what would be the size and shape of the weapon and what kind of airplane would be able to carry it — depended ultimately on the Los Alamos's scientists' calculation of the critical mass.

Other groups started working on ways of putting the bomb together as rapidly as possible. Speed was all important, because if the two subcritical pieces were put together slowly, the mass would become critical when they got near each other, the reaction would begin, everything would melt and explode into vapor, and the reaction would die before reaching the optimum conditions. The mass might also become critical by accident, merely because there were enough cosmic rays around to trigger an explosion.

The scientists decided to assemble the bomb in millionths of a second by the "gun method." The idea was to take a normal, sawed-off artillery gun and put half of the uranium as a target at the end of the muzzle, then shoot the other half of the uranium into it. It was not a very good method, and the Los Alamos scientists adopted it reluctantly only because it was a proven one; artillery was an old, reliable technique, and its problems had been studied for years.

A young physicist from the Bureau of Standards, Seth H. Neddermeyer, proposed a new method that he had invented. He called it "implosion" — the opposite of explosion. Neddermeyer's idea was to make a hollow sphere of uranium thin enough to be subcritical; then explosives would be detonated outside the uranium sphere, and the metal, instead of exploding outward, would be compressed *inward* into a ball of critical mass.

Such a principle was radically new, but it sounded too complicated, especially since it required absolutely uniform and simultaneous pressure on all points of the sphere's surface. Neddermeyer propounded his implosion idea during the April conferences, but failed to find any support. The gun method was adopted.

Army engineers erected more and more barracks and laboratories atop the isolated mesa. An unusual new town took shape — a dusty town without sidewalks, a compound of log cabins and ugly temporary structures surrounded in the distance by breathtaking mountain scenery. Site Y, as Los Alamos was called, was smaller than the other two secret cities of the Project — Oak Ridge and Hanford. But like them, its name did not appear on any map, neither was it used as an address. All mail was directed to "P.O. Box 1663, Sante Fe," the only official residence for Los Alamos's thousands of citizens.

If the town had the appearance of an Army camp, its population was nonetheless predominantly civilian. The scientists went around in casual dress — blue jeans or wrinkled pants, no neckties, unpolished shoes. Though Los Alamos was run entirely by the Army, the civilians had their town council, which met regularly to discuss the local problems. They were many, ranging from complaints about the "Black Beauties" — huge, wood-burning cooking stoves installed in the middle of rooms, real museum pieces — to protests about excessive security measures.

The relationship between the scientific community and the Army was often marked by strain and mutual irritation. The Ph.D.'s thought that security was ridiculously exaggerated. They were particularly sensitive about the censorship of their mail and about the "compartmentalization," which hindered the flow of precious information between them and other laboratories. The Army, on the other hand, found it difficult to deal with some of the "longhairs" who readily displayed a distaste for what they called regimentation.

As a result, *de facto* segregation between scientists and the military was established in Los Alamos's social life. It was natural that General Groves's name should become the lightning rod on which most criticism and irritation, just and unjust, was discharged by the scientists. But Groves believed that this reaction was inevitable, merely a part of every boss's job. He did not care about his popularity — or lack of it.

Security measures at Los Alamos were extraordinarily tight. The site, enclosed by a high barbed-wire fence, was patrolled by armed MP's on the outside. Everyone had to show a pass to be admitted inside, and special passes were needed for the Technical Area. The homes of Oppenheimer, Captain Parsons and other top men were guarded continuously by MP's, and even Mrs. Oppenheimer and Mrs. Parsons had to show their passes before being allowed to reenter their homes.

Except for a small area around Los Alamos, special authorization was needed for traveling, and it was granted only for official business. Even trips to Santa Fe were restricted. Children were not allowed to be sent out to camps or schools, and those already in school outside could not come home to their parents for vacations. Driver's licenses had numbers instead of names and were not signed. Everyone's occupation was listed merely as "engineer" and the sole address was "P.O. Box 1663," a fact that at first puzzled state troopers whenever they stopped a speeding car on the road to and from Santa Fe. Since Los Alamos people were not allowed to appear in court, the state police had to discuss violations with the MP's and let the drivers go.

The local Manhattan District security office monitored outside telephone calls and censored mail on a spot-check basis. The outgoing mail of the important scientists was censored 100 percent to avoid inadvertent security breaks. Security agents were even placed as desk clerks and waiters in all Santa Fe hotels.

The censoring of mail provoked great emotion among the scientists, and after many protests and even threats of leaving, some rules were drawn up in common agreement. Families were notified that letters were being read and the civilians agreed to avoid any mention of the words "Los Alamos," "uranium," "atom" and "fission," as well as the names of distinguished scientists, such as Niels Bohr.

The greatest headache that Army censors had was caused by a bright, twenty-seven-year-old physicist in the Theoretical Division, who took impish pleasure in teasing them. Dr. Richard Feynman's practical jokes became a nightmare for the security officers. When Feynman's wife had to go to a hospital in Albuquerque, they began writing to each other every day. The moment he realized that their letters were being censored, Feynman started sending strange messages to his wife and also to his father, and even stranger letters began to arrive addressed to him. They were covered with mysterious letters, such as "W Z Q R F T," and liberally sprinkled with dots and dashes. When the alarmed censorship officer called him in for an explanation, Feynman said that his hobby was cryptography, and that he had simply asked his father and his wife to send him letters in code, but without revealing the key, so he could amuse himself deciphering them. It was quite true; Feynman could crack any code. "Would you like me to teach you?" he asked the furious officer who did not consider it a laughing matter.

Feynman had so many squabbles with the security officers that he became an expert in matters of censorship for his colleagues. Scientists started coming to him for advice each time they had to write a letter that they hoped would not be changed or held up. "Will this pass or not?" they would ask. Feynman was even taking bets and making some money on the side on how to beat the censorship problem.

A handsome, dark-haired physicist from Far Rockaway, Long Island, Richard Feynman had a reputation for possessing exceptional mathematical talents and a degree of self-confidence that bordered on brashness. He had first become involved in nuclear research while working on his thesis at Princeton. One morning Bob Wilson came into his room in the dormitory and said, "Feynman, we're starting up some very important secret work here, and we want you. I'm not supposed to say what it is, but I'm going to tell you because when you hear it, you'll definitely want to come." Wilson then told about the bomb and explained his plan for separating uranium by a new method.

At that time, however, Feynman was only interested in theoretical physics. His intention was to dedicate his life to understanding nature, to finding out what the world was like. "No," he told Wilson, "you've made a mistake. You shouldn't have told me, because I'm not going to do it. But I'll keep the secret."

"All right," said Wilson, but as he left the room, he added, "We're having a meeting at three o'clock this afternoon."

Feynman resumed work on his thesis but could not concentrate. "This bomb is quite possible," he thought, "and the Germans may make it, too — what a catastrophe!" At 3 P.M. he went to the meeting, where there was exciting discussion about which man would do what experiment. Put in charge of theoretical calculation, Feynman was asked to find out whether the method of isotope separation would work in theory.

Forgetting his thesis, he started feverishly making calculations right after the meeting was over. Around him other scientists bustled in and out, carrying instruments from other rooms, borrowing apparatus from the laboratories, dismantling their own research apparatus and setting up new experiments. The dozen men in Wilson's group were working at a frenzied pace. As they assembled apparatus and started building a vacuum, Feynman jumped from behind the rolltop desk where he had been doing his calculations and waved his papers, yelling like a madman, "It works! It will work, it will work!"*

When Oppenheimer came to Princeton and enrolled Wilson, Feynman and the rest of the group also promised to join the Los Alamos project. But before leaving for New Mexico, Wilson sent Feynman to Chicago. "Go and find out everything you can about what they know there, then come back and tell us what the problems are and how the bomb works, so we won't waste time building apparatus until we know."

The self-confident Feynman visited every group in Chicago, and was briefed by men like Compton, Wigner, Teller and Fermi. Surprisingly enough, he even solved, in half an hour, a mathematical problem that had been plaguing the Chicago group. "So I paid them back a little for my lessons," he reported later to Wilson.

When Feynman returned to Princeton with the information, a meeting was hastily called in one of the classrooms. Before all the scientists who had been let in on the secret, he gave a lecture on how the bomb was supposed to be released. When the meeting was over, the mathematician Paul Olum came over to him and exclaimed, "What a dramatic moment! All these people learning for the first time how the bomb will operate, all of them ready to go out to work in New Mexico — in the middle of nowhere — to make the thing! I wonder how this historic moment in

---

* Later, work on this particular separation method was discontinued as being less efficient than the others.

human life will be described in the future. Probably there'll be something about a solemn, tense physicist bringing secret documents from Chicago in a leather briefcase, then in the midst of deep silence, making a startling speech to wide-eyed scientists. My foot! Just look around, Dick, and see how it really is — look at yourself!"

Feynman, in shirtsleeves, was reading from a bunch of wrinkled papers held together by a clip, mixing scientific formulas with jokes. Most of the scientists, their coats off and their feet on the desks, were asking questions and shouting wisecracks. If they felt the drama of the moment, they did not show it. Yet their lives and careers were about to take a new direction after the meeting. All over the country, other scientists, having received secret briefings about the latest developments in nuclear science, were also packing to leave for New Mexico. As a result, General Groves was later able to make a famous remark to the military personnel of Los Alamos: "Here we have assembled the greatest bunch of prima donnas ever seen in one place!"

32

RICHARD FEYNMAN'S voice could be heard from the far end of the corridor: "No, no, you're crazy!" His colleagues in the Los Alamos Theoretical Division looked up from their computers and exchanged knowing smiles. "There they go again!" one said. "The Battleship and the Mosquito Boat!"

The "Battleship" was the division's leader, Hans Bethe, a tall, heavy-set German who was recognized as a sort of genius in theoretical physics. At the moment he was having one of his frequent discussions with Dick Feynman, the "Mosquito Boat," who, from the moment he started talking physics, became completely oblivious of where he was and to whom he was talking. The imperturbable and meticulous Bethe solved problems by facing them squarely, analyzing them quietly and then plowing straight through them. He pushed obstacles aside like a battleship moving through the water.

Feynman, on the other hand, would interrupt him impatiently at nearly every sentence, either to shout his admiration or to express his disagreement by irreverent remarks like "No, you're crazy!" or, "That's nuts!" At each interruption Bethe would stop, then quietly and patiently explain why he was right. Feynman would calm down for a few minutes, only to jump in wildly again with "That's impossible, you're mad!" and again Bethe could calmly prove that it was not so. But Bethe had great respect for the quick, imaginative mind of his younger colleague and enjoyed their stimulating discussions.

Feynman's attitude toward everyone was equally fearless, even when it came to Professor Niels Bohr, the Danish Nobel Prize winner and the venerated prophet of nuclear science. Early one morning Bohr's son, Aage, telephoned Feynman at his dormitory. "This is Jim Baker," he said (the Bohrs traveled under the false name of Baker for security reasons). "We've just arrived and my father wants to hear your opinion on a new idea we have."

"Me?" asked the amazed young physicist. "Are you sure you've got the right guy?" He could not believe that the Prophet would call an unknown and very junior scientist and ask his opinion.

But the moment Niels Bohr started his explanation on the blackboard,

Feynman lost all inhibitions. "No! That's wrong!" he shouted. "You can't do it that way!" And, in an excited voice, he gave his reasons. The Danish professor listened attentively, and then with one phrase destroyed the young man's arguments. But two minutes later Feynman was interrupting again. "That's crazy! I think I can do it a better way!" The discussion lasted for two hours, with Feynman shouting questions, alternately criticizing and applauding wildly. At the end Bohr said, "Well, I guess we can talk to the big shots now."

"Why did your father choose me?" Feynman asked Bohr's son later. "I really can't understand."

"It's simple. After we had been here the first time, my father noticed you and later told me, 'There's a young man whose name we must remember. He objects and argues and doesn't seem to care about my reputation. The next time I'll test my ideas against him. The others are too polite in front of me, and too many of them have studied under me!'"

For a rehearsal before his meeting with the laboratory leaders, Bohr could not have found a better intellectual sparring partner than the impertinent twenty-five-year-old scientist from Long Island. Richard Feynman was the son of a businessman who had little scientific background but was utterly fascinated by the natural world around him. He was the kind of father who would point out a sunset to his little son and explain how the light beams were refracting, or turn over a rock to show him how the ants carried their young. On Sundays he would take the boy for walks in the woods and tell him about the trees, how they struggled for life, how they grew and died. He would explain how birds migrate and their wonderful sense of direction. He did not know their names, so he would make them up: "This bird? . . . In Germany it's called *Swiedenleben,* in Sweden it's called *Oot-Oot,* and in China, *Ching-Wong, Tong.*" To him, all this was not important; what mattered was nature's marvels, the mysteries of life, the secrets of the physical world around us.

Mr. Feynman early awakened his son's interest in the wonders of numbers — their funny relationships, the tricks of arithmetic. When the child first asked what algebra was, his father, not knowing how to explain, simply made up an example: "A house and a garage cost twenty thousand dollars. How much does the garage cost alone? You can't answer, but with algebra, you could!" For years after that the child dreamed of this magic science that one day would give him all the answers.

Dick Feynman set up a laboratory in his room, and when family friends worried about his experiments and the danger of explosion, his mother answered calmly, "My son knows more about chemistry than I do, and I don't think he wants to blow himself up." Very early in life he became interested in the formulas for things, in the laws that governed nature.

Under the approving eye of his father, Dick played scientist as other children play fireman. "That boy will one day go to MIT, the best school in the country," Mr. Feynman often declared proudly to friends.

The prophecy came true. After MIT, Feynman quickly established himself as one of the brightest young scientists in the field of theoretical physics. If the old saying about the difference between the theoretical and experimental physicist was true in general ("the first knows what's the matter with a doorbell, while the second doesn't but can repair it"), this did not apply to Dick Feynman. He was officially in the Theoretical Division at Los Alamos, but each time a calculating machine broke down, he would take it apart and repair it. It became a hobby with him, but when he started repairing the secretaries' typewriters, the mild-mannered division leader, Bethe, was forced to put his foot down. "I think your time and talents," he suggested gently, "should be used for solving more important problems."

Feynman, of course, obeyed. Like all the "theoreticals," he had immense respect for Hans Bethe.

Bethe, a German refugee who came to Cornell in 1935, had long held strong feelings about the Nazis. After the fall of France, he decided that he could somehow help the West's defense efforts by studying the penetration of armor plate by artillery shells. His paper on the subject was so valuable that the Army classified it and Bethe, still an alien at that time, was not allowed to see it again.

After working on explosion shock waves, Bethe finally received his security clearance and was asked to help with radar, the most important scientific war project at the time. In May 1942 he moved from Cornell to MIT, where work on radar was being conducted in the greatest secrecy. Oppenheimer had not known Bethe well before; they had merely met from time to time at scientific conferences. But by the summer of 1942 he was insisting strongly that Bethe join the preliminary bomb study. There was a great mutual admiration between the two theoretical physicists, and Oppenheimer felt that the Cornell professor was a man that the Project badly needed.

Bethe was at MIT when Oppenheimer asked him, by both letter and phone, to come to Berkeley. He told him a small group of theoretical physicists was gathering there to discuss the possibilities of assembling an atom bomb if enough fissionable material could be produced. Oppenheimer did not give any further details about the Project at the time. Although Bethe thought that radar was far more important militarily than atomic energy, he accepted Oppenheimer's invitation because it was scientifically more challenging. Oppenheimer's personality also appealed to him. From their few conversations earlier, Bethe considered the Berkeley professor the best-educated person he had ever met.

On the way to Berkeley, Bethe stopped for two days in Chicago where his good friend, Edward Teller, briefed him in detail. Bethe learned for the first time of Fermi's work on the pile, of plans for plutonium production, of gaseous diffusion and electromagnetic separation. While Lawrence's process struck him as an unbelievably expensive method using brute force, Bethe was greatly impressed by the intelligence, the talent and the single-mindedness with which Fermi was working on chain reaction. Teller continued the trip with him and they joined Oppenheimer, Serber, John H. Van Vleck and a few other scientists for several conferences on bomb assembly at Berkeley.*

In November 1942, Groves, Bush and Conant decided that a special laboratory should be immediately organized for bomb work. The scientists who had participated in the summer conference at Berkeley met again in Chicago and agreed to leave for New Mexico. "We'll need a lot of people," one physicist remarked. "Maybe fifty scientists and a hundred technicians!"†

Leaving his teaching post at Cornell and his radar work at MIT, Hans Bethe arrived at Los Alamos at the beginning of April 1943 (his wife was already there, having been recruited by Oppenheimer to take charge of the housing office). Despite the magnificent natural surroundings, Los Alamos was a depressing sight in those first days. There was a lot of dust or mud, according to the weather, and no houses — only big shacks standing in the middle of nowhere. Many people had to sleep on the porch of the former boys' school; others stayed at ranches around Santa Fe.

The houses that the Army engineers soon put up were quite comfortable in spite of their austere exterior appearance. The only really unpleasant thing was the heating. The system was serviced by Spanish-American janitors, who — according to a joke current among the scientists — when they were sober, came around and put in as much coal as possible and drove room temperatures up to 90 degrees; when drunk, they didn't come at all and then the room temperatures went down to 50 degrees. Since they were more often sober than drunk, the main problem was the excessive heat. Another annoyance was the unpredictable, wood-burning kitchen stoves. The physicists could never understand the strange prop-

---

* One of the main topics of the meeting was Teller's idea of the "Super," the future hydrogen-fusion bomb. The theoretical physicists had greatly underestimated the practical difficulties of making the atomic bomb, and were already discussing, prematurely, the next step. However, some important work was done on calculating the efficiency of the atom bomb and its critical mass.

† Two years later five thousand people were working at Los Alamos, and yet it was hardly enough.

erty whereby the stoves would heat the kitchen up to 110 degrees but without heating the food at all.

During the months that followed, an impressive Theoretical Division was organized under Bethe's direction. Including such brilliant men as Teller, Serber, Donald Flanders and Feynman, the theoreticals were often too abstract to communicate with the experimental scientists. Fortunately Bethe had brought with him his old Austrian friend, Victor Weisskopf, who was unusually good at understanding the concrete needs of the experimentalists.

A famous authority on the theory of the atomic nucleus, Weisskopf worked mainly by intuition (somebody put on his door a sign reading *The Los Alamos Oracle*). Scientists from other divisions came to him daily with questions such as "What is the plutonium cross section at 2.5 million volts?" Weisskopf would go into a trance and say, "Two point two." Most of the time his answers proved absolutely correct.

Another European friend of Bethe's joined the theoreticals later in 1944: Rudolph E. Peierls. As a German refugee in England, he had already played an important role in the Project earlier by making predictions of critical masses and doing pioneering work on gaseous diffusion. His firm belief that an atomic bomb was possible had been an important factor in convincing American scientists in the early days. Bethe, who had asked especially for Peierls, put him in charge of work on the theory of implosion.

Foreign-born scientists played a vital role at Los Alamos, where their participation was proportionally greater than at Oak Ridge or Hanford. Fermi, Teller, Bethe, John von Neumann, Weisskopf, George B. Kistiakowsky and others were former Europeans who, as mature men and for different reasons, had chosen to become Americans. Intellectually, morally, politically, they already belonged irretrievably to America; as scientists and as men, they scarcely had any further affinity with the mentality of their former homelands. In their thinking and actions, these men, though often speaking their adopted language with heavy accents, had become amazingly American in a very short time.

Most of them were assigned full-time jobs as division or group leaders. Enrico Fermi had just become a permanent Los Alamos resident when he assumed, in September 1944, the function of associate director of the laboratory. Before that, he had commuted regularly between Chicago and Hanford, concentrating mainly on the "Water Boiler," the first reactor to be made of enriched, rather than ordinary, uranium. This was an important new research tool for determining the critical mass of uranium. The precious enriched element, which was held in a liquid solution, was placed in a spherical, stainless-steel container, which was one foot in diameter and surrounded by a three-foot-high black cube of beryllium oxide. The Water Boiler was so small that it sat on a little table, but a five-foot-thick concrete wall was erected to protect it.

A slight, unpretentious figure in his worn leather jacket, Enrico Fermi would drive out every day in his sand-colored Chevrolet to the bottom of deep, wooded Omega Canyon. There he conducted experiments in which he used the Water Boiler as a source of neutrons. The Purdue University group, which built and ran the reactor, was composed of Marshall G. Holloway, Percy King, Raemer Schreiber and Charles Baker. They followed the work of the master physicist with fascination. Modest and friendly, he took part in their experiments and solved many of their problems with incredible facility. But he did not like them to use a pencil in calculating. "You must first solve the problems in your minds, *think* them out well, and only then write! Use a pen! I don't want you to erase and not leave any trace of a change!"

Another category of foreigners was represented by the British mission. Led first by James Chadwick and then by Peierls, it consisted of twenty eminent scientists, among them Otto Frisch (the German physicist who, with his aunt, Lise Meitner, first explained atomic fission in 1939), Sir Geoffrey Taylor, William Penney and Klaus Fuchs (later to become the most important atomic spy). The British scientists were assigned to the existing groups in the laboratory (seven among them were experimental physicists; two were electronics experts; five worked on theoretical problems; and five on explosives). No distinction was made in the assignment of work nor in social life between Americans and Britishers. The collaboration was perfect, and the contribution of the British mission was inestimable.

Professor Niels Bohr (code name Nicholas Baker) was a special case among the foreign-born scientists. The eminent Danish professor came to Los Alamos with his son Aage from England, where he had sought refuge late in 1943. Staying in Nazi-occupied Copenhagen had become dangerous for Bohr, whose mother was Jewish; the Danish underground had managed, with the help of the British Secret Service, to smuggle him out in a small fishing boat to Sweden one night. Three weeks later he was flown to England in the bomb bay of a Mosquito bomber. (The oxygen mask the RAF gave him to wear was too small for the scientist's unusually large head, and Bohr fainted during the flight.)

It was from England that Bohr came to the United States to help with the atomic project. His arrival had a greatly stimulating effect on the laboratory, where he found several of his former students. Bohr was not given responsibility for any particular division, but acted as a consultant and adviser to all the groups, helping them solve many knotty problems. He arrived at a moment when the scientists, absorbed by the practical questions of production, were neglecting some of the fundamental aspects of their research. Bohr's presence boosted the research effort and also gave the younger physicists more confidence.

Oppenheimer, who had special admiration for Bohr and was constantly asking his advice, was one of the few intellectuals who could understand the rather esoteric Dane. Not only were most of Bohr's theories and formulas above the head of the average physicist, but his speech was unusually hard to understand. Listening to his mumbling of complicated sentences and eating half his words, it was hard to believe that this inarticulate man was an acknowledged genius. Several of his ideas were never understood, especially the ones on future world collaboration on atomic energy which he tried unsuccessfully to get Roosevelt, Churchill and other statesmen to espouse. He was a man who lived in the clouds.

His absent-mindedness often worried General Groves and security officers. The general was working once in his Washington office when a terrific screeching of brakes, blowing of horns and furious patrolmen's voices were heard from the street below. "Here's Niels Bohr coming to see me again," said Groves to an aide, without even looking out the window. He was right. But when the illustrious jaywalker left the building a little later, Groves sent an officer along to escort him across the street.

In the beginning, the twenty scientists of the Theoretical Division used only simple, desk-type calculating machines. Modern electronic computers did not yet exist. The machines were operated by wives of staff members — Mrs. Frankel, Mrs. Teller and Mrs. Brodey had studied mathematics — and by a few hastily trained WAC's. The known methods were much too slow for the complicated calculations and Dick Feynman's job — and hobby — was to invent new, faster ways of setting up calculations. But the desk machines were still too slow.

At a meeting of the laboratory's governing board, the Procurement Division's head, Dana P. Mitchell, mentioned one day that he had seen men in the astronomy department at Columbia using business machines for calculating orbits of planets. "Why don't you try them?" he asked Bethe.

Stanley Frankel, group leader in Bethe's division, investigated the possibilities and ordered several of the machines from IBM. They were mechanical devices operated by means of perforated cards, like mechanical pianos, and were much faster than the finger-operated desk calculators. Another great advantage of the IBM machines was the rapidity with which they could sort things. In a matter of seconds they could find, among thousands of cards, all those that contained a certain name or datum. Once the card received the general instructions, all calculations were done automatically and there was no need to do every operation separately. Each machine could perform hundreds of operations; then the cards were collected by operators and carried to the next machine to do a further operation. Feynman and Frankel invented some extraordinarily imaginative methods of preparing the mathematical data in a form suitable for the punched cards. To practice them, before the arrival of the IBM's, they used eight girls with hand calculating machines, simulating different stages of the new computing system.

The IBM machines represented a great improvement, a valuable addition to their capacity. Without them, it is doubtful whether the complicated implosion calculations could ever have been made. Normally, IBM rented out the machines and sent their own repairmen for periodical inspections. But because of the distance and the secrecy at the laboratory, this was impossible at Los Alamos. The problem was serious because the machines had to be used twenty-four hours a day, seven days a week. So the Army searched its records for a former IBM repairman now in uniform and sent him to Los Alamos.

The machines arrived before the IBM man, and the impatient Feynman and Frankel could not resist the temptation to explore. They took the parts out of the crates and spent the better part of the week trying to put them together, without ever having seen an IBM machine before. When the repairman finally arrived, he was amazed to see that the machines were practically assembled.

The scientists became so fascinated with the machines that they started playing with them as a pastime and exploring new mathematical possibilities. Some of them began to neglect the original problem and the work was getting slower. Finally, one machine was put aside especially for "playing games," but only during off-hours. Strict orders were given that the other machines must not be used for hobbies. So the scientists used to come every night to "play" and to test original theories.

Unlike the scientists, the young IBM operators, who worked three shifts a day and who had replaced the wives and the WAC's, were operating the machines without interest. Enlisted men from the Special Engineers Department, they felt that they were wasting their time punching holes in cards instead of fighting a war. Dick Feynman had never had a group of people under him before, but he thought that it would be good for their morale if they were told about the Project.

This was strictly against regulations, but Feynman pleaded with Oppenheimer and obtained special permission. He then explained the bomb project to the young soldiers. It worked miracles: the soldiers became so excited that their work soon improved 100 percent.*

---

* It was the first time science had used computers in operations of such size and complexity. Use of IBM machines at Los Alamos proved of inestimable value in the later development of modern electronic computers. It was there that a mathematical genius, John von Neumann, saw the machines in operation for the first time and became fascinated by the possibilities they offered. Their value in solving implosion and hydrodynamics problems convinced him that computers would play an enormous role in modern science. Inspired by what he saw, von Neumann developed some of the theories on which modern computers are based.

WESTFIELD MEMORIAL LIBRARY
WESTFIELD, N. J.

33

EDWIN L. JONES, a tall, erect man of fifty-two, had never touched liquor in his life, never smoked, and never missed a Sunday service at the Methodist Church in Charlotte, North Carolina. There was an air of great sobriety about him — in his disciplined way of speaking, in his conservative dark suit, in the friendly but serious eyes behind the rimless glasses. Every morning Jones, a construction contractor, arrived at his office at 209 West Fourth Street at precisely 8 A.M.; every evening at precisely 5 P.M., he put away his papers and left for home. As far back as anyone could remember, Edwin Jones had never missed a working day, and had never been sick in his life. He firmly believed in hard work, temperance, and living according to Holy Writ.

His father, James Addison Jones, a mechanic with no formal education, had come to Charlotte at eighteen from a farm. He built up a successful construction business from scratch and was able to send his sons, Edwin and Raymond, to college. But he always considered that his most notable accomplishment was to have instilled in his sons a clear and simple set of values, the values of a pious Methodist family at the turn of the century.

Very few people in America knew exactly what the J. A. Jones Construction Company was building at Oak Ridge, Tennessee; even the company people didn't know the purpose of the gigantic secret construction. The work force at Oak Ridge numbered twenty thousand men, and the payroll amounted to five million dollars a month. Huge quantities of materials were required — 350,000 cubic yards of concrete, 40,000 tons of structural steel, 15,000 tons of sheet steel, 5 million bricks.

Never had such a colossal plant been built before — the floor area of the U–shaped K–25 building covered forty-four acres of ground, and each side of the gigantic U was a half-mile long. When finished, this four-story plant would be the world's largest construction under one roof.

For the J. A. Jones Construction Company, the contract was a tremendous challenge. They were a relatively unknown company, but the Army had chosen them because of their excellent record in building Army camps and other installations. General Somervell, Groves and many officers in the Corps of Engineers knew the capacities and the integrity of old James A. Jones and his two sons. They did not run a major construction firm, but their word was worth ten contracts. When the Joneses agreed on an estimate and a deadline, the job was certain to be done. At the outbreak of the war, J. A. Jones had twenty-two construction projects under way, but when the Army asked them to help on some urgent jobs, they dropped all private work and built twelve complete Army bases, several hospitals and a shipyard in Florida. They operated the shipyard so successfully that they were asked to build 212 Liberty ships at the Brunswick yard in Georgia.

Edwin Jones had not been particularly concerned by the fact that he knew nothing about ships. "You learn by working," he often said. "You select the right people and you work; you put all your heart and your mind in the project, and again you work; then you can do anything — Army camps, ships, everything!"

"What about building a huge power plant?" General Groves asked on the telephone one day. Edwin Jones was working at the Brunswick shipyard. "Have you ever built a power plant?"

"Yes, we have."

"But this will be different. This one plant alone will use more electricity than Boston. When can you start?"

Edwin Jones paused for a moment to make a few estimates. "Tomorrow," he answered calmly.

General Groves loved it. "I knew that was my man!" he said to an assistant after hanging up.

The same evening Jones flew to New York to see Colonel Marshall. The plane arrived at dawn on Friday morning, and it was only 7 A.M. when he stepped into the Fifth Avenue office. But only fifteen minutes later, another early riser appeared — Colonel Marshall did not want to lose any time. By eight o'clock all details were settled and a simple "letter of intent" was signed by Marshall, commissioning J. A. Jones to build the electric power plant at Oak Ridge. Five million dollars was allocated without any formal contract having been drawn up. The colonel did not give any details about the plant, and the builder from Charlotte did not ask any questions. The Army and the Government had told him that the project was very important, secret and urgent; for Edwin Jones that was sufficient reason to accept.

Jones knew Oak Ridge because he was already building one thousand homes for the plant being constructed there by Stone and Webster. On June 1, 1943, work began on the power plant, which had to be completed in ten months. Then on September 10 of the same year, construction began on the stupendous K–25 gaseous-diffusion plant. To millions of Americans, the name of Oak Ridge was completely unknown; there was no suspicion that towns were being built in complete secrecy, towns with populations in the tens of thousands.

Relatively unknown builders like the J. A. Jones Company and its sixty-four subcontractors were tackling construction problems of unprecedented difficulty. To prepare the uneven terrain for the foundations, for instance, enormous volumes of earth — two million cubic yards — were removed. It took four months to level 130 acres for the main building area. The topography of the site required fills of up to twenty-three feet in height, while a cut of forty-six feet had to be made into one hill.

The question of how to lay the building foundations of the huge plant, which would house very heavy processing equipment, presented tremendous problems. Anything less than perfect construction would affect the clocklike precision of the future process. One plan was to spread concrete footings on undisturbed soil and extend columns up to the basement floor level. Fill was subsequently to be placed between the footings and columns by dump trucks. But no grading subcontractor could be found who would undertake the filling in the time allotted. Another plan was to complete all grading operations as rapidly as possible, and drive pile supports separately for each footing. This was also eliminated as being too slow, expensive and inadequate.

Finally, a revolutionary idea was adopted: all fillings would be laid in six-inch layers, which would be thoroughly compacted with sheepsfoot rollers after the manner of earth-dam construction; then the footings could be founded directly on top of the new fills. But in making the fills, J. A. Jones encountered a major difficulty: the red clay contained an excess of natural moisture, too much for good compaction. In spite of the enormity of the area, it was decided that all the soil used in compacted fills had to be plowed, aerated and dried out.

No excavation was composed wholly of one type of soil. The engineers became exasperated when they discovered that nine different soil types were intermingled throughout the entire site. Since it was not possible to identify them by eye, Jones finally had to use methods of soil-testing and identification developed earlier by TVA. At least once a day, samples were cut out of the embankment with a ring-cutter, and the dry density of the soil determined in the laboratory.

When the Kellex people first told Edwin Jones the cleanliness requirements for the new plant, he thought they were simply using figurative language in order to emphasize their point. "A thumbprint in the whole plant would represent contamination, and therefore can't be tolerated," he was told. A thumbprint in a four-story building with sides half a mile long! But very soon he realized that they were perfectly serious.

There would be thousands of people working around the clock on a floor covering an area of 5,560,000 square feet. How could that be kept as clean as an operating room? But the order came from above, and though unprecedented in the history of big construction, it was imperative that the cleaning and conditioning of the equipment when installed in K–25 be done under surgical conditions. This meant the complete removal of dirt, grease, oxide, scale — even the smallest amount could cause a complete failure.

In this respect, the J. A. Jones Company, the engineering firm of Ford, Bacon and Davis and other subcontractors performed a job that bordered on the impossible. Construction workers had to change into special clean clothes from head to foot upon entering a restricted building. Special lockers were provided for all, including General Groves and Colonel Nichols, who had to change like everybody else when they entered the area, even if they were going to stay only a few minutes. Everything possible was done to eliminate dirt and dust — vacuum cleaners were used instead of brooms, wet mops were used in order to avoid raising dust by dry sweeping. All process equipment from individual valves to sub-assemblies of pipes had to be put through as many as a dozen cleaning operations, including sandblasting, degreasing, alkaline cleaning and acid pickling. After cleaning, equipment was dried and then tightly capped to prevent contamination during handling. Certain items of equipment were filled with dry nitrogen to preclude any possibility of moisture infiltration.

Once cleaned, dried and capped by the Ford, Bacon and Davis crews, the equipment was subjected to a procedure known as "cleanliness control." The first step was to partition off the building in which the equipment was to be installed, and thoroughly clean it from roof to basement. Not only was all construction debris cleared away, but all building surfaces, even the ceilings, were wiped down by hand, or vacuum-cleaned. To keep the building clean, it was placed under forced draft ventilation and all air was filtered; only essential trucks were permitted to enter and these were hosed down.

The task was grandiose, the challenge enormous. Future generations, looking at the incredible K–25 plant, will like to imagine the men who erected it as exceptional pyramid builders, defying and overcoming the technology of their time. Undoubtedly they will be disappointed to discover that the frugal Methodist brothers from Charlotte, North Carolina — Mr. Jones, "Mr. Edwin," and "Mr. Raymond" — were just good, ordinary professional people, solid citizens with a deep interest in public philanthropies. They were men of great technical competence, but unlike the heroes of novels and movies, they did not spend sleepless nights dreaming of greatness, were never torn by dramatic doubts of the success of the job, and uttered no historic words.

34

THE DIFFICULTIES were piling up at Kellex. Barrier problem, pump problem, corrosion problem, cascade problem. One of the major difficulties was the extraordinarily corrosive power of uranium gas; it ruled out the use of practically every known metal. Another one was the requirement of airtightness. Such a requirement exceeded – and by far – anything that had ever been conceived before, even in small systems. To incorporate such airtightness on a gigantic scale, in piping hundreds of miles long and through two thousand cascade stages, seemed an impossible dream. The gaseous-diffusion system could be ruined by even an infinitesimal leakage. Such minute leakage, however, seemed unpreventable: extrasensitive instruments recorded perceptible leaking in valves, even through solid metal three feet thick. No existing valve, no welding technique and no pipe joint could guarantee such optimum airtightness.

Technology then could boast several kinds of excellent valves and joints preventing leakage to a high degree. For years they had been perfectly satisfactory for the most demanding industrial processes – no higher degree of airtightness had ever been needed. But now a new requirement had emerged: separation of the bomb material would be impossible if several hundred miles of pipes were not made completely leakproof – and kept that way for months, perhaps for years.

As the summer of 1943 progressed, grave anxiety descended over the Kellex organization quartered in the Woolworth Building in Manhattan. Experts were consulted right and left; countless designs were examined. But it became more and more doubtful that anyone in the country could build the ideal valves and joints that would keep the whole piping system absolutely airtight.

Then, fortunately, Ludwig Skog, the engineer in charge of designing the Oak Ridge power plant, thought of hiring J. C. Hobbs. Others knew his reputation – Dobie Keith and Al Baker, particularly at Kellex – and were immediately interested in the idea. But would he come? J. C. Hobbs was making a great deal of money in industry, and was famous not only for his inventiveness, but also for being a testy, difficult person and a complete individualist.

Ludwig Skog had met Hobbs in 1940 in Chicago. A client of Sargent and Lundy, where Skog was a vice-president, took him one day to visit an unusual plant that the Diamond Alkali Company had just built. Skog already knew that the plant's designer, J. C. Hobbs, was probably the best boiler builder in the country, but he was still enormously impressed by what he saw. Hobbs had convinced Diamond Alkali that their chemical plant could produce its own power more cheaply than they could buy it outside. Hobbs had made a bold, unorthodox design using a new type of boiler that replaced all the thirty-two boilers they had had before. J. C. Hobbs was an outspoken, slightly grouchy man in his fifties, very self-confident and with a passion for mechanics. "The trick was to start with seven hundred pounds' pressure of steam, instead of the usual two hundred pounds," he explained to his visitors that day as they went around the Diamond Alkali plant. "Then I raised the temperature up to seven hundred degrees. Everybody always starts with three hundred and fifty degrees. But that's all wrong.

"It's like a waterfall: the higher you start, the more power you get. Then I heated up to eight hundred degrees, then to one thousand, and two thousand five hundred. And that is red-hot steam — a Niagara Falls! It takes me less coal to make a pound of steam at two thousand five hundred degrees than at four hundred. Surprised, eh? I'm gettin' a lot for less than nothin'."

Hobbs had made everything himself, personally designing and arranging all the pipes and boilers. "The only thing I bought from the outside was this turbine," he said, pointing to it with disdain. "An awful thing! I had to change everything but the manufacturer's nameplate, and rebuild the whole thing."

Skog, like everybody in the business, knew about Hobbs's numerous inventions and patents, the best-known being the "theoretical combustion" boiler, which he had originated in 1914 for the William Penn Hotel in Pittsburgh. It was a gas burner combined with a meter that measured the mixture of gas and air automatically and kept it at optimum functioning.

Hobbs had also designed many successful power plants, as well as a city-wide heating system comprising the pipelines and tunnels beneath street level, and the largest boiler in the world in Pittsburgh before World War I. During the war, when Pittsburgh became an important munitions center, the Hobbs-designed power plants were vitally important. During the next twenty-five years engineers and designers everywhere in America were copying Hobbs's bold innovations. His drawings, always done in different colors, had become his trademark in the profession.

When Hobbs's name was first mentioned at Kellex, some engineers were both critical and skeptical. "J.C." was known to be an independent free-lancer who had no taste for working within an organization. "They say the old man is not only a lone wolf, but he's a true prima donna," one young Kellex engineer remarked.

Ludwig Skog (at fifty, he was also one of the few "old men" at Kellex) told his younger colleagues some of the tales of Hobbs's unusual accomplishments. He did not argue about Hobbs's temperament, although Skog himself had no trouble getting along with him. "But when it comes to designing boilers and power plants and inventing gadgets! . . ." Skog broke off, unable to find enough superlatives in English to describe what J.C. was capable of doing. He made Hobbs's boilers and valves sound like the pipes and keys of a superb organ played by a great, if temperamental, maestro.

Hobbs's reputation for having a difficult personality stemmed largely from the fact that he had quit several jobs when his employers had not agreed with his radical engineering ideas. In his speciality, he would never make a compromise. He knew only one way of doing things: his way. Extremely impatient in the face of stupidity or incompetence, stubborn and self-confident, he was perfectly sincere when, while candidly lecturing his clients and superiors, he would exclaim, "Look, it's not *my* way; it's the *only* way. It's not a matter of agreeing or disagreeing — it's just how nature works. You can't change the law of gravity by majority vote, can you?"

Some company presidents, however, took the risk of going against those laws of nature and disagreeing with Hobbs. J.C.'s reaction was simple: he would just take his hat and his drawings and go to work with another company, without any argument.

That was the way he left Allegheny County Light of Pittsburgh, a utility company where he had worked for eighteen years, and the parting nearly broke his heart. In 1924 he had designed a new type of boiler using water-cooled tubes for walls instead of bricks. Some consultants, hired by the company president, recommended that the design be changed and the usual air-cooled, refractory walls be used instead. Although Hobbs voiced his disgust for the "appalling design," the company president reversed him. J.C. left without even saying good-bye. "I am not angry," he said later, "but I will not work with anyone who doesn't cooperate on progress."

Hobbs went to work in the chemical industry, where he made even more money than his generous salary at the Pittsburgh light company. But leaving the public utilities company had been like walking out on a wife after a silly quarrel. In spite of his interest in and respect for the dollar, Hobbs's puritanical heart belonged to public service. "One thing about the utility business: it's a national asset, because they are non-competitive and cooperate with each other," he said regretfully. "We would trade ideas, help each other solve problems. Utility people are dedicated, they want to feel they are part of the community — anyhow, in Pittsburgh we did and I liked that. I like the spirit of fellowship among utility people all over the country. When you go to another city, you can walk into offices and sit down and have a talk."

Hobbs kept in continual touch with inventors, engineers and mechanical people, and loved discussing technical problems. He felt less attracted to intellectuals and academic scientists, and had little respect for desk engineers who depended too much on books and learned nothing from practice. They were the "theoreticals," and Hobbs delighted to shock them by some unorthodox but brilliant design. "It's not according to the books, but it works better," he would chuckle. "I had the scholars a little bit worried, because they had already determined — on paper — what the characteristics should be, and my boiler just didn't fit them!"

J. C. Hobbs's attitude was not based on real animosity — the kind he felt, for instance, for what he considered to be left-wing demagogues, or for cigarette smokers, or for parasites who lived on public money. He simply distrusted the theoreticals. "What is all this about doctor's degrees and theses nowadays?" he often complained. "That's the wrong incentive; all studies are keyed directly to having a degree, a doctorate. I wasn't a doctor, but I'd had more training than the doctors had. I didn't waste time and work on some theoretical thing that might never have any practical value. If you're a bookworm, or one of those with a photographic memory — you get ahead, see? All these fellows that sit at the front desk and read some kid's report, made from impressions he's had in school and not from practical experience. You don't get anywhere that way!"

The theoreticals sometimes had their feelings hurt by the blunt-spoken, grouchy engineer; but popularity did not concern him too much — not when it was measured against making something work. He usually refused to attend meetings, and abhorred decisions made by committees. Some Kellex people who had heard of his reputation simply did not believe J.C. could ever fit in on their team. "Imagine a character like that working under Keith!"

But Keith's ideas were different. He knew that the only chance this impossible project had was to assign each problem to the best man in the field. The job had to be done and all other considerations were secondary. "Look," he told one assistant, "if Toulouse-Lautrec made me a painting, I wouldn't start asking whether he drank and what his private life was!"

221 (

Some of the engineers didn't know much about Toulouse-Lautrec, but the argument seemed conclusive enough.

Ludwig Skog picked up the phone and called Hobbs, who was at his home in Ohio. "J.C., could you come down to New York?" he asked. "There is something very important going on and they need you badly. I am not free to discuss it, but you should come down here for a conference."

Hobbs accepted and came to New York. In the Woolworth Building, Keith and Baker were waiting for him. "We're in trouble," said Al Baker. "We need somebody to solve a lot of problems that we haven't been able to solve so far. You've had experience building big new things and making them work." Nothing was said about gaseous diffusion or the bomb. Keith merely stated, "When this plant goes into operation, the war ends."

Both of Hobbs's sons were in the service, one in the Pacific. Moreover, he liked the two Kellex engineers — they were real "pros" — and he trusted Skog. So he mumbled something like "Let me think," which sounded like a favorable answer. They gave him a pile of papers and applications to be filled in for security clearance. Hobbs went through these suspiciously. "I've been checked so doggone many times that they won't have to go very far to check me out. I built a magnesium plant for the Government and I've been through all this nonsense before. They even want to know who your grandmother was!"

When he came to the forms concerning patents, Hobbs grew even more suspicious. The routine was to assign to the Government all inventions made during work on the Project. But Hobbs had no intention of giving away his inventions, past, present or future. He already had about thirty patents that earned him large sums of money. He was a firm believer in free enterprise and its monetary incentives for people who create and improve things. He had built his fortune with his own hands, dollar by dollar, with no outside help, and he had a profound aversion to anything that smelled of "socialism." Shortly afterwards, when Hobbs came back to Kellex with the papers filled in, he put the patent sheet aside. "This one I won't sign," he said, "and I can't work for you if you insist on it." To make an exception for Hobbs would be against the rules at Kellex. But Baker and Keith just exchanged a look and said, "OK, we want *you!*"

Salary presented another problem. Compared with the money Hobbs had been making before, the salary fixed by the Government seemed ridiculously low. Besides, J.C. could not devote more than half of his time to the job: the other half was fully occupied by work for the Navy, and he could not quit that. With the Army's approval, Keith and Baker decided to put Hobbs on the payroll at the top full-time salary, even though he would be working only part-time.

But for Hobbs, "part-time" work was only a manner of speaking. When he was interested in a problem, he would dive into it head first, and time would cease to exist for him. He never allowed anyone to tell him when and how to do things.

In his work, as in his life, J. C. Hobbs had very decided views of right and wrong, and the idea of doubting these basic values was completely foreign to him. He was a minister's son, like so many others in the Manhattan Project — notably, Groves and Bush, Compton, Urey and Hilberry. Actually his father was an educator from West Virginia, who went to Florida as a superintendent of schools when J.C. was only five. But he was also an evangelist on the side. J.C. started working as captain of a small yacht, then went to Pittsburgh to study engineering at the Carnegie Institute of Technology. Graduating in 1910, he kept on studying for several years in night classes. It was an unusual situation: Hobbs graduated from college in engineering without ever having been to high school. The Florida areas where evangelist Hobbs moved his family simply had no high schools in those days. But the preparation given by his father and mother was quite sufficient to enable J.C. to pass every exam easily.

"What is the secret of your success with inventions, J.C.?" someone once asked him.

"I get my information through my fingers," was the reply. "Look at my hands — they've always been tough — and through my eyes, and my ears, and all my senses. If you see me around a plant, you'll just as often as not see me *in* a piece of equipment. I've gone down into big chemical equipment while it was operating, trying to find out just what was goin' on. If you know what's goin' on, you can do somethin'. And when I visit a plant, I say, 'Take me first to the scrap pile!' There I see what trouble they have. Scrap and waste — that indicates wrong design usually, or wrong operation. There I get the most reliable information, and not by listening to those people with degrees in the front office!"

J. C. Hobbs started working at Kellex on September 8, 1943. The next day, September 9, he asked to see the overall drawing for the entire plant. He studied it with care, stood silently by the chief engineer's big double desk; then looked down again. At that time he did not know anything about details of operation, or any troubles that Kellex had had. But after a long examination, he took a fat grease pencil and slowly went over the drawing freehand, making what he called "chicken scratches." With a few brisk movements, he took out about two-thirds of the miles of piping on the complicated blueprint. (This represented six months of work and twenty million dollars' worth of piping.)

An uncomfortable silence fell over the stunned engineers. Finally Allen Fruit, the amiable chief engineer, took a deep breath and looked again at the mutilated blueprint. "The original design looks foolish, all right. . . . But you probably don't realize the horrible problems that the cascade and the barriers and all the rest give us."

"I don't," replied Hobbs. "But nevertheless, from a purely mechanical standpoint, the drawing stinks!"

Thus began J. C. Hobbs's first day of work on the Manhattan Project.

35

IF JUDSON SWEARINGEN had to pin down the exact moment when he invented his leakproof seal, he would place it on a gray Saturday afternoon in December 1942, while he was working at the Elliott Company in Jeannette, Pennsylvania. That day, after three hours of mentally reducing all the requirements for an ideal seal down to the absolute essential, he suddenly visualized a mechanical device that would do the job. The seal would not be a modification of any existing model; it would be built on a principle that was altogether new and revolutionary. *

The following Monday morning Swearingen immediately proceeded to make a model, a very complicated job because of the unusual requirements. He was forced to improvise new techniques right on the spot. After two weeks of exhaustive work, he had a handmade model ready on New Year's Day, 1943 — in time for a meeting, called by Dobie Keith in New York, of scientists and engineers working on the cascade pump.

The purpose of the conference was to evaluate the feasibility and chances of success in building the needed pumps. By accepting the task of building a gaseous-diffusion plant, M. W. Kellogg Company had made an enormous commitment in money, effort and reputation, and Dobie Keith wanted the specialists to answer the question whether it was reasonable to believe that the formidable pump problems could be solved in the time available.

At this conference, however, no special attention was paid to Swearingen's model; most of the discussion was devoted to a promising seal being developed by Henry Boorse of Columbia. Swearingen's device was only briefly mentioned, and then merely as one more possibility to be explored in the unlikely event that Boorse's seal did not work.

Watts, Swearingen and O. C. Brewster† who had not met each other

---

* Exactly what the Swearingen seal represented is still one of the few secrets of the atomic bomb and cannot be described. All that can be said is that it made possible the building of centrifugal compressors operating at very high speeds and without any leakage.

† Brewster, a Quaker, had serious qualms about his participation in the Project and even wrote a letter to Groves, asking to be relieved of his duties. Groves showed the letter to Secretary Stimson. "This man is a man of integrity," he said. "I thought

before, were moved to several modest offices on the twelfth floor of the Woolworth Building, where they started working, helped by a few assistants, on the pump design. Several lengthy meetings were immediately set up with Professor Boorse, who explained his seal and expressed his belief in its success. George Watts was impressed by the elaborate test data obtained in the well-equipped Columbia laboratories. Swearingen, however, was still skeptical about Boorse's solution and continued to perfect his own invention. He aired his views to Watts, who had primary responsibility for the pump development. But Watts, after having received both Boorse's and Swearingen's seal models within a short period of time, was still hopeful that several additional ideas would be forthcoming. He therefore asked Swearingen to build a "universal" seal-tester — an instrument on which various seals could be installed and tested comparatively.

Swearingen had had two models of his seal built by the Sharples Corporation before the news came in from Kellex's pilot plant in Jersey City: Boorse's seal had failed its first tests. From that day on, all attention was focused on the Swearingen seal.

Only then could Swearingen persuade Keith to build full-scale models, a difficult and expensive task. The Columbia laboratory readily picked up the development of many phases of the new seal. Swearingen, realizing that some mathematical studies were beyond his capacity, gladly accepted the help of the Columbia scientists. Boorse and his group concentrated all their efforts on helping Kellex build the exact-size seal models.

Once the principle of Swearingen's revolutionary seal was understood, a new problem arose: what material would be used? The difficulty proved to be infinitely greater than anyone at Kellex had suspected. To begin with, Watts's pump division had to eliminate practically all known metals and alloys because of the intensely corrosive power of uranium hexafluoride gas. Those metals that remained as possible choices made up a very meager list indeed.

Finally, after one corrosion-resistant metal had been selected, new and even harder problems arose. If the seal was to be bottle-tight to prevent any leaks, a fantastic degree of precision was imperative. While the current manufacturing tolerances were on the order of a thousandth or a ten-thousandth of an inch, Swearingen and Watts were talking about tolerances of less than one-millionth of an inch! Since no instruments existed for such ultraprecise measurement, a method of measuring by different wave lengths of light had to be used.

---

you should know what he wrote." After talking it over with the Secretary and Dobie Keith, General Groves explained to Brewster that he must remain with the Project for the good of his country. Brewster agreed to stay.

Unfortunately, the metallurgists discovered that the first material Watts recommended was unstable — it tended to change its characteristics when heated to different temperatures. In other words, when the pump was in operation and generating heat, the metal expanded; when cooled down after operation, however, it did not come back to its original dimensions. The seal therefore lost its tightness.

"You must use another metal!" the discouraged metallurgists pleaded with Watts. They had tried, without success, every possible technique to lick the problem. "You will never build the thing with this unstable material." The seal development thus reached still another impasse. The problem looked insoluble to most specialists. Many Kellex people grew more and more pessimistic. To make matters worse, word came to Watts's pump division that the British scientists, after examining the plans for the compressor and the seal, had declared that they would never work. Many of their colleagues at Columbia shared the British view. Pessimism even won the builders of the pump; Brewster was the first to lose faith, then doubts began to assail the mind of the overall leader, George Watts.

The men who relentlessly tried to keep up morale in the pump division were Dobie Keith and John Dunning. The head of Kellex, never showing any doubt or discouragement, personally joined the engineers of Watts's group to give them a hand. As for the Columbia physicist, he was not only confident but even enthusiastic. Although there was no concrete reason for Dunning's optimism, his regular visits to Kellex were like a ray of sunshine on a gloomy day. And simultaneously what the pump builders were hearing from Groves indicated a remarkably unchanging mood on the part of the general: he was incessantly dissatisfied.

Dobie Keith's vigorous, if unorthodox, leadership proved to be a bulwark of strength for Watts and his engineers. In moments of depression, when they needed to talk to someone, they instinctively turned to Keith. His show of unlimited confidence was reassuring. Once he believed in somebody, the usually impatient Texan was ready to listen carefully to the smallest details, to offer his analysis and to back his engineers to the utmost. Keith gave Watts full authority and freedom of action. Each time the pump division came into conflict with the representatives of the Army, the Kellex boss intervened energetically in favor of his men — and not necessarily only when they were right. Both Keith and Watts disliked meetings and red tape; they were not models of good organization men. They often ignored established channels, to the great irritation of Kellex's chief engineer Al Baker, a sober, meticulous executive who was struggling to keep some order in this conglomeration of individualists. "I don't believe in committee solutions," Watts used to say, "because they are always a compromise between the best and the worst. Committees are fine for setting up the problems and looking at them, but not for resolving them." One man he certainly did not have to convince on this point was his own boss, Dobie Keith.

Solution of the seal-manufacturing problem came only after several agonizing months of experimentation. It eventually became possible to make a stable and dependable seal according to Swearingen's specifications.

As far as mass production of the compressors at Allis-Chalmers was concerned, the harmony was less than perfect. Both the Kellex and the Army men had the impression that the company had little faith in the program and was cooperating only because the Government directed them to do so. Swearingen, especially, became more and more impatient with the Allis-Chalmers engineers, suspecting them of marking time, and frictions developed between him and them. Some Army people even suspected that sabotage might be the cause for the lagging work pace.

The reason for the company's initial slowness was something else, however. Allis-Chalmers engineers, unaccustomed to moving so fast, knew nothing about the intended purpose of the compressors, nothing about the atomic bomb or the separation of uranium isotopes. To most of the workers at the Hawley plant, it was just another war job; moreover, it was one that interfered with other important contracts, such as the building of the giant magnets for Oak Ridge and some vital Navy projects. The Allis-Chalmers people were irritated by the impatient Army and Kellex men constantly breathing down their necks. Keith had sent seventy-five inspectors to the plant; the Manhattan District's representative, Lieutenant Colonel Stowers, also had his men there, and security people were all over the place. "We have so many inspectors and advisers, we can't get any work done," moaned one Allis-Chalmers man.

The engineers, who were producing five different sizes of compressors simultaneously, were driven nearly mad by constant revisions and model changes. They had never seen such erratic methods. They had never been asked to observe such incredibly strict standards of cleanliness either. In the final-assembly room, for instance, workers wore white coveralls, white hats and white nylon gloves and maintenance crews cleaned and dusted the premises around the clock. "Are we running a plant or a hospital operating room?" grumbled one old hand.

Security measures added to the difficulties. At the Hawley plant, the engineers' offices were completely separated from the shop. No shop worker could move freely about the plant. Everyone was restricted to his particular work area, and one shop even had a high wall around it. Employees were placed on the payroll only after the most careful scrutiny of their backgrounds. To work under such conditions, with relentless prodding and no explanation of the reason for the frantic urgency, was extremely trying.*

Groves was told by Allis-Chalmers's James M. White that it was difficult to maintain his men's morale without being able to give them any reason for the pressing haste. Groves could only repeat that the Manhattan District was engaged in work of the utmost importance to the war effort. To stress the point, Groves wrote a letter to the president of Allis-Chalmers, Walter Geist: "It is necessary that the utmost secrecy be maintained within your organization. . . . The importance of the work in the Hawley plant cannot be overemphasized. This work is for a project of the highest possible importance to the prosecution of the war. It is desired, therefore, that you do everything within your power to obtain and maintain an adequate staff of skilled personnel and necessary plant equipment and materials. . . . It is further desired that you make available needed engineering and supervisory talent from any part of your organization, regardless of the work engaged upon, in order to maintain the manufacturing schedule now set for the Hawley plant. This letter may be shown to such persons as necessary in order to insure the success of the Hawley plant program, but must not be reproduced or copied." After Groves's signature, Geist read: "I concur in the above, Donald M. Nelson, Chief, War Production Board."

Groves's letter raised morale somewhat, but production was still too slow for the taste of Kellex and the Army. Swearingen, who had moved temporarily to Milwaukee, was so harsh at times in his goading that heated arguments broke out between him and John Avery, the engineer in charge of the Allis-Chalmers compressor department. Several complaints reached Keith and Watts. The Allis-Chalmers people, fed up with Swearingen's impatience, requested his removal. Watts called him back to New York to hear his side of the story. On the train Swearingen wrote a twenty-page report on his plan for the pump-and-seal combination and on its manufacture. Watts was so pleased with the report that he would not allow time for a smooth typing — he literally tore the report from Swearingen's hands and ran to discuss it with Keith, and he mentioned nothing about the Allis-Chalmers request for Swearingen's removal. Keith, delighted to find someone as keen as himself in getting things done fast, backed his fellow Texan all the way and refused to replace him.

Independent of Swearingen, Lieutenant Colonel Stowers was also waging his own battle for efficient compressor production. Even when Allis-Chalmers doubled the number of employees in the Hawley plant to 1878 people, he thought the work force was still inadequate and the

---

* During the period when thousands of compressors were produced and shipped to Oak Ridge, four Allis-Chalmers employees had nervous breakdowns.

control system not effective enough. Finally, Avery agreed to increase the work force. And Stowers found yet another way to speed up production. Allis-Chalmers had often explained that its shipping only a limited number of compressors to Oak Ridge was motivated by its concern not to send any pump that was not absolutely perfect. "From now on," a new directive said, "every unit that is mechanically OK — that is, every unit that can be run without the possibility of destruction of any of its parts — should be shipped from the Hawley plant."

Once initial difficulties were overcome and production moved into high gear, Allis-Chalmers did an excellent job. It developed new materials and new techniques, special welding equipment. In one year, Allis-Chalmers shipped seven thousand compressors to Oak Ridge. (Counting all the spare parts, seventy thousand pieces were produced in one year.) The contract was executed on time; construction of the gaseous-diffusion installations at Oak Ridge would not be held up for want of compressors.

36

MOST OF KNOXVILLE was still asleep and the streets were almost deserted when Pat Patterson, a tall, eighteen-year-old brunette, left her home at five-fifteen in the morning to go to work. A car picked her up and, as on every working day, then stopped to collect other sleepy-eyed girls before heading west out of the city. There was already a long string of cars forming on the two-lane highway to Oak Ridge, and near the entrance to the town, traffic slowed down to bumper-to-bumper crawl, as guards stopped each vehicle and checked the identity of each passenger.

It was a long drive to Oak Ridge — over an hour — but Pat Patterson did not mind it at all. For the first time in her life, she felt independent — important. Though just out of high school, she was making more money than many people she knew — enough to afford buying, every two weeks, a fifty-dollar war bond. On pay day she was even rather embarrassed to admit how much she made to the GI she was dating — poor boy, he was only getting thirty dollars a month.

On the way to Oak Ridge, the road wound through beautiful hilly country, where trees and grass had grown luxuriantly green after the abundant rainfall during the early months of 1943. But it was a different picture at Oak Ridge itself: hundreds of bulldozers were tearing the whole place apart and transforming it into a huge construction yard, which was covered with thick, sticky red mud. Daily rains sluicing the unpaved streets made mud a major problem for the tens of thousands of people working on the Project. Like all the other girl employees, Pat wore clumsy GI boots when walking to the cafeteria through ankle-deep mud; when she got home, her mother refused to let her in until she had hosed down her boots in the basement.

Pat's father and mother never learned exactly what her job was; on taking the job, she had sworn never to discuss it — at work or outside — and she took the pledge seriously. Her only brother was serving with the Navy, and she felt proud to be helping her country, too. Her parents knew that she was doing some kind of war work, and the only thing they demanded was that she live at home with them in Knoxville. No eighteen-year-old daughter of his, Pat's father had said, was going to live in the

WESTFIELD MEMORIAL LIBRARY
WESTFIELD, N. J.

women's dormitories at Oak Ridge, and that settled the matter. Pat, however, was allowed to spend the weekends with the other girls at Oak Ridge and go to the Saturday night dances in the recreation hall.

About the plant itself, Pat knew little more than her parents. After finishing high school, she had read some of the want ads in the local papers, and had gone to Tennessee Eastman's employment office in Knoxville. It was a small, crowded room with girls waiting on benches or standing in line. She filled out an application — the pay was better than in other factories — and then had to wait three weeks for her security clearance. It was a job essential to the war effort, she was told, and highly secret. When the clearance arrived, Pat was fingerprinted and given a badge. After this she submitted to a series of tests — mostly for manual skill, concentration, and the ability to match different things together. Then she was taken to Oak Ridge, shown a fenced-in area called Y–12, and was told that she would be working in a building called Alpha One.

For the next few weeks she went through training courses with other girls, learning how to operate some big control panels that looked like switchboards with dials and knobs, and which were part of tall, cabinet-like units called cubicles. She learned how to read the meters, how to keep a record on a sheet attached to a clipboard, and how to operate the knobs. But despite many rumors that the Oak Ridge plants were producing this thing or that — poison gas and airplane fuels were the most common rumors — Pat Patterson never learned what they were actually making.

The man sipping his soft drink at the counter was a stranger in Murphysburg, Tennessee, but he had a kind, friendly face. "What's your name?" he asked the young girl behind the counter.

"Helen Hall."

"Is this your first job?"

"Yes, I just graduated from high school." She was eighteen, and the drugstore paid her $27.50 a week, which was good money for a beginner.

"How about doing something for the war effort and also make more money than you do here? I'm with Tennessee Eastman and we need girls like you for an important job near Knoxville. You can start at seventy-five cents an hour, six days a week."

It was a higher wage than any factories paid in the area, and "helping the boys" was the popular thing in 1943. Besides, going away sounded like an attractive adventure. Helen discussed the offer with her family and agreed to go to Knoxville for an interview. An important factor in the family decision was the reputation that Eastman Kodak enjoyed all over

Tennessee. Nearly everyone had some friend who worked for the company and proudly spread the word about its bonuses, workers' participation in benefits, and extremely friendly management. There was never a strike at Tennessee Eastman, never a serious labor conflict, and there was not even a union.

Helen and a school friend cashed the four war bonds they owned — all their savings — and took the bus to Knoxville. There were no available rooms in town, but the company had made arrangements for them in a home in Maryville, where two beds were waiting for them. The next morning a bus came to pick them up and drove them to the employment office, where they spent most of the day filling out applications.

After the formalities, they were put on the old trailer buses to Oak Ridge, which became known as the cattle cars. The name was hardly an exaggeration: standing in the aisles, pressed against one another in the suffocating heat, the smothered passengers had to endure the slow bumpy ride to the gate of Oak Ridge, where guards inspected identifications and examined every piece of luggage with all the zeal of suspicious customs officers. Then one guard jumped on the step of the bus and accompanied it to Jackson Square, where everybody received a series of shots — typhoid, tetanus and diphtheria.

Helen and her friend were assigned a double room in a new dormitory. The room was not bad — two beds, a chest of drawers and a closet, all in bleached wood. Each wing of the dormitory had bathrooms with showers.

Two days later the girls were sent to the main administrative building, "the Castle," for training courses. The first lectures were on security, on patriotism and on the company's policies. Then for two weeks they studied meters and dials drawn on paper. Nothing made any sense to them until they were finally taken to the plants, three miles away, and shown the real cubicles.

The little Tennessee country girl was tremendously impressed by the appearance of the plant; the equipment looked fantastic to her. "Lord, what will I do with all that?" she murmured to another girl.

The instructors took over, showing the manipulation of each knob and correcting the girls' reading of the meters. These supervisors constantly consulted manuals or looked for help from the handful of young scientists around; it was obvious that the supervisors were also just learning their jobs. But no one ever explained to the girls what the function of the control boards was, and no questions were asked. Everyone wore blue coveralls, with a stripe on the sleeves — yellow for the operators, red for the electricians; in the chemical plants, the girls wore white coveralls. Helen made many friends among them, but she never asked them what they were doing — they all knew that any indiscreet question was reported to the security people.

The girls learned the job very fast. Taking readings every hour or half hour became a routine, and when the machines ran smoothly, there was not much to do. The only problem was concentration, especially during the "owl shift" from 11 P.M. to 7 A.M. No smoking was allowed on the job, and no food could be carried into the plant. The girls had one hour for their meal in the crowded cafeteria, which invariably served fried potatoes and grits for breakfast.

The first few weeks away from home seemed very long to the girl from Murphysburg; many a time the mud and the food and the fatigue after a night shift made her think of quitting. But according to the standards of her upbringing, few things in life could be worse than being known as a quitter. She stayed on, and in time she made new friendships, and joined the softball and basketball teams which practiced at the school at night. Then there was the skating rink and numerous little canteens with jukeboxes where she and other young people could have fun jitterbugging. Life in such a big place soon fascinated Helen, and because she became a good cubicle operator, she felt more important than ever before.

Pat Patterson and Helen Hall arrived at the gate of the Y–12 area and showed their blue badges to the guard. A different color of badge was required for each area; the girls never found out where the people with red or green badges went every day, or what they were doing. Surrounded by a high wire fence, the Y–12 plants spread over an area of several square miles. It was an impressive complex: several dozen buildings of varying size, with high-voltage power lines running from them in every direction and an intricate piping system. Some of the buildings were still only half finished, and construction was going on all around. But the most striking thing was this unexpected sight of feverish human activity, thousands and thousands of people and machines and tools — three miles from the town of Oak Ridge, hidden between two peaceful wooded ridges. Inside the huge brick buildings were the calutrons. Each plant contained two sets of calutrons: one set, in the so-called Alpha plants, was arranged in the oval shape of a racetrack; the second set, in the so-called Beta plants, had a rectangular shape.

In these buildings were the largest magnets ever built — monsters weighing from three thousand to over ten thousand tons, and so powerful that hammers and screwdrivers would be jerked out of workers' hands when they came too close; men even felt the pull on the nails of their shoes. Built by Allis-Chalmers, most of these magnets had coils made out of the silver obtained from the United States Treasury Department — between twelve and twenty-one tons of silver in each of the hundreds of coils, which were enclosed and welded into huge rectangular steel cases that looked like fifteen-foot-tall portrait frames.

It took some time for personnel to remember to remove watches and keys before going near the magnetic fields. Hairpins suddenly flew into the air as if by magic, leaving women's hairdos in grotesque shapes. Once the whole operation had to be stopped because a section of heavy pipe was jerked from the hands of a workman and became stuck on the magnet. Three strong men tried, with all their strength, to pull the pipe loose, but it remained glued to the magnet until the current was cut.

Pat and Helen walked with the other girls to the section where the cubicles were located — a long double row of tall control boards facing each other. One girl stood in front of each four boards; supervisors were slowly walking between the rows, ready to act if a problem arose. A scientist was also assigned to every group of operators and supervisors.

It was a crowded floor, but the operators had to stay in front of their cubicles and were not allowed to go to other sections. Judging by the high ceiling and the faraway walls they could see behind the cubicles, the girls knew they were working in a huge plant. But they could not see what was going on beyond their row.

The work of Pat and Helen, like that of all the other operators, consisted of constantly watching the oscillations of the needles of several meters on the control boards in front of them. At first sight the cubicle looked quite complicated, with about twenty dials and a dozen knobs; but after long months of training and always repeating the same readings and movements, they became familiar with it.

The work was not difficult but demanded the fullest attention and patience. The girls were told that the needle should stay within certain limits on the dial. If it didn't, the operator turned some of the knobs slowly until the needle resumed its normal position. She had to try two or three different knobs — or a combination of them. Sometimes the meters did not respond, and the needle refused to come back to normal position. In such a case, the operator would call the supervisor, or would use the telephone, which hung on each board. Technicians would appear immediately, try to correct the oscillation, and phone some incomprehensible messages to somebody in another place. Then everything would work again, and Pat and Helen would never know who repaired what, or where.

They never knew why they were turning those knobs, or what the meters controlled. Neither did any of the several hundred other girls operating the cubicles. They had no idea what sort of plant this was, or what it produced. The supervisors, although they had had some technical training, did not know either, and nobody asked questions. They were all told in no vague terms that their work should never be discussed with anyone. Not with their families, not with any other Oak Ridge employees. Everything they saw and did had to remain an absolute secret.

Over the next two years, the girl operators at Oak Ridge never learned that there were five Alpha plants and four smaller Beta plants at Y–12, with each building containing two "racetracks." (Originally so called because of their shape, the name was retained also for the rectangular ones.) Each Alpha racetrack contained 96 independent separating units, or calutrons, which could be shut down and reactivated separately, and each Beta had 36 calutrons, or separators. Some of the calutrons operated with four ion sources, which meant that four beams were formed simultaneously instead of one; others had only two ion guns. The original calutrons, with which Ernest Lawrence at Berkeley had separated a few grams of U–235, were now reproduced on a much vaster scale at Oak Ridge and were separating several thousand times more fissionable material.

The calutrons were worked almost continuously for a number of days, then they were disconnected in order to remove the receivers, which collected the separated isotopes, and to clean up the equipment. The electric power supplied by TVA was tremendous — enough to serve a large city. The Tennessee Eastman operating crews worked day and night on three shifts. And yet the fruit of this extravagantly expensive operation seemed pitifully unspectacular to the workmen: all that the flat, metallic receiving baskets contained were a few grams of a blackish powder.

The mixture of uranium, graphite and metallic dust was so impure that the precious uranium element had to be extracted by a long and difficult chemical treatment in another building. During each continuous "run," only about 10 percent of the uranium found its way into the two collecting receivers marked U–238 and U–235. The other 90 percent was scattered and deposited on the walls of the apparatus. About every tenth day for the Alpha system, and every third day for the Beta, each calutron had to be dismantled, washed, scrubbed and repaired and the receivers replaced before it could be put to work again.

The few grams in the receiver (and often something went wrong and the envelope was found empty) were by no means pure uranium–235. The best enrichment hoped for at the time was in the vicinity of 20 percent; but usually not more than 13 to 15 percent of the isotope was found in the mixture. After "washing" it chemically, the 15 percent of enriched uranium that had been separated in the Alpha plant was then fed into the smaller Beta calutrons, which would raise the enrichment level.

In the meantime, other chemists would scrape and wash the equipment, trying to recover the 90 percent of uranium that had been lost. Then it was run back through the calutron, which would again waste 90 percent of it. Thus, many of the atoms were being reprocessed hundreds of times before they followed the right beam into the right receiving basket.

This method of collecting U–235, atom by atom, in a receiving pocket did not seem realistic. The so-called "batch" method — reproducing the same operation thousands of times and using thousands of independent apparatus — certainly did not sound like a modern, efficient way to mass-produce enriched uranium. Scores of Ph.D.'s working at Berkeley had earlier produced, with great effort and complicated instruments, only a few grams of enriched uranium. Did this mean that, in order to separate several thousand times more material, men and machinery had to be multiplied by the thousands? It was like solving the problem of manufacturing one million pairs of shoes by putting one million shoemakers to work on one million stools, with one million hammers. There simply had to be a better way!

If there was a better way, however, Lawrence did not know of it. Moreover, he was in too much of a hurry now to stop and experiment. True, the electromagnetic method was not efficient and would be tremendously costly in manpower and money. But farfetched as it sounded, it was the only method so far that had produced enriched uranium, something that one could see and work with. Time was the important factor, not money or effort. And who could guarantee that Hitler's bomb would not be ready first? Lawrence had enough courage and prestige to impose his idea, which, under other circumstances, might have seemed not only extravagant but amateurish.

Through the year 1943 the idea became a reality, brought to the remote Tennessee countryside by the bulldozers of Stone and Webster and by the thousands of engineers and construction workers. The Berkeley dreams of science-fiction magnets materialized into steel and silver and became just another industrial fact, with an Allis-Chalmers label. At the same time Westinghouse and General Electric, with impressive effort and ingenuity, developed and produced unusual bins and transformers, electric generators, high-voltage units and meters that never existed before.

The vision came into being under the code name of Y–12. Twenty-two thousand people were assembled inside the guarded wire fences to try, in complete secrecy, to separate a uranium isotope, according to a never-tried method proposed by Lawrence and his Berkeley colleagues. The first Alpha plant was ready by the end of 1943, and the other buildings were progressing rapidly.

In the beginning, uranium separation on a mass-production scale had seemed hopeless to the Berkeley scientists. The reason: the obvious impossibility of training several thousand scientists for the tedious, precise and vital job of controlling the separation process twenty-four hours a day. Then, with time, the idea was born that perhaps an understanding of the process was not really essential for an operator.

Many scientists were shocked at first by such heresy, but the idea gained more and more adherents. "Our wives all drive automobiles," the argument went. "Do they have to know about the principles of combustion? They've never seen what's under the hood, but they are perfectly able to operate an engine." The idea that a woman would ever be able to operate an electromagnetic isotope separation was a bitter pill to swallow for some scientists. But boards with control knobs, buttons and meters were designed and connected to the calutrons; then tests were made, comparing the results of scientist-operators with those of young girls not familiar with the process. The result of the tests represented a surprising victory for the laymen! The scientists got impatient, it seemed, and were always trying to improve the process by experimenting too much with the knobs and meters.

Tennessee Eastman Corporation, contractor for the operation of the Y-12 plants, organized an extraordinary recruiting and training program for girl operators. It was a particularly difficult time to recruit personnel for a large new organization. The labor market was being raided by many other war projects, and without the priority obtained by the Manhattan District, enough workers could hardly have been found. The figure of needed personnel changed constantly. Early in 1943, Eastman's Dr. Frederick R. Conklin came back from Berkeley with the figure of 4459 persons needed. In July, it grew to 7500, and in August to 13,500, with no indication that it would stop at that level.

As job applicants arrived by the hundreds at the Knoxville and Oak Ridge employment offices, a training program was started for future instructors. It was quite a problem to teach anyone how to operate the still nonexistent cubicles, but wooden models were built, with a few dials and knobs for training purposes. Several of the future instructors were sent to Berkeley to learn at the source. But the technique itself was changing constantly, and the dummies built one day were not good the next. All trainees were pledged to absolute secrecy; the ones sent to Berkeley were told that they were going to Chicago, and only when the train reached Chicago were they told the real destination was the West Coast.

Most of the girls trained as operators were from the area — high school graduates, young housewives or farm girls. None of them had had any technical education or had ever heard of nuclear physics. The electromagnetic process was never explained to them; but even if it had been, they would not have understood one word of it.

For the average operator, the initial training (called vestibule training) lasted for six to eight weeks. Several more months were taken up by on-the-job training. Training in Oak Ridge began in June 1943 in two special buildings after each girl had received her security clearance. Instruction was only on a lecture basis since there was no actual equipment. Some blueprints of the future Y–12 buildings were made available and proved very valuable at this stage. After a week of general lectures, the group was divided according to specialized jobs, the courses being constantly revised as new developments occurred in Berkeley or in the pilot plant in Y–12. The results surpassed all expectations. The country girls showed a remarkable ability to learn a technique which until then had been mastered only by highly educated men.

The experimental Alpha unit was completed in August 1943, and the first Alpha racetrack was scheduled for operation in September. But the giant new machine began to develop bugs; failures of one kind or another were reported almost every day. Many small leaks developed in the vacuum tanks; some welds in the magnets gave way and spilled oil on the floor; there was some leakage and also short circuits in the magnet coils; the stress imposed by the huge magnets caused some vacuum tanks to move several inches out of line. One by one, the failures were corrected, and Alpha seemed to be ready to go.

In the middle of September 1943, Track I in the first Alpha building was turned on, while the Y–12 team was still struggling heroically with all sorts of problems. But before it had run a month, serious short circuits developed in one coil. The track was closed for six weeks to remove the coil and replace it with one from the other unfinished tracks. By December, everything finally seemed in place, every defective part repaired and checked. The moment had come for the first Alpha track to try the electromagnetic method on a big scale.

The slow process of the start-up began. The powerful generators were started up and the magnet turned on. When the operating level was reached, it was time to create the vacuum, which took about eight hours. Only then was the accelerating voltage turned on, at a low level first, with a large amount of sparking from the electrical discharge. As all the equipment was heating, the voltage was gradually raised and the sparking disappeared. This "baking-out" period lasted for another couple of hours, while the pressure meter, telling the vacuum condition in the calutron, was coming back down.

When the pressure went down, the voltage for the arc filament was turned on. Everybody watched tensely as the uranium tetrachloride was heated up gradually and the ion gun started functioning. An arc was formed, small in the beginning, but increasing quickly. Somebody shouted, "The J's are struck!" (In plant jargon, the J was the arc, and striking meant that the beam was reaching the other end.) The process was working! Smiles appeared on the tired faces. At the cubicles, the girls read the dials, and without knowing what was happening in the other parts of the plant, reported to the supervisor, "I'm striking my Y!" (Meaning, "Mine is working!"). The Alpha track was in operation.

But the rejoicing was premature. From the first day, the performance of the machines became steadily more erratic. Some of the arcs straightened and the beams missed the receivers. Other beams could not hold together, and the ionized atoms were scattered in every direction. The curve in the arc was gradually disappearing, and the beam began to weave like a waterhose in the hands of a drunk. Short circuits appeared in the magnets with increasing frequency. Then suddenly, everything stopped. The magnetic field disappeared; no beams came out of the ion guns. The whole system had died.

For days anxious electricians looked for the possible causes of trouble, and worried scientists frantically checked and rechecked every piece of equipment. The engineers tried every imaginable way to restart the operation. Ever alert for possible sabotage, Army security personnel redoubled their effort. But after a thorough search no evidence of sabotage could be discovered. In the meantime, on the floor of the huge silenced plant, hundreds of men and women stood idle, patiently waiting.

Then, little by little, everybody realized what had happened. The Alpha racetrack simply did not work. It was a disaster, and black despair fell over Y-12.

37

AT OAK RIDGE, the electromagnetic plant was in deep trouble. Several days had passed since the start-up failure, yet the Alpha racetrack was still not operating. As soon as the bad news was reported to him, General Groves, greatly displeased, arrived hurriedly from Washington, inspected the magnet and angrily demanded explanations. It was clear that there were some shorts in the magnet coils, but none of the Stone and Webster, Westinghouse or Allis-Chalmers engineers could find anything wrong with their particular part of the magnet network.

Groves ordered one of the heavily welded steel casings of the magnet to be broken open; then the reason for the shorts was found: the cooling oil, while circulating in the coils, was carrying a sediment of rust and dirt. As the oil passed through, iron particles accumulated between the silver bands of the coils and shorted the magnet. In the hurry to get the plant in operation, the impurities had somehow been left in the magnet.

Groves was outraged — and let everyone know it. "Unforgivable!" he said time and again, cutting short all explanations. To him, there was no excuse whatsoever for allowing such slipshod design and manufacture. Why hadn't perfect cleanliness been maintained during manufacture of the magnets? Why didn't the oil-cooling system use filters? Why hadn't the designers placed the coils farther apart? And above all else — why hadn't he, himself, forseen the trouble and taken steps to avoid it? Everybody involved received his share of the general's blame, including Professor Ernest Lawrence for not having said that he once had had similar trouble with a cyclotron.

Before returning to Washington, Groves, still in a very bad mood, issued a curt order: "Send the magnets back to Milwaukee!" They were removed from the Alpha track; the heavy parts were then sent back to Allis-Chalmers to be cleaned and rebuilt. The silver bands were unwound, then rewound with greater spacing between them. A special pickling plant was built at Oak Ridge; every pipe was taken out of the process, passed through the pickling plant to eliminate every speck of rust, then reassembled. Special oil filters were added to the system.

The repair work lasted several weeks, and meanwhile attention was switched to Track II. Waiting for the magnets to be returned by the manufacturer, thousands of Alpha One operators, on all three shifts, continued to report regularly for work, and keeping them busy had become a major problem. Lectures, conferences and games were organized around the clock. Tennessee Eastman men raided the entire state for checkers, dominoes and chess sets. Every available movie was commandeered for the entertainment of the personnel, so that they would not leave their jobs out of sheer boredom.

The morale at the Y–12 plant had sunk to its lowest point. There was doubt in the minds of many scientists and engineers: Would the method *ever* work? But daily contact with Ernest Lawrence, who had flown in from Berkeley, was the best cure for doubt — the tall, energetic professor was as enthusiastic and as sure as ever, and his contagious optimism soon swept through the plant.

At the same time, the construction of the other Alpha and the Beta plants was progressing with great speed, and the aspect of the entire area was changing every day. After the start-up failure, Stone and Webster's manager at Oak Ridge had been sent to another job, and an outsider, Frank C. Creedon, had been appointed in his place, due to the urging of Groves. Most Stone and Webster people felt that the choice of the new manager had been forced on them, but, anxious to remain on good terms with the head of the Manhattan Project, they accepted his recommendation. Creedon, a hard-driving civil engineer who had done construction work with the general in the past, proved to be a very efficient, if sometimes tough, manager, rigorously observing all deadlines. However, as calutron equipment was retested in every plant, breakdowns continued to occur. Electrical failures were frequent, leaving the night shifts in complete darkness and resulting in the creation of a whole folklore of juicy stories and jokes about experiences of the young female personnel in the dark. Insulators cracked under high voltage, chemical tanks became corroded; once a vacuum area was even spoiled by a dead mouse.

During this period, Lawrence and his team of physicists were more or less taking it for granted that, if the arc succeeded in separating the enriched uranium into a distinct receiver, recovery of it would be a relatively minor chemical problem. At the Berkeley lab, chemists had seemed to be successful with the recovery of enriched uranium. They had no way of telling, however, how much enriched uranium had been wasted by admixture with impurities in the receiving pocket.

The recovery from the steel-and-graphite receivers did not at first seem to present problems at Oak Ridge. Then newly perfected instruments detected an alarming fact: after washing out the graphite and other impurities, only fractions of the enriched uranium were recovered. A large proportion of the precious material whose production had resulted only from the most painstaking effort, remained unaccounted for. Then, finally, the explanation became evident: the big calutrons projected the uranium beam against the walls of the receiver with such energy that the atoms buried themselves in the stainless steel and thus remained embedded. There seemed to be no way of recovering them.

The new problem could not have been predicted at Berkeley, where the machine's power was not nearly as great. Now, however, the whole project was again endangered. What was the point of building a good strong separator if the separated material could not be recovered afterward? Consternation struck the Y–12 team. All eyes turned toward the chemists for a solution. Many techniques were tried, but the stainless steel still refused to release the embedded uranium atoms.

At the Y–12 plant there was a professor from the College of the Pacific, a chemist who had come with the Berkeley group to join the Tennessee Eastman forces. Dr. Clarence Larson, a blue-eyed Minnesotan in his early thirties, knew Ernest Lawrence well and had worked in the past with radio isotopes from Berkeley's cyclotron. One day, after weeks of struggling with the problem, he came up with a new idea and approached Lawrence about it. "Look, if we can't recover the uranium from stainless-steel receivers, why don't we try to copper-plate the receivers? The atoms will be buried in the layer of plating, but it will be relatively easy to recover them from copper."

Lawrence had always had the gift of recognizing a good idea — and selecting the most workable one — from among hundreds. He was enthusiastic about Larson's suggestion: "That's it! Let's do it — right away! How long will it take you to plate the receivers?"

Larson thought a moment. Plating on stainless steel was a difficult job. "A couple of weeks," he said finally.

"Good," said Lawrence, "but we can't wait that long. Take everything and everybody you need from the plants, and make some receivers by tomorrow!"

There was no use arguing with Lawrence; he would not take no for an answer. Since there was no possibility of ordering the copper-plating from a specialized plant, Larson and his colleagues ripped sinks out of the buildings, requisitioned four generators, borrowed some tools and worked throughout the night and most of the next day. But they met Lawrence's deadline, and the homemade, copper-plated receivers, when installed in the operation, worked beautifully. The plating could be dissolved in a chemical solution, and all the uranium recovered. While the copper-plating process was being organized on a larger and more efficient scale, Larson and his team collapsed in bed, utterly exhausted and still thinking that Lawrence could not have been serious in asking that the job be done in one day.

The breakthrough achieved by Larson's team heartened all the scientists and engineers working in the Y–12 plant. They thought that, with a few grams already separated, the production of kilograms of enriched uranium would merely become a matter of time, money and effort. It was going to be a very difficult and expensive way, of course; but it was a sure way.

One of the characteristics of electromagnetic separation was that each unit operated independently. In case of trouble in any unit, it could be removed without stopping the whole process. The development of the Beta tracks enormously increased the chances of success. These were smaller but more sensitive calutrons perfected by Robert Thornton of Berkeley, who was now in charge of them at Oak Ridge, as a temporary employee of Tennessee Eastman. The Alpha track took the natural uranium and enriched it up to 15 or 20 percent. Then the enriched material was fed to Beta, the second stage, in which the enrichment was brought to a much higher degree, almost high enough for bomb purposes.

Alpha and Beta, however, shared the same inefficiencies. They operated by means of a great number of small units, which could concentrate only a few grams of enriched uranium at a time; then the units had to be dismantled, cleaned and reassembled after a run of a few days (three days for Beta, longer periods for Alpha). There was thus a need for an army of operating personnel and for an exorbitant amount of power; moreover, 90 percent of the uranium was scattered all over the equipment during the process.

This problem became particularly serious at Beta; since the feed material was already enriched, any loss amounted to a small disaster. The chemists, asked to recover the uranium that had been scattered all over the walls of the equipment, faced a real problem, even graver than the recovery of the material from the receiving pockets. The stainless-steel walls of the tubes were being washed carefully with nitric acid every third day, but the deposit containing the precious enriched uranium also included a high amount of impurities, mostly steel particles. Under the circumstances, recovery of the uranium looked like an impossibility. Several different solutions were proposed, and groups of chemists started working around the clock on three competing processes. The chemical operation of Y–12 became a gigantic operation involving between five and ten thousand people, independent of the track operators.

The method that Clarence Larson was working on was based on a very unique property of uranium: its precipitation by hydrogen peroxide —

the ordinary peroxide sold in drugstores. Since other elements are not precipitated by hydrogen peroxide, this offered a good way to separate the uranium. But when Larson tried it, it did not work. Peroxide had one great disadvantage: it decomposed in the presence of iron. Before Larson even had time to congratulate himself on his successful precipitation of uranium, the peroxide had decomposed all over the room, creating one more cleaning problem. The chemists were plunged into gloom. The entire Beta separation was worthless if 90 percent of the ultraprecious material was going to be lost on the walls. The problem had become even more serious than that of uranium recovery from the receivers.

In Larson's mind, however, the decomposition of peroxide rang a bell. He remembered a similar decomposition in body fluids, plant proteins and other biological materials from the years when he had experimented as a biochemist. He recalled that simply by keeping the materials cold, decomposition had been prevented. The materials were hardly similar; but Larson tried precipitating uranium in double-walled vessels where he had installed a cooling system. This time no decomposition occurred. The uranium was successfully separated from impurities. Once recovered, it could thus be reintroduced later into the Beta system.

38

GRACE GROVES smiled when she found Gwen's message on the hall table: *Dear Mother: I will be at Kate's. Turned on the oven to 300 at 4 p.m. Got an A on the French test. Gwen.*

For months the Groves family had been communicating by message. The general, when in Washington, was in the habit of leaving the yellow brick house in the Cleveland Park district at seven o'clock each morning and did not get back till late at night. But most of the time he was out of town. For years the family had been trained never to ask questions about the general's work, and during the war his wife usually did not know whether he would be at home the next day. She almost never accepted invitations for him.

Grace Groves had taken a part-time job at Garfinckel's suburban store. With thirteen-year-old Gwen in school most of the day, and their only son Dick away at West Point, the narrow, three-story house at 3508 Thirty-sixth Street was empty most of the day and Mrs. Groves was glad to have a job to occupy her time. In addition she occasionally worked for charity organizations or as a chaperone at dances for young officers.

Her messages were by far the most amusing in the family and she always added a funny cartoon, showing her teen-age daughter in some comical situation. The general — "Deeno" to the family — also tried at times to compete as a cartoonist, but his drawings were totally lacking in resemblance and proportion.

The door opened noisily and Gwen, dark-haired and tall for her age, rushed in. Dressed in a purple Cathedral School blazer, she was carrying a pile of books and the huge brown purse in which she kept her first lipstick and a glamorous photo of her brother in his plebe uniform, which made all her friends very envious.

"Hi, Mother! Aren't you supposed to be giving that boy his piano lesson now? How can he ever learn?"

"No, his lesson is tomorrow. Call Mrs. O'Leary, dear — Deeno wants to play tennis with you."

"Oh, not today! Kitty and I wanted to go and see the new Fred Astaire movie."

"You'd better do what Deeno wants, Gwen. Tennis, after all, is his only diversion, and he needs it."

As a matter of fact, the young girl was delighted. Behind the façade of gentle teasing going on constantly between father and daughter, they had great affection for each other. There were few things Gwen enjoyed more than the evenings her father allowed her to visit him at his office before a game of tennis. Often they would dine together in some restaurant in the vicinity of the War Department.

"Mother, why does Deeno have to work all the time?"

"I suppose he's doing something important."

"I bet he doesn't do anything at all!" Gwen, of course, did not believe a word of what she was saying, but that was one of the ways she teased her father. But neither his wife nor his daughter had the slightest idea about the general's work, and he tolerated no questions. They never bothered to ask him.

Gwen Groves was always very impressed by the security measures and formalities at the entrance of the new War Department Building,* at Twenty-first Street and Virginia Avenue, where her father worked in Washington. In the high-ceilinged, dark hall each visitor had to fill in a form — "Name of Visitor, Purpose of Visit" — and then sit down on the bench by the front door. The wait was usually very long, but the young girl was fascinated by the people coming in and out, dutifully showing their credentials to the guards.

The general finally appeared, very busy and surrounded by other Army officers and serious-looking civilians carrying briefcases. When he caught sight of his daughter, he smiled, said good-bye to the others, and went to the basement to get the car, a green Dodge that he drove himself. After driving to the Army-Navy Country Club, father and daughter were on the tennis courts within a matter of minutes.

Despite his weight, the general was surprisingly agile once he got a racket in his hand. He was a sure, strong player, and he enjoyed every minute of the game. After one set, his teen-age daughter was exhausted, but Groves himself was as fresh as ever.

"Come on now — move your big feet!" he scolded her, dropping a short shot just over the net. When she missed getting her racket on it, he grinned delightedly. "Where were you?"

Gwen couldn't finish the second set; she was completely out of breath, while her overweight, strategy-minded father seemed tireless as he played his usual fiercely competitive game, attacking, running, chopping and

---

* Now the State Department Building.

cutting. He constantly criticized her for not trying hard enough, but in spite of his good-natured scolding, Groves was very pleased with her game. "Not bad! Some day you'll learn," he teased her as he went off to shower and change.

When Groves reappeared, father and daughter returned to the office, as they sometimes did. Often they would pick up his secretary, Jean O'Leary, and take her out for a hurried dinner. By this time Mrs. O'Leary had become the general's office executive and almost invariably her hard-working days stretched into the evening. For even when he was going home, Groves did not leave before seven or eight o'clock. Her only respite came when he was out of town. He had quickly discovered that Jean O'Leary combined qualities of intelligence and efficiency to an unusual degree. She was a devoted but independent-minded secretary who consistently displayed exceptional initiative, intuition and good judgment. The general was not in the habit of complimenting his subordinates; but in Jean O'Leary's case, he elevated her far above the position of a mere secretary; she became his *de facto* chief of staff.

"Where do you want to go?" Groves asked them.

"Any place but the Allies Inn," said Gwen. "We always go there. Let's go to Fan and Bill's."

"That's a nightclub," said Mrs. O'Leary. "It's not for young girls."

"Oh, Deeno, please!"

They ended up at their usual eating place, a cafeteria, the Allies Inn, where the food was good and they could eat quickly. After a few mysterious phrases exchanged between the general and Mrs. O'Leary ("Mr. You-Know-Who telephoned, General," and "After dinner don't forget to call You-Know-Whom"), the conversation returned to Gwen's level. The dinner finished with the general's downing an extra portion of dessert, while lecturing his secretary about smoking with her coffee. But as usual, Jean O'Leary enjoyed her cigarette to the last puff, though appearing to listen attentively to his sermon.

After dinner they went back to the office. Even though she was with her father, Gwen still had to go through the procedure of signing the book in the lobby — name, nationality, address; then the guard gave her a numbered badge to pin on her lapel.

"What if a spy got in here, Deeno?" she asked as they passed another uniformed guard, who saluted smartly. "I mean, what if somebody had a duplicate key to your office?"

"Nobody would get in here who didn't belong," her father replied seriously. "And even if somebody did, this building is so well wired and watched that the alarm would be heard all the way to San Francisco."

The general unlocked a door and after they entered the office he locked it carefully from the inside. The head of the Manhattan Project occupied only two rooms, 5120 and 5121, on the fifth floor of the War Department.* They were very simply furnished — a green carpet, two big desks, an oak conference table and a leather sofa. Two heavy safes were the only pieces of furniture which General Groves himself had added after taking over his post in September 1942. Always mindful of security, he had ordered one outside door and another door leading to a conference room locked and bolted, and the ventilating louvers sealed. The general shared the inner office with Jean O'Leary, while the outer room — the only access to his office left open — was occupied by the gray steel desks of three assistant secretaries and several more safes and locked file cases.

Gwen remained in the outer office, studying her homework and feeling very important among the telephones and typewriters, the IN and OUT trays, the rack with rubber stamps marked SECRET, CONFIDENTIAL, TOP SECRET. But there was not a single paper to be seen — they were all locked up. The general and Mrs. O'Leary resumed work in the next room.

"Gwen, do you want a piece of candy now?" the general called out through the open door. He unlocked the safe and handed out the boxes of chocolates and caramels lying among the top-secret files.

"Aren't there any peppermints left?" Gwen asked mischievously.

Mrs. O'Leary grinned. Winking at Gwen, she said, "The general finished those up last night."

"Out, out!" shouted the general, half delighted, half embarrassed. He was quite sensitive about the family joke accusing him of eating too many sweets on the sly and not observing the strict diet that his wife tried in vain to make him follow.

The general worked late that night. Then, with the security officer who had to stay until every safe had been locked, they dropped Jean O'Leary off at her car, and Groves drove his daughter home. The head of the Manhattan Project stretched out on his bed and started correcting Gwen's algebra homework, eating fruit from a big bowl, while his daughter watched him intently, waiting for his usual reproaches about sloppiness and lack of concentration.

"Do you think my hair looks better when it's up on the sides?" Gwen asked.

Groves paid no attention. Concentrating hard on the algebra, he was

---

* For the first year, these two rooms comprised the entire office space of the Manhattan Project. Late in 1943, however, five more rooms were allocated to the Project to accommodate Groves's assistants and his intelligence section. But true to his dislike for large staffs, he never let his offices grow to the proportions of the huge and vitally important project he directed.

WESTFIELD MEMORIAL LIBRARY
WESTFIELD, N. J.

almost disappointed not to find any mistakes. Finally he handed her homework back. "It's OK. Not bad," was his only comment. His eyes were growing weary and his voice faded a bit behind his tired smile.

"Good night, Deeno," Gwen said, "and thank you for checking my algebra."

"You're not at all welcome," her father said, with mock gruffness. "And hey! Don't swipe any of my grapes on your way to bed!"

39

GENERAL GROVES read every word of the long confidential document marked *Transcript of Interview with Dr. Oppenheimer by Lieutenant Colonel Lansdale, September 12, 1943.* Although he had a high opinion of his chief intelligence officer, Groves never relied entirely on the conclusions of the security officers. He made it a point to demand the full text concerning every important investigation.

This time the case was particularly crucial because the future of the entire Los Alamos project was at stake. Groves had to act swiftly, but before making any decision, he wanted to see Oppenheimer again and have a frank discussion with him. The last time they had talked, the general had not succeeded; the Los Alamos director had not exactly refused to give the information Groves wanted, but he had said, "General, I can't tell you who the man is. If you order me, I'll tell you, but you have to give me the order."

"No, I am not going to order you," Groves had answered. At that time, he did not think that he should pull rank; but now all other ways of getting the valuable information seemed to have been exhausted. Even the tactful approach of Lieutenant Colonel John Lansdale, Jr., a shrewd, thirty-one-year-old lawyer from Cleveland who served as head of the Project's security service, had come to nothing. Oppenheimer steadfastly refused to divulge the name of the mysterious academic figure who had been used as an intermediary by Soviet agents.

Oppenheimer's intransigent attitude was certainly not enhancing his reputation in the eyes of the Counter-Intelligence Service. He had received his security clearance, in the first place, only by special order from General Groves. But the security service of the Manhattan Project had continued a thorough investigation of the director of the Los Alamos laboratory. They kept him under surveillance whenever he left the Hill; they opened his mail; they listened to some of his telephone conversations. The entire security organization remained suspicious of him.

The latest reports received by Groves made Oppenheimer's security file appear even worse. A memorandum of June 29, 1943, signed by Lieutenant Colonel Boris T. Pash, chief of the Counter-Intelligence branch in

San Francisco, began with this statement: "Information available to this office indicates that subject may still be connected with the Communist Party. Results of surveillances conducted on subject, upon arrival in San Francisco on June 12, 1943, indicate further possible Communist Party connections. Subject met and is alleged to have spent considerable time with one Jean Tatlock, the record of whom is attached."

This was serious. Jean Tatlock, the daughter of an English professor, had been very close to Oppenheimer between 1936 and 1939 — they had even considered marriage. She was a member of the Communist Party and moved in a coterie of fellow travelers. After 1939, however, Oppenheimer saw her very rarely.

On the particular trip that Oppenheimer made on June 12, 1943, from Los Alamos to San Francisco, he had called her up and then visited her at her home on Telegraph Hill. A few hours later the security service received the alarming report sent out by the agents who had followed him: the head of the most secret laboratory in the whole Manhattan Project had spent several hours with a known Communist.

In the summer of 1943, Lieutenant Colonel Lansdale went to Los Alamos to talk with Oppenheimer about some scientists recruited from the West Coast whose appointment to the Los Alamos project was opposed by the security service. A group in a nearby industrial laboratory in California was suspected of collaborating with Soviet agents. Oppenheimer, very cooperative, emphasized his belief that no member of the Communist Party should be admitted to the Project. Loyalty to the party was, he said, "incompatible with loyalty to the Project."

Shortly after this conversation with Lansdale, during a visit to Berkeley on August 25, 1943, Oppenheimer went to see Lieutenant Lyle Johnson, the security officer at the Radiation Laboratory. The information unexpectedly volunteered by the Los Alamos director was extremely valuable. He said that ever since Colonel Lansdale had told him about Soviet espionage activities at Berkeley, he had been worrying about the situation. When he learned that some trouble was being caused by the Federation of Architects, Engineers, Chemists and Technicians (FAECT), which wanted to unionize the Radiation Laboratory, he remembered that Dr. George C. Eltenton, a Communist sympathizer, had been active in FAECT. He also had other reasons to suspect Eltenton of pro-Soviet activities but had so far preferred not to talk about them. Now, having changed his mind, he strongly advised the security services to put Eltenton under surveillance.

An interview was arranged the next day between the scientist and Lieutenant Johnson's superior, Lieutenant Colonel Boris Pash. Oppenheimer revealed then that Eltenton had attempted to approach, through an intermediary, three members of the Berkeley Project on behalf of a Soviet consular attaché. Eltenton's intermediary asked the three scientists whether it would not be a good idea to give some information about the United States atomic project to the Russians, who, after all, were allies of America but were prevented from access to atomic knowledge by a group of overzealous, anti-Soviet fanatics in the State Department.

When Lieutenant Colonel Pash asked who the intermediary was, Oppenheimer refused to answer. He said it would be unethical to reveal the man's identity; it would merely disturb some of his associates who were in no way guilty.

Several times afterwards, Lansdale, and then Groves, tried to learn the name of the mysterious Professor X, who had transmitted Eltenton's proposals to the three still-unidentified scientists. Oppenheimer, however, obstinately continued to keep his secret.

The transcript General Groves was reading now had been taken from the recording of Lansdale's interview with Oppenheimer in Groves's office in Washington. For several hours the colonel had tried to persuade the physicist to give him the name of Eltenton's intermediary. He talked about the Soviet Union's efforts to penetrate the secrecy surrounding the Manhattan Project.

"They know — we know they know — about Tennessee, about Los Alamos and Chicago," Lansdale said. "We know they know that the, uh, spectrographic method — I may state it wrong — is being used at Berkeley. They know that you would be in a position to start practical production in about six months from, say, February and that perhaps six months thereafter you would be in a position to go into mass production.

"It is essential that we know the channels of communication," pleaded Lansdale. "I think we know now who the man was that you referred to. I wonder if you feel that you're in a position to tell me?"

But Oppenheimer remained adamant. "I think it would be wrong," he said. "This came to me in confidence, and the actions of this intermediary were reported as essentially negative."

"You stated that he contacted, I believe it was three persons on the project," Lansdale said, "and they told him to go to hell in substance. How do you know that he hasn't contacted others?"

"I don't. I can't know that. It would seem obvious that he would have."

"Now you can see, therefore, from our point of view the importance of knowing what their channel is."

"Yes."

"Is this man a friend of yours by any chance?"

"He's an acquaintance of mine I've known over many years."

"Well, there are acquaintances and there are friends. Do you hesitate for fear of implicating a friend?"

"I hesitate to mention any more names," Oppenheimer replied, "because of the fact that the other names I have do not seem to be people who were guilty of anything or people who I would like to get mixed up in it. They are not people who are going to get tied up in it in any other way."

Colonel Lansdale was discouraged. "Now, here is an actual attempt of espionage against probably the most important thing we're doing. You tell us about it three months later," he grumbled.

Oppenheimer did not change his position. "The reason I mentioned Eltenton's name," he said, "was because I thought it was likely that Eltenton would persevere in this. But the reason I mention no other names is that I have not felt that those people would. They were all just accidental."

Lansdale tried to compromise. "While I would like to have those names very much, it's not as essential as our knowing the contact. Because there are other channels we know of. We've got no way of knowing whether the names that I know of are identical with this man. Now, that's a simple reason why I want that name, and I want to ask you point-blank if you'll give it to me. If you won't, well OK, no hard feelings!"

"No," answered Oppenheimer. "I've thought about it a good deal because Pash and Groves both asked me for the name and I feel that I should not give it."

"I don't see how you can have any hesitancy in disclosing the name of the man who has actually been engaged in an attempt at espionage for a foreign power in time of war. I mean, my mind just doesn't run along those channels."

Oppenheimer assured the colonel that he not only understood his point of view perfectly well, but that he also hoped "devoutly" that if, by some improbable chance, this man was still operating, Lansdale's organization would find him. But he confessed a "very strong feeling" on his part that he ought not give the name himself.

"What I want to say is this," Oppenheimer said. "I'm not kidding you and I'm not trying to weasel out. It's my overwhelming judgment that this guy isn't involved. That isn't judgment which is based on hope but on his character. If I'm wrong, then I am making a very serious mistake, but I think that the chances are very, very small."

Lansdale tried every possible approach, but to no avail. "Now, are these three people to your knowledge members of the party or have they been?"

"No — no!"

"Why did they come to you?"

"I suppose for two reasons: first, because I was more or less responsible for the work, and second, because they thought I wouldn't hit the roof over it. I might say I did."

"You probably have administratively the best running outfit in the Project," said the colonel with a certain amount of admiration. "And that's largely because of the intense personal loyalty which you seem to be able to inculcate in the people that work for you. I can see one of the reasons for it — they stick by you and you stick by them, which after all is the secret of obtaining people's loyalty."

At the end of the interview, the two men parted amicably, but Lansdale knew that he could not report that his mission had been a success.

After finishing the transcript, Groves reread one passage that seemed to sum up his own dilemma. "Try to put yourself in our position," the exasperated Lansdale had said during the conversation. "We've got the case of Dr. J. R. Oppenheimer, whose wife was at one time a member of the party anyway; who himself knows many prominent Communists, associates with them; who belonged to a large number of so-called front organizations at one time and may perhaps have contributed financially to the party himself; who becomes aware of an espionage attempt by the party six months ago and doesn't mention it; and who still won't make a complete disclosure. I've made up my mind that you yourself are OK, or otherwise I wouldn't be talking to you like this, see? Now, what are we to do in a case like that?"

Yes, Groves wondered, what should he, as head of the nation's most important military project, decide in such a case?

WESTFIELD MEMORIAL LIBRARY.
WESTFIELD, N. J.

40

THE SLENDER FIGURE wearing a checked shirt, and usually trailed by a group of attentive disciples, had become a familiar sight in the corridors of the Los Alamos laboratory. Robert Oppenheimer could also be seen early each morning leaving his home at 1967 Peach Street and walking to his office on the other side of Ashley Pond. He usually wore the same wide-brimmed hat which exaggerated the thinness of his face. From time to time he would escort his young son Peter to nursery school before going to his 8 A.M. job.

For Robert and Kitty Oppenheimer, life at Los Alamos was happy, in spite of the tremendous pressure of his job. Their home was simple but pleasant, one of the original Ranch School stone houses on "Bathtub Row" — so called with some envy by other scientists who were not so well housed. Oppenheimer loved the pure crisp air of the Los Alamos mornings, when the fragrance of pine trees and mountain flowers drifted in on the wind from the Pajarito Plateau. When he could spare a weekend, he and his wife enjoyed going on horseback over the Sangre de Cristo Range and into Pecos Valley, camping overnight and, for protection's sake, accompanied by a GI on horseback. For a man of delicate health, Oppenheimer's endurance was surprising. But in everything he undertook, including riding over precarious trails, this fragile-looking intellectual always gave the impression of knowing very well what he was doing, and just how to do it.

His office was on the second floor of a two-story frame structure of the type seen on any Army base of that period. Everything about it was utilitarian except for a beautiful view over the pond and lodge, and reaching far out to the mountain ranges. There was a desk at one end of the room and a long table at the other, with blackboards all along the wall. The moment he got to his office, Oppenheimer would start to read progress reports, dictate to his secretary, Priscilla Greene, and receive the visits of colleagues. He paced the room while he talked, smoking constantly and coughing frequently. He expressed himself well but spoke slowly, thinking out what he wanted to say first and phrasing it in eloquent, often rather literary language.

He had the reputation of being a hard worker, often returning to his office after dinner and working on Sundays. There was never any question about who was boss of the laboratory. In his informal and considerate way, the friendly, thirty-eight-year-old Oppenheimer had quickly established his authority over his colleagues, many of whom were older. There was no trace of the dictator in his leadership. He seldom raised his voice, rarely reprimanded a subordinate. He was "one of them" — the fellow worker who was called "Oppie" and who used persuasion, rather than the director, Dr. Oppenheimer, who gave orders. But behind his courteous air, it was not hard to sense a potential for impatience and anger — and people were careful not to arouse it. His delicate physical appearance concealed a steely character, one that possessed that high degree of self-assurance which makes most born leaders always *sure* that they know better than other people. Extremely sensitive and emotional yet controlled, he evoked the image of a dramatic hero.

True or false, the heroic image fascinated people and created a special aura around his personality. Of all the atomic scientists, Oppenheimer became the most intriguing, the most adulated. His former students imitated him. Junior scientists admired him fervently, and young secretaries blushed in his presence.

From the beginning a good relationship existed between Oppenheimer and Groves. The general followed the progress at Los Alamos closely and visited often. Though he reserved the right to make final decisions on all important matters, he left the actual running of the laboratory entirely to Oppenheimer. He also made a point of contacting the scientists, when this became necessary, only through the director, and he never discussed their individual problems except in Oppenheimer's presence.

Intelligence reports about the head of the Los Alamos laboratory, however, were disturbing indeed. In the Eltenton case, the scientist's behavior had been peculiar, and his account about the three professors, who had been contacted through X, a mysterious intermediary, contained several inconsistencies. Nevertheless, Groves continued to trust him and he never questioned his loyalty. The general's conclusion was that Oppenheimer was trying to protect somebody who was very dear to him.

Groves was not at all surprised by this; on the contrary, he expected a man like Oppenheimer to act that way. ("The typical attitude of the American schoolboy is that there is something wicked about telling on a friend," Groves wryly told an aide.) By then, Groves, Colonel Lansdale and Colonel Pash knew that, in telling some of the details, Oppenheimer had contradicted himself. Some of the security officers saw in these contradictions certain proof of the scientist's guilt.

Groves, however, was primarily interested in finding out why a man of superior intelligence, whom he considered a loyal American, would ever get himself involved in such a "cock-and-bull story." A thought had crossed his mind: Had the approach been made through Oppenheimer's own brother Frank, a onetime Communist? Naturally, he would try to protect him. The general did not consider such an attitude as necessarily wrong — quite the contrary. But the moral aspect was not material in this case. The important thing was to block a potential channel for the transmitting of vital, highly secret information to the Soviet Union. After reading Colonel Lansdale's report of his interview with Oppenheimer, it was clear to Groves that the scientist would not reveal the identity of X to any intelligence officer. On his next visit to Los Alamos, Groves decided to try, for a last time, to find out the name himself.

Thus, two months after their first discussion of the Eltenton case, Groves asked Oppenheimer point-blank who the intermediary had been. "If you don't tell me, I'm going to have to order you to do it," he added.

This time Oppenheimer spoke. One evening in the winter of 1942–1943, when the Oppenheimers were still living in Berkeley, a friend, Haakon Chevalier, had come to their home. Chevalier, a Frenchman, was teaching at the university, and both he and his wife had become close friends of the Oppenheimers. When the scientist went out to fix the drinks, Chevalier followed him into the pantry. "I saw George Eltenton recently," he said casually. Then he revealed that Eltenton had said he had means of getting technical information to Soviet scientists. Oppenheimer told Groves that he had been shocked and had said something like, "But that's treason!" or, "This is a terrible thing to do!" and that Chevalier had agreed completely. That was all — Chevalier had never talked about it afterwards.

The reason Oppenheimer had first mentioned the matter at all had long been evident to Groves: Oppenheimer had wanted to warn Groves about Eltenton without, however, involving his friend Chevalier. The French professor was completely innocent, Oppenheimer insisted; but, with a long record of leftist associations in the past already, he could have been put in a very vulnerable situation. Haakon Chevalier had been very active in left-wing teachers' unions and such causes as Spanish Relief. In fact, Oppenheimer had met him for the first time when Chevalier was presiding at a meeting for Spanish Relief.

Only a few minutes after Oppenheimer revealed the name of the intermediary, confidential telegrams were sent between the offices of Groves, Nichols, Lansdale and Pash. Chevalier was put under strict surveillance, and serious pressure was brought to bear on General Groves by the security service and the FBI to remove Oppenheimer from his post as director at Los Alamos. (Colonel Lansdale, disobeying Groves's desires,* had informed the FBI of the general's suspicions that Oppenheimer was protecting his brother.)

How could a man who had committed at least two serious breaches of security — in the cases of Jean Tatlock and Haakon Chevalier — be allowed to continue as head of the most sensitive of all war projects? Should a man with associations that made him potentially vulnerable, through his family and his friends, be entrusted with the highest secrets of the country? General Groves was faced with the decision.

Both alternatives involved risks. If he relieved Oppenheimer, there would probably be a slowing-down of the Project. If he was retained, there might be a grave breakdown of the entire security system. In assuming the tremendous responsibility of this choice, Groves had no Congress to share the burden, no public opinion to dispute or commend him. He was responsible only to the Military Policy Committee: Bush, Conant, General Styer and Admiral Purnell. By now, their role was greatly reduced, but they still had the responsibility of ensuring that Groves was proceeding along proper lines. At any moment they had the power to recommend to Secretary Stimson that the head of the Manhattan Project be fired.

Things were usually clear in the general's mind, and he did not allow sentiment or the desire for popular approval to color his opinions. In his eyes the important thing in each situation was to establish a precise goal, then act accordingly. For the former West Pointer, the Los Alamos predicament was not particularly difficult — the goal was simple and obvious: to make the bomb as fast as possible. In this task he considered Oppenheimer as essential and difficult to replace. He worked well with the scientist and saw him at least once a month; sometimes they talked on the phone four or five times a day. He had never had to push him. In fact, Oppenheimer worked harder than the general wanted him to. Groves had seen his health record and was constantly worried that the professor might break down under the strain of his heavy work load.

Groves, relying on his judgment of people, had no suspicions about Oppenheimer's own loyalty. Yet even if he were wrong (a possibility the general considered purely theoretical), he felt that an important figure like Oppenheimer would become potentially more harmful if he were dismissed from the Project and became embittered. In any event, by that time the scientist knew a tremendous amount of details about Manhattan Project.

Groves could never understand or approve many of the young physi-

---

* At this time Lansdale was not under Groves's command, but under the War Department's military intelligence (G–2) under Major General George V. Strong.

cist's ideals and actions. But that was another story. In this particular case, in December of 1943, the question was whether Dr. Oppenheimer should remain as head of the bomb laboratory.

Without much hesitation the general made his decision. "Dr. Oppenheimer stays," he announced flatly to his security people.

41

General Groves was elated to hear of the promising barrier that had been developed by Clarence Johnson at Kellex. At the same time, he realized that the new development called for an immediate and irrevocable decision that he alone could make. Once again, suddenly, he found himself the arbiter in an acute, impassioned conflict. This time, it was between two perfectly logical, but diametrically opposed, viewpoints held by two men of equally outstanding achievement.

Because of the self-assurance and finality with which he habitually formulated his decisions (even in matters well outside his experience), Groves had gained the reputation of being an autocrat who believed his own opinion superior to that of anyone else. Actually, this was a false impression, although the general's customarily overbearing attitude did nothing to belie it. He was even rather pleased with his public image, knowing the psychological value of a formidable reputation.

But the truth was different — one of Leslie Groves's greatest talents was an ability to listen to different opinions, then choose the best one. He was not handicapped, like most scientists, by the difficulty of defining such words as "better" and "best" in a complicated situation. To him, better meant any faster way toward building the bomb; best meant the *fastest* way — it was that clear and simple.

The paradox was that in problems he was not equipped to understand himself, this man, supposed to be lacking in human understanding, always relied on his judgment of men. Between several possible solutions he would pick the one proposed by the person he trusted the most. But once his choice had been made, after careful examination of all the arguments, General Groves invariably announced the verdict as his own decision. He did so resolutely and in an almost authoritarian manner, with a minimum of explanation and certainly without hesitation or apology. If he ever experienced the pangs of confusion and incertitude, the general never showed it. West Point had taught him that the worst crime for a leader was to appear indecisive.

The barrier decision was perhaps the most difficult one he had ever had to make. On one side was the newly invented Johnson-Kellex barrier, combining some of the contributions made by Norris, Adler, Nix and Groff. So far, it looked superior to the material that would be manufactured at the Houdaille-Hershey plant in Decatur. Dobie Keith was passionately advocating adoption of the Johnson barrier even if it should mean abandoning the old barrier, which he contemptuously called the "lace curtain." All efforts, he pleaded, should be concentrated immediately on the new Johnson barrier, because the lace curtain would never work. It was too fragile; it was difficult to weld — the material burned or disintegrated under welding conditions; and its separation characteristics were not uniform. To prove his point, Keith would take a piece of lace curtain and crack it across his desk. Even the Columbia scientists were discouraged by this time and admitted their product was inadequate for the job.

But the opposite viewpoint — that held by the Norris-Adler supporters — also had some formidable arguments in its favor. These were voiced by Harold Urey, scientific head of the entire program, and with no less fervor than Dobie Keith's defense of the Johnson barrier. Although he admitted that the Johnson barrier did look better than the Norris-Adler, Urey nevertheless insisted there was no time to switch from the old to the new model. It was much too late, he said, if the deadline for the K–25 plant at Oak Ridge was to be met.

Houdaille-Hershey was already building a production plant geared to the Norris-Adler barrier. Urey admitted that it was not yet satisfactory, but at least it was there waiting to be produced, and there was still hope of perfecting it. There was no assurance that the new Johnson model would be acceptable when it entered the production stage. What if, at that point, it failed to work? The program would be without any barrier at all — and just when the K–25 plant would have to start production. There was only a short time remaining before the deadline. "Let's put our entire effort," Urey proposed to Keith, "into a crash program to improve the old Norris-Adler barrier, instead of taking the risk of starting something entirely new and unknown." Urey adamantly refused to divert the resources of the Columbia laboratory to the new Johnson barrier.

When the conflict between them reached an impasse, Urey and Keith took the problem to Groves and asked him to arbitrate. The general recognized the validity of both viewpoints, and on November 5 announced his decision: they would go ahead, temporarily at least, with both barriers. The Norris-Adler model had to be improved as soon as possible, he said, in order to be ready for the completion of the K–25 plant; no effort should be spared. But while Columbia scientists worked on this, Kellex and Carbide should continue developing the Clarence Johnson model and produce a better barrier for later use, or for use in case of failure of the Norris-Adler. Neither Urey nor Keith was happy about the compromise.

By that time, tests on the new Kellex material were well advanced. Richard C. Tolman, the distinguished dean of Cal Tech, who, with Conant, was one of the two officially appointed scientific advisers to General Groves since January 1943, had visited the Kellex laboratory in Jersey City and found Clarence Johnson's product very satisfactory. But it was still a small-scale, handicraft kind of operation, and there was no guarantee that mass production of millions of square feet could ever be turned out.

This problem had become Dobie Keith's major headache. The first small samples of barrier — about the size of an airmail envelope — passed the quality tests; but ways had to be found to produce an enormous quantity of sheets of material with the same perfection. For this job, Keith called on a British-born friend, Professor Hugh Taylor of Princeton, who was already associated with the Manhattan Project on assignment from Harold Urey.

A prominent chemist who had been living in America since 1914, Taylor had been assigned by the British government to help Urey with his heavy-water program in Trail, British Columbia, where a plant had been built. Since his instructions were to place himself at Urey's disposal, he was put on the spot when the Nobel Prize laureate called him long-distance from New York one day in June 1943 and asked him to make the long trip from Trail to New York and take on a new and mysterious job.

"I can't tell you what it is over the phone," said Urey.

"I don't accept any job unless I'm convinced I can do it," answered Taylor. "I'll be in New York in ten days and talk it over with you."

"I have to know *today*," said Urey. His voice was urgent.

"And who says that I'm needed in this job?"

"Dobie Keith insists that you are badly needed for this particular work, and that you have the necessary techniques."

"Oh well, if Keith says so, then I accept."

The British scientist had great respect for and confidence in Keith's judgment. The cocky, ebullient Texan had impressed him ever since their first meeting in 1935. Taylor had been in Philadelphia at a scientific conference when a long-distance call was put through to him and a rather impertinent voice said, "This is P. C. Keith. I want you to come to New York to talk to me. I'm with the M. W. Kellogg Company."

Taylor was slightly irritated. "I'm too busy, Mr. Keith. I'm not doing any consulting work. I've got too much to do at Princeton with my teaching. And I don't *want* to come, besides."

But Keith was persistent. "At least you can do me the favor of coming to see me and talking to me face to face rather than over the phone."

Taylor was growing curious; his resistance weakened. "Well, let's see. Today is Friday — I can come next Wednesday afternoon."

"Why can't you come on Monday?" asked Keith.

Taylor replied coldly, "Because I have classes, and when I have classes, Mr. Keith, I don't do anything for anybody else!"

At their Wednesday meeting Keith made Taylor a strange offer.

"You've done a lot of work on catalysts, but you've never brought hydrocarbon into contact with a catalyst. I will contribute five thousand dollars to Princeton if you will pass a hydrocarbon over a catalyst."

"Which hydrocarbon?" Taylor asked.

"That's up to you, not me."

Back at Princeton, Taylor said to his assistant, "I've met a curious chap who says he'll give us five thousand dollars if we pass a hydrocarbon over a catalyst. I think I'll play a joke on him. He's interested in petroleum. Let's do it with a hydrocarbon that is of no use to the oil industry — pure heptane! We'll collect the five thousand dollars — and teach him a lesson!"

They did it — and produced a product that they were at a loss to understand. It turned out that they had converted heptane into toluene grease, an important substance that would be the base for a kind of petroleum used later during the war. After this episode, Keith and Taylor became good friends.

Ten days after Urey's call, Taylor returned to Princeton from British Columbia and found his laboratory stripped and his Belgian assistant, Georges Joris, working on something new. "I see we've got a new job," he said. "What is all this?"

"It's a hell of a job, Dr. Taylor! It's called the 'barrier' — the British call it a 'membrane.'"

Hugh Taylor became a troubleshooter for the barrier program. On his first visit to the SAM and Kellex laboratories he was immediately dissatisfied with the testing methods that consisted of testing only three points, which were chosen at random, on the barrier material in order to determine its separation efficiency. "What about the other 90 percent?" he asked. The laboratory could not test more than three points, he was told, because the testing of each point required an entire hour.

Taylor went back to Princeton and started working with Georges Joris on a new test. They soon devised a system by which they could determine barrier efficiency at any one point in fifteen seconds. Taylor then divided a square foot of barrier material into 144 square inches and asked his assistants to tell him the efficiency of each square inch. They could do it rapidly with the new system, after which they marked the results on a similar piece of cardboard divided into 144 squares.

The quality ranged from one (very poor) to ten (very good). The numbers from one to ten were represented by pieces of paper of ten different colors, so that the efficiency of the 144 squares could be seen by a quick glance at the cardboard. In order to pass the test, each square foot of material had to have an average quality of nine. Taylor's method of statistical analysis greatly impressed the Kellex people.

When Johnson had produced his first samples of the new material, Keith convinced Hugh Taylor to join the Kellex forces and take charge of barrier production. The professor accepted, but on condition that he could continue teaching at Princeton. Thus started a hectic schedule of commuting between Columbia's Schermerhorn laboratory, the Nash Building laboratories in New York and Princeton. For a year and a half, Taylor gave his morning lecture at 7:30 A.M. in order to catch the 8:40 train to New York. He came back home on the six o'clock train, had dinner with his wife and two daughters, then went directly to his laboratory, often staying until midnight to work with the forty people assigned to barrier analysis.

Hugh Taylor refused any money from Kellex or the Army. He continued to live on his professor's salary. By becoming one of Keith's assistants at Kellex, he contributed greatly to the improvement of the Johnson barrier. The color charts of his statistical analysis method showed a better average quality for each new piece of sheet arriving from the Jersey City laboratory. Taylor began to share Dobie Keith's optimism in spite of the peculiar way the Kellex boss intended to solve the problem of mass production.

"If you can do it in postcard size," Keith told Taylor and Johnson, "then I can do it on a big scale. I can do anything in the plant that you can do in the laboratory!"

When the first barriers were made in the pilot plant in the Nash Building, General Groves arrived promptly in New York to see them. The plant was making a square foot at a time.

"How can I get a million square feet?" asked the general, trying to hide how pleased he was by the quality of the samples.

Dobie Keith did not seem to be confounded by the question. "Well," he said, "how would the Japanese do it? Let's assume the Japanese had to produce a million square feet of this material, and they knew how to make a square foot of it. They'd have no difficulty. They'd make one square foot, then one more, and then one more, and then hundreds more.

And finally they'd have a million square feet. And that's just what we're going to do!"

Taylor was rather perplexed. "You mean you want to make them one by one — in the *millions?*"

"Why not? The alternative to the batch process is the assembly line, like an automobile factory; and that wouldn't work for the barrier. If I have enough high-quality nickel powder, I'm sure we can produce a million square feet."

Groves was listening attentively. "Why don't you investigate the sources of nickel powder, Mr. Keith?" he suggested. "I'll see that you get it."

Urey was extremely disappointed by Groves's decision to go ahead with both barriers. More and more convinced that the gaseous-diffusion process was impossible, he urged a last all-out effort on the Norris-Adler barrier before abandoning the whole project. It was a courageous, agonizing position for the head of the program, and Harold Urey had reached it so painfully that his tense nerves seemed about to snap. Emotionally, Urey was already deeply involved in what he considered the failure of the barrier battle. Nevertheless, he was willing to lead a last offensive on the Norris-Adler front. Willard Libby, the outstanding Berkeley chemist in the group, still insisted that with an all-out effort, the old barrier could be developed successfully in six to eight weeks. There was one major condition, though: all men and all resources would have to be mobilized into a single program.

Instead, Kellex and Carbide were now coming up with a new, unproven idea; at the eleventh hour they were trying to change everything, diverting dozens of specialists from the main effort, requisitioning material, and even occupying large portions of the Nash Building laboratories.

Urey protested vehemently. He argued with Keith every time he had a chance to talk about barriers. His relationship with Dunning had not improved, and some other feuds also erupted at the same time among scientists at Columbia. The strain was too much for Urey. He became a harassed man on the brink of exhaustion. He was taking the failure of the barrier program and the conflicts in his organization so deeply and personally that his hands started shaking during business meetings; he could not even hold a glass of water steady. Finally, after a quarrel with Keith, Professor Urey exploded. He wrote an angry, impulsive letter to General Groves, saying that any war project that required such enormous expansion of research effort should be abandoned. Now Keith was planning still another major expansion, which was absurd considering the time limitations. Urey concluded that the K–25 plant could not be finished during the war and no more funds should be expended on it until afterwards. If any diffusion plant were to be built, it should be based on British design and technology.

Urey's letter brought the crisis at the Columbia laboratories to a climax. It was impossible, especially when the Manhattan Project was gambling so much on the gaseous-diffusion program, to continue the work there under the direction of a man who now openly and passionately advocated its discontinuation. On the other hand, Groves felt, to fire Urey at this point would result in grave psychological damage to the morale of his co-workers.

Groves was certain that Urey's state of nerves and doubting attitude in general would harm the project if he were left in command of the Columbia laboratories. To avoid hurting the scientist's feelings, Groves tried to kick him upstairs, sending him on a mission to England (hopefully, to last a long time) to investigate the state of the British atomic program. But the painfully conscientious professor was so worried about problems at home that he came back within a week! Then he was sent to British Columbia to inspect the heavy-water project at Trail. Groves, knowing that Urey had lived in Montana in his youth, arranged to have him go on a fishing trip there, and thus spend at least a week getting some badly needed rest. But Urey was so keyed up that he would only stay twenty-four hours before rushing back to work.

Groves then decided to replace him as effective head of the laboratories, but without stripping him of his title, thus sparing him any humiliation. Some of Urey's prerogatives were gradually transferred to Professor Taylor, whom Urey had trusted enough to make his assistant director in the Columbia program. On the recommendation of Rafferty and Felbeck, Groves assigned the delicate job of replacing Urey (but still keeping him nominally on the project) to Dr. Lauchlin M. Currie, a Union Carbide engineer.

A pleasant Southerner with charming manners, Currie had all the qualities necessary for such a diplomatic mission; not only was he a competent chemist and a good organizer, but he also had unlimited reserves of patience, tact and modesty. Currie gradually assumed all the executive functions for the barrier program, with the help of both Urey and Dunning, who accepted his presence without resentment. The Carbide engineer was directly responsible to General Groves, who was ready to back him on any decision concerning the barrier. His official title was Associate Director of the SAM laboratory (the code name for the Columbia atomic project) — but Currie never let anyone forget that Urey was the great world-famous chemist, that Dunning and Booth were the real pioneers of the diffusion method, and that he himself was merely a relatively unknown engineer, a coordinator whose role was not to boss but to serve his illustrious colleagues. Carefully avoiding any outright announcement, Groves thus relieved Urey of any real responsibility for the gaseous-diffusion program.

Urey had not been replaced because his views on the barrier conflicted with Keith's. His views were not regarded as necessarily wrong, nor Keith's as necessarily right. Neither Groves nor anyone else at the time knew which of the two proposed approaches would work. One thing Groves did know was this: it was impossible to give up, which was what Urey had done.

Groves's mission was clear: to try every possible way to produce fissionable material. The investment in the K–25 project was already colossal: it was unthinkable to abandon it. Kellex had nine hundred employees in New York; the SAM laboratory at Columbia employed seven hundred people; and several hundred more worked at other laboratories. Allis-Chalmers was building the $4-million pump factory in Milwaukee; Houdaille-Hershey, a $5-million plant for barrier production; and Chrysler was converting its Lynch Road plant to diffuser assembly. At Oak Ridge, ten thousand workers were erecting the K–25 plant. It was much too late for second thoughts.

Of all Urey's suggestions, General Groves followed only one: he authorized a review of the gaseous-diffusion project by a team of British scientists, who had been working for a long time in their laboratories on this process. Ever since Groves took over in 1942, the British had not been kept fully informed about the Manhattan Project. The signing of the Quebec Agreement, however, provided for certain cooperation between the United States and the United Kingdom. The British approach to gaseous diffusion was very different. It was not adaptable to American manufacturing and construction methods. It was based on low pressures and hence relatively coarse barriers, while the American process worked with high pressures. The British required such huge pumps that the "separation machine" designs of Imperial Chemical Industries and of Metropolitan-Vickers had been described by Dunning as "mechanical monstrosities incapable of being built or operated." The whole British nuclear program had had low priority because of other urgent war efforts.

But since the quality of British nuclear scientists in this area was widely recognized, Groves agreed that they send over their experts on gaseous diffusion. A fifteen-member British delegation,* led by Wallace Akers and including Franz Simon and Rudolph Peierls, met the American experts

---

* From the moment the visitors opened their mouths, the Americans became increasingly amused by their English. The accents of several of them — refugees from Central Europe — were anything but Oxonian. The joke spread quickly that the British delegation did not speak English.

on December 22, 1943, in the Woolworth Building. General Groves showed up with his two scientific advisers, Conant and Tolman. Keith, Baker, Arnold and Benedict represented Kellex; Felbeck, Clark Center and Lyman Bliss came for Carbide; and Urey, Dunning, Taylor and Currie were the spokesmen for the SAM laboratories. Groves's concern was that the British might go back to England and tell Churchill that the Americans didn't know what they were doing; he was worried that Churchill would complain to Roosevelt, and Roosevelt then would talk to Bush and create unnecessary complications. So Groves wanted Conant and Tolman to be present and see for themselves that the American plan was wise.

The guests were briefed in full detail, then each expert went off to visit the laboratory of his United States scientific counterpart. Some of them went to Oak Ridge. Groves wanted to hear not only the opinions of the British delegation on the barrier problem, but also their ideas on the plant as a whole.

In the meantime George Felbeck threw all Carbide's support behind the new Johnson barrier and managed to persuade Keith to let Carbide take entire charge of production. Even Houdaille-Hershey, whose Decatur plant for producing the Norris-Adler barrier was nearly built, took a stand against the old barrier. Their own pilot plant experiment had led to the conclusion that the Norris-Adler barrier could not be produced, at least not for a very long time.

On Christmas Day 1943, Walter Pinner of Houdaille-Hershey informed Groves and Kellex that Houdaille would not be able to manufacture it. Expecting dismay and anger, Pinner was surprised to see signs of relief. He did not know he was giving the final argument to Groves, Keith and Felbeck, in whose minds a bold new plan was taking shape.

The anxiously awaited meeting with the British delegates started at eight-thirty in the morning on January 5, 1944, in the heavily guarded conference room in the Woolworth Building. For four tense, dramatic hours the American and British viewpoints clashed and remained diametrically opposed. Barrier was not the only topic in the discussions. The British disagreed with the entire design of the American diffusion cascade, such as conceived by Dunning, Booth and Benedict, and offered their own design. They were particularly skeptical about the possibility of controlling the process through thousands of diffusion stages and insisted that it would not work. But in spite of their warning, the Americans remained determined to go ahead with their design.

The visitors were startled when Groves asked their opinion of a plan to abandon the Norris-Adler barrier, which had taken two years to develop, and gamble the Project's fate on a crash program to produce millions of square feet of the newly discovered Johnson barrier, which was just being tested. The British agreed that the new process was more promising for future use, but they insisted that, owing to the time factor, it would be absurd to discard the results gained in developing the Norris-Adler barrier.

Then Keith took the offensive. In his fiery and articulate manner, he stated bluntly that the old lace curtain was too flimsy to work, and that the Manhattan Project had no choice but to gamble on the new barrier without any further delay.

"There is not enough evidence to judge which of the two is really superior," answered the visitors. "But wouldn't it be wiser to continue work on both?"

"Impossible!" snorted Keith. "With the limited resources and time at our disposal, we must make our choice right now!"

The British reminded him that no assembly-line technique yet existed for continuous mass production of the enormous quantities that would be required. They were flabbergasted, no less than Urey had been before them, when Keith declared, with almost arrogant self-assurance, that he could do without the continuous assembly line. "Kellex produces the new barrier in the laboratory by a very simple hand process," he said. "If production can be multiplied by the use of thousands of employees doing piecework, there will be no problems of translating a laboratory process into an industrial one."

When Keith sat down, the Carbide representatives continued the battle. Lyman Bliss offered a concession to the old barrier: "Let's continue research on it," he suggested. "But as far as production goes, the all-out effort should be concentrated on the new process."

Then George Felbeck, the top Carbide man who was going to organize the barrier production, dropped the bombshell. What he suggested left the British, and even most of the Americans present, speechless. "If we want to start production right away, *and we have no time to waste,*" he said, "then all the installations in the Decatur plant, designed for the old process, will have to be ripped out and replaced by new machinery. It's a hard decision to make at the last moment, but there's no other way."

To rip out a nearly completed plant, after the millions already spent there? "That is absolutely reckless!" one British scientist exclaimed. The new barrier was still at the test stage. What if it failed? Would there be time to re-install the Norris-Adler machinery? Keith admitted frankly that there would not be time to switch back. One had to play it "all or nothing"!

At 11:20 A.M., Hugh Taylor rose and announced that he had to return to Princeton. Before leaving, he said, "This is one occasion where I, as a

British subject, wish to disagree profoundly with my British brethren. In my judgment, you ought to decide to go ahead, take courage in your hands and push for the barrier as it has been developed by Johnson, Groff and the others. It *is* feasible."

But most of the British were convinced that such an undertaking, even if successful, would delay production of U–235 till the summer of 1946, at the earliest. Even after pilot plant experience, building much less complicated installations always took a minimum of two years. Keith and Felbeck wanted to start production in four months, and to have all the millions of square feet manufactured in another four months! "It would be something of a miraculous achievement," said one of the visitors.

Groves listened carefully to both sides of the argument without announcing his verdict. As far as he was concerned, only one thing mattered: to have the Decatur plant in production by May, as Dobie Keith had solemnly promised it would be. Whether he would use the old barrier or the new — or both — the Kellex boss was not going to be driven in any way from his commitment.

Exhausted but excited, Keith went back to his corner office across the corridor. While he was locking his papers in the files, he noticed a cartoon that had been clipped from a newspaper and sent to him by Groves. It showed a turtle walking with its head stretched far out. The caption read: "I advance only when I stick my neck out." A dedication followed, written in ink: *To Dobie Keith, Leslie R. Groves, Brigadier General, U.S. Army.*

On Sunday, January 16, 1944, the men gathered in the small office building at the front of the dirty, dingy Houdaille-Hershey plant. They looked tense and tired. It was a cold gloomy morning and most of them had arrived in Decatur late the previous night in order to be on time for the decisive meeting scheduled for 8:30 A.M. They were told that the new Garfield plant was nearly completed — the foundations were in, the walls were up, the roof almost finished, the administration building practically ready for occupancy.

The conference was to take place in a long, narrow room in which there was a large table with two dozen chairs arranged around it. Urey, having just arrived from the West Coast, was already there, and was talking to the Houdaille engineers — Walter Pinner, Don S. Devor, Jay Gould and R. C. Smith. Leon Merrill of Carbide took his seat and began chatting with the Manhattan District representatives — Colonel Stowers, Major Alphonso Tammaro and Captain Brannan. In a corner, Zola Deutsch and Peter B. (Ben) Gordon of Kellex were discussing the latest details with Keith, the man who made the agonizing proposal that Groves would either ratify or reverse that morning.

At nine o'clock Groves and Felbeck strode into the room, disheveled and unshaven after the long trip from Oak Ridge. The general had left the afternoon before, by train, but his railroad car had missed the connection in Cincinnati. From the station, Groves had telephoned the local district engineer and had asked for a car with an officer-driver to take him immediately from Cincinnati to Decatur. When the car arrived at the railroad station at midnight, Groves sat next to the driver and told him, "Now I'm going to talk to you all night long, just to be sure that you'll stay awake." They arrived in the morning, only half an hour late, but without having slept at all. The general carried a large paper bag containing a quart of coffee and some rolls which he placed at the head of the table. "Well," he said, "let's get the meeting going."

After a short discussion, the entire party inspected the plant in detail and then resumed the discussions, at the end of which Groves announced the decision. The plant would be stripped for the new Johnson barrier. Carbide was to take responsibility for the development and supervision of barrier production, with Leon K. Merrill representing the company in Decatur. Houdaille-Hershey would convert and operate the plant.

There was no argument, no criticism of the decision. The general read it out like an order, and that was it. In fact, the Houdaille-Hershey people were not really very surprised — Walter Pinner had already brought from New York the news that such a decision was possible. After frustrating months of working with the lace curtain, their reaction was one of intense relief that it was at last being given up. Groves, wasting no time in meditation over the tremendous gamble, left for Washington as soon as the meeting was over.

The next day, hundreds of engineers and construction workers who had come to continue their job at the new Garfield plant were told to start stripping it. "That's where the taxpayers' money goes!" some of the men said in disgust. "Those military men never know what they're doing."

42

In the spring of 1944, few people in the United States, not even high government and military officials, knew of the fantastic events taking place in an isolated, wooded area near Oak Ridge, Tennessee. In an area cryptically designated as K-25, an army of twenty thousand workers was feverishly erecting the largest and most unusual plant ever built. If successfully completed, the plant would be the scene where a group of determined scientists and engineers would attempt an olympian task: the separation, for the first time in history, of some uranium isotopes that had been linked together since the beginning of time.

Though the J. A. Jones Company's labor force was rushing ahead with the construction of K-25's gigantic buildings, most of the important equipment to go into the plant still did not exist. Some components had not yet been designed, and production of the most vital part — the barrier — had not yet begun. A series of miracles had to be performed if the plant was to get into operation within the short time limits imposed by Groves and Nichols. An entirely new industry had to be created from scratch — and in record time. All necessary resources had to be mobilized in a crash program of staggering dimensions. It was indeed a question of winning — against the clock — a number of crucial, concurrent races. In many parts of the country, factories were starting up mass production of parts and instruments whose ultimate use remained a mystery to company engineers. Large sectors of industry were put to work for the K-25 plant, their work coordinated by Colonel Nichols and Al Baker of Kellex.

The April deadline for starting barrier production had passed, but still nothing was coming out of the Houdaille plant in Decatur. Development of the new Johnson barrier proved more difficult than Groves and Keith had anticipated when they made the decision to gamble the Project's fate on it alone. A pilot plant for its production was installed in the big Nash garage at Broadway and 133rd Street in Manhattan. There Clarence Johnson, inventor of the process, redoubled his efforts to produce material good enough to stand the rigid statistical analysis tests carried out by Hugh Taylor at Princeton.

But the results were still heartbreaking: Taylor's colored charts indicated a quality that was scarcely 5 percent of what plant standards would require. To raise the quality extraordinary measures were taken at the Nash Building to assure conditions of maximum cleanliness during fabrication. In order to avoid even the slightest presence of organic materials, the girls engaged in the processing not only wore white gloves but were even asked, by embarrassed engineers, when thir menstrual periods were due. True or false, the popular belief that women's hands tend to perspire more during their periods caused concern. The Kellex team could not take the risk of questioning the scientific basis of the legend. Hence charts were prepared on which, next to the name and shift of the girl, there was a column carrying the date of her period. On those days, she would be switched to another job.

The quality of the nickel powder was also of prime importance. Fortunately, Groves and Nichols had foreseen the need for highly purified nickel a year earlier and had approached the International Nickel Company about supplying it. Nichols had financed the construction of special equipment in one of the company's plants, which by now had produced and stored eighty tons of pure nickel powder. The International Nickel Company continued to refine the powder so as to meet the Nash pilot plant's requirements; by the end of April 1944, Johnson's team was beginning to receive the first reasonably good nickel.

Until then, though, the only source of nickel powder had been England. The precious powder, obtained at the International Nickel Company's Mond plant on the south coast of England, was shipped by convoy to Philadelphia, then sent to the barrier plant. For the top men in the Manhattan Project there was good reason to keep an anxious eye on convoy movements across the Atlantic.

While the progress of the new barrier at the Nash Building was not very promising, some better news about the old barrier came unexpectedly from Columbia's Schermerhorn laboratory. Edward Mack, brought from Ohio State University by Urey to help with the nearly abandoned Norris-Adler barrier, succeeded in eliminating some of the defects of the process. His samples sent down to Princeton passed the tests much better than anybody had expected. Was Norris-Adler, after all, perhaps the best barrier?

But it was now too late to switch again. The Houdaille-Hershey Company had already remodeled its Decatur plant. It was decided that the old, more complicated process, as improved by Mack, should be kept in reserve as a standby for the easier newer Johnson method in case of production failure. Both pilot plants, Nash and Schermerhorn, now joined efforts with the rest of the SAM laboratories, Kellex and Carbide in concentrating on pilot plant production of the Johnson barrier. Some promising material started arriving at Taylor's laboratory for analysis in April. By May the quality had jumped from 5 to 38 percent. Now it was time to go on to the next stage: industrial production of the material.

But this proved to be a different story. Conversion of the plant could not go ahead full blast once the Decatur decision to scrap the old process was made. Drawings had to be revised and materials procured. The Houdaille people had no idea what would be involved in the production of the new barrier. The first problem was to keep the nearly one thousand construction workers from leaving the job. As more information on conversion began to arrive, Houdaille-Hershey teams headed by Walter Pinner started converting the buildings and equipment. The heavy foundations, which had been specially designed for equipment necessary for the Norris-Adler process, now had to be leveled. For months, Houdaille engineers had been striving to get equipment and material lined up for the Norris-Adler method. Now, work had to begin all over again in order to line up equipment and material for an entirely different process. Mysterious material in long wooden boxes began arriving in trailer trucks. Fortunately, only about 40 percent of the Garfield plant had to be changed completely; the rest of the plant's space and equipment was easily adapted to the new process.

The Decatur decision had turned over supervision of the entire barrier production to Union Carbide. That was the agreement with Felbeck made by Dobie Keith, whose shoulders were already bending under the tremendous weight of his numerous responsibilities. Previously, though all plans needed Carbide's approval, Kellex had been in charge. Many Kellex people were upset by this transfer of power. They felt that development and production of all K–25 components should be their responsibility, especially since their colleague, Clarence Johnson, had developed the barrier. But the Bakelite methods devised by Frazier Groff played a large part in the new barrier. Carbide, the parent company, was thus considered better equipped to organize mass production.

A special new group was formed with the code name of K–1, with headquarters on the fourteenth floor of the Woolworth Building. K–1 included Merrill and Al Tenney of Carbide, Ben Gordon and a small Kellex group, and Pinner and his men from Houdaille. They worked with Johnson at Jersey City and Nash, with Frazier Groff at Bakelite, and with Hugh Taylor and the SAM scientists, as they tried to find out as much as possible about the process in order to adapt it to industrial production.

The man who became Carbide's proconsul in Decatur was Leon K. Merrill of the Bakelite Division, the engineer who had originally selected Frazier Groff to tackle the barrier job. Ken Merrill was the complete opposite of Groff, who was impulsive, disorganized but nonetheless an inventive genius. A forty-seven-year-old engineer from Cleveland with his feet firmly planted on the ground, Merrill was a first-rate organization man who knew how to get things done. None of his superiors could ever accuse him of being a yes-man. When he did not like something, he simply shouted, "It stinks!" And he often manifested disapproval of his bosses' opinions with phrases like "You're nuts!"

Difficulties in preparing the Garfield plant came from all sides. Special, complicated machinery had to be designed and installed, machinery capable of producing thousands of units per day of material hitherto made only in small laboratory amounts. No furnaces that would be adequate could be found anywhere. Huge quantities of hydrogen and nitrogen gases were to be used in the process, and nobody seemed to be able to procure these gases. No one knew how many tubes would be needed. At the end of January, bids for the immediate manufacture of two special furnaces, with the possibility of a later order of seventy-two more, were sent out to General Electric, Westinghouse and other manufacturers.

Shortly afterwards, a tall, weather-beaten man in his late fifties who introduced himself as Sam Keener from Salem, Ohio, came to the Woolworth Building with some furnace designs. A onetime cowboy who finished his schooling with the sixth grade, Keener was a picturesque character of wide-ranging business interests that included, among other things, ownership of several flying schools in Colorado. He had founded his own engineering company in 1934 and now, ten years later, was a wealthy builder of mills and ammunition plants. Keener was known to be unorthodox in his business methods and highly eccentric in his clothes. In the office he sometimes wore red cowboy boots with silver spurs and shirts embroidered with rodeo scenes and his badge as deputy sheriff of Cheyenne, Wyoming. Otherwise he was likely to show up in one of a series of flashy, pale-blue uniforms, complete with gold stripes and silver stars, which he had designed himself.

Despite his eccentric dress, Keener presented some preliminary drawings for a furnace that looked good. Ben Gordon of the K–1 group asked him how long it would be before he could submit final plans. "Tomorrow," Keener replied promptly. "I have my own plane. I'll fly back to Salem. My staff won't mind working all night on this job, then I'll fly back tomorrow."

Eventually Keener got the contract, and in eight months turned out fifty-two furnaces. He did an excellent job, although he admitted later, "I never knew what the hell I was doing!"

The problem of getting enough hydrogen and nitrogen gases within the time limit was another headache. At first, while only two furnaces were operating, Air Force trailers with hydrogen generators, the type normally used for inflating observation balloons, were used. But this would not be an adequate source of supply. The plant would need over a million cubic feet of hydrogen and six million of nitrogen.

The Girdler Corporation of Louisville, Kentucky, was recommended as a builder of hydrogen plants. But it would require six months to fabricate the parts, plus another two months to assemble them. The K–1 group learned that Girdler had just fabricated a plant like the one they needed. To their consternation, however, they found out that the plant, which had been ordered for Russia by lend-lease, had already been shipped out. The Manhattan District moved fast and located the shipment, which was headed by rail for Seattle, where it was to be loaded aboard a Russian cargo ship sailing for Vladivostok.

Ben Gordon rushed to Lieutenant Colonel Stowers. "Write me a memo saying what would happen if you didn't get the plant," Stowers instructed him. "I'll get in touch with Groves's office in Washington."

Two days later the plant became the property of the Manhattan District. The United States Army wrote a letter to the Soviet Army Purchasing Mission promising to replace the "borrowed" plant. The entire shipment — twenty-two freight cars of it — was then routed to Decatur and assembled near the barrier plant.

One by one, pieces of equipment were found or improvised, and in June, barrier production started at the Garfield plant. By then the total cost of K–25 and its components had reached $281 million and was still climbing. But barrier quality was still so poor that Professor Taylor declared most of it unacceptable. Lauchlin Currie, now heading the SAM team at Columbia, mobilized all his resources, and Mack at Schermerhorn laboratory increased his work shifts from two to three a day. Currie himself was sent by Groves to work with Merrill in Decatur. By now everyone seemed to have joined the production effort, and each had something to say about it — the Army, Carbide, Houdaille, Columbia, Kellex — thus creating a veritable Tower of Babel. When the confused Currie admitted to Groves that he really didn't know to whom he should report, the general settled the matter in one second: "Me. That's who."

On the Houdaille side, Don S. Devor supervised the entire effort. A bright young man, Frank Fisher, was assigned the full-time job of superintendent of the Garfield plant. Walter Pinner headed the group called Research and Technical Control, which already numbered 279 scientists and engineers. There was no assembly line; everything was produced by the batch method. The Houdaille engineers and workers had no idea of the purpose of the product, and no one ever told them.

A few times trouble did occur with the unions. The finished barrier

WESTFIELD MEMORIAL LIBRARY
WESTFIELD, N. J.

tubes had to be shipped by truck in big coffin-like crates under armed guard from Decatur to Chrysler's Lynch Road plant in Detroit. There was a different truckers' union in each place, and both claimed the right to do the entire job.

With the improved quality of the nickel powder and perfecting of the techniques, Houdaille began to produce a better barrier. Professor Taylor's analysis finally showed a uniform quality superior to the required standard of 7½. From that time on, the flow of good barrier between Decatur and Detroit was uninterrupted, and all deadlines were met.

In the winter of 1944, Oak Ridge's muddy K–25 area was beginning to look like a gigantic Cecil B. de Mille set for a movie about the building of the pyramids. The time for installing the intricate piping system was fast approaching, but as yet no pipes had actually been made. No pipe known could meet the requirement of resisting corrosion by uranium hexafluoride. The scientific team made up of Dunning, Booth, Benedict and Cohen had designed the cascade brilliantly. But the process nevertheless required no less than three million feet of special piping that no one in America could produce.

Only one metal could resist corrosion — nickel. And the scientists felt that, with the corrosion problem much worse than it was in the case of the Chrysler-built diffusers, the pipes must be made of *solid* nickel. Because of its scarcity the piping problem at first seemed insoluble. Could not nickel-plating be used for steel pipes?

Impossible, said the specialists. To plate even a flat surface with nickel was very difficult anyway. But to achieve perfect plating — and nothing short of perfection would suffice in K–25, where a microscopic pore would create corrosion and leakage — just did not seem feasible, especially not on the curved surface of very narrow pipes extending for many miles. A further complication was that the pipes also had to be weldable.

After discussing this new impasse with Keith, Groves decided to ask the advice of the most practical man he knew: Chrysler's K. T. Keller. Keller's reaction was prompt. "The job is impossible!" he said. "Solid nickel pipes would eat up all the nickel mined in America for two years, and the entire free world's production won't be enough to finish the job!"

"In that case even a Triple-A priority for nickel would be worthless," remarked Groves.

"Of course," said Keller. "A Triple-A wouldn't be enough." Being involved in arms production, he knew the demands for nickel in armor-plating, guns and other war equipment. "To free the nickel, some other process of hardening steel would have to be developed, and that might take years. That would be the wrong way to go about it. It would mean about a two-year tie-up in the production of the rest of our war stuff, and the nickel supply would still not be enough."

Groves and Nichols, who accompanied him, recognized the difficulty, but stated firmly that some way must be found to overcome it.

"I see only one solution," Keller said finally. "The pipes, and particularly the larger sizes, will have to be nickel-plated. No matter what your scientists say, I'm sure that the plating could somehow be made just as noncorrosive as the solid nickel."

Groves went away quite satisfied. He had gotten what he wanted: the reassurance of Keller. The question was now who could do the job.

More than ten years earlier, Groves, then a lieutenant, had been responsible for antiaircraft searchlight research and procurement. The model in use had a glass mirror that was quite unsatisfactory. A Swiss-born inventor named Blasius Bart had developed a metal mirror produced by electrodeposition. He had come to see Groves accompanied by his son Sieg, a high school boy who seemed to know everything about his father's business and who was very impressed by the Army officer's appearance and manner. Groves liked the process and for several years worked closely with Bart. Now he remembered the Swiss inventor, who had established himself in Belleville, New Jersey. "I know someone who is good at plating things, especially curved surfaces and exotic shapes," he told Dobie Keith. "His name is Bart; he's a Swiss and Gorham Silver Company brought him to this country in 1913 to teach their men a process he had invented. He's been working in New Jersey ever since. I want you to get in touch with him. If anyone can do this, he can."

The older Bart had just retired. So Keith and Baker asked Sieg Bart, now a young man of twenty-nine with a degree in chemistry, to come and see them in Jersey City. "Do you think you could plate nickel inside of steel pipes?" they asked him.

"I don't know. Never did it. But we can try."

Sieg Bart returned to the small red-brick plant in Belleville, called in his chemist, Millard Loucks, and started working on the new problem. They tried all sorts of electroplating tanks, liquid solutions, baskets made of rubber, lucite baskets. Nothing worked. It seemed impossible to achieve a heavy and uniform deposit. The older professionals, watching them work frantically day and night, shrugged their shoulders skeptically. The pipes were twenty feet long, but Bart's tanks were only six feet long. The laboratory was much too small to install big new tanks.

After days of hard work, Bart and Loucks came up with a completely new and original solution: instead of tanks they used the pipe itself as the processing vessel. A special solution was then introduced inside, and in order to obtain uniform coating, the pipes were rotated during the operation. Previous electroplating techniques had followed the exact contours of the surface, which was never perfectly smooth. In the new Bart process, however, the coating filled every tiny hole in the steel pipe's face, and the heavy nickel deposit on the base met the exacting requirements.

Kellex was enthusiastic, but the problem immediately arose of where to build the plant for mass production of nickel-plated pipes. The Belleville laboratory was too small; there was no railroad siding, and the Bart personnel had had no experience with pipes. In spite of these handicaps, Kellex and Groves decided to give the huge contract to the tiny and relatively unknown laboratory.

Thousands of pipes manufactured by United States Steel were trucked to Belleville. Four hundred workers, mostly from Harlem, were hired immediately to work in three shifts, twenty-four hours a day, seven days a week. The technique was improved as production progressed. By February 1944 the first large pipes were plated. Because of development problems and lack of experience, production had reached only 15 percent of schedule by May. Soon afterwards, Bart was able to plate pipes as small as two inches in diameter. International Nickel, Midwest Piping and Supply Company and Republic Steel Corporation joined in the production effort. All deadlines were met. Furthermore, only 2 percent of the nickel originally estimated as needed was actually used.

While Houdaille-Hershey was struggling with barrier difficulties, K. T. Keller at Chrysler was getting increasingly impatient. To keep him occupied, Merrill sent ten thousand unacceptable barrier tubes to Detroit for training Chrysler personnel in assembly and testing. Then, at the end of the summer, trucks started delivering good barrier.

One hundred and fifty people were working on the engineering side at Chrysler, and more than one thousand others — each having security clearance — were engaged in production under J. M. Hartgering and his chief engineer, Alan Loofbourow. None of the workers had the slightest idea of the purpose of the huge cylinders in which they were installing barrier tubes.

The cylinders, which looked like ordinary boilers, came to Detroit in different sizes, the largest being about ten thousand gallons, ready to be plated. Chrysler* did the drilling, welding, plating, treating and installing of the barrier sent from Houdaille-Hershey. Half a dozen huge vertical tanks were used during the process, and the cylinders were hoisted and dipped into the tanks by a big crane. They were chemically washed in the first tank, degreased by vapor in the second. Eventually they reached the

---

* During the two years that followed, Chrysler nickel-plated about sixty-three acres of steel surface.

plating tank, equipped with pure nickel anodes. After the nickel was deposited on the interior surface, the cylinder was immersed in a hot-water bath for forty minutes, then lifted out. It dried instantly because of the heat in the steel, and if there was any porosity in the nickel-plated surface inside, a rust spot would show, visible to the naked eye. The cylinder was set on the floor and an operator went inside to inspect the surface with a high-powered light.

Preventing any leakage was another of Chrysler's main concerns. A tremendous vacuum installation was built inside the plant and new pumps were designed to supplement the pumps brought from outside. Then a mass spectrometer was hooked to the tank, and the tank itself was covered with a plastic hood. Nitrogen was put on the outside. If any of the nitrogen leaked into the unit, the mass spectrometer would detect it. The leak detector had enough sensitivity to indicate one molecule of nitrogen in thirty million molecules of air! If it showed a leak, the hood was taken off the tank and small probing nozzles were run along all the welded joints until the hole was found. Sometimes leaks would be detected even in the solid-steel metals that had only the very slightest degree of porosity through which infinitesimal amounts of gas could escape.

The welding presented enormous problems and new techniques had to be developed during the production. The complete chemical analysis of all materials arriving in the plant required the organizing of a test laboratory, where the exact composition, density and temperature of every single piece of material had to be checked. As a result, fifteen hundred to two thousand chemical analyses of samples around the plant were taken every day.

Security measures were extremely strict. Every employee, including janitors and typists, was investigated by the FBI and by Army security people assigned to Chrysler by the Manhattan District. Everyone had to sign a security agreement not to talk about his work. In the matter of clearances, the only difficulty was how to handle K. T. Keller. When the security officer brought the questionnaire to his office, Chrysler's president pushed it aside. "To hell with that!" he snorted indignantly. "You should have found out that personal information before you came to me in the first place about this job. If you're not satisfied that I'm OK, take the contract away or send me to jail! I'm not going to fill out that question-naire!" K. T. Keller got his way.

The finished diffusers were shipped from Detroit by rail. Chrysler engineers had to design a special suspension because transporting the diffusers on standard flatcars would have ruined the fragile barrier tubes. To test the first suspension system designed, a concrete dummy of exactly the same weight as one of the diffusers and with a barrier tube in it was put on a flatcar and shipped to Oak Ridge. A Chrysler man rode the car all the way to check the accelerometers and vibration instruments en route. The tube was broken on arrival, but the Chrysler engineer had gotten enough information from that one trip to redesign the suspension satisfactorily.

The special flatcars were soon shuttling back and forth between the Chrysler plant and Oak Ridge, with the diffusers covered so casually that no one could guess whether they were oil tanks or stores of chemicals. Once on the K-25 site, the diffusers were installed by Carbide and Kellex and their subcontractors.

Finally the gaseous-diffusion plant was built, and all the components — barriers, diffusers, pumps, pipes, valves, instruments — were on hand. A few weeks would tell whether the whole process was going to work or not.

43

At the beginning of 1944, the difficulties involved in building the fantastic K–25 plant were growing bigger and bigger. In his austere office in the Woolworth Building, J. C. Hobbs, assisted by an enterprising young engineer, Evan A. Johnson, from Los Angeles, was struggling with some of the most urgent problems. He attended the weekly meetings in Dobie Keith's office but usually said little. He listened carefully, and if things seemed to be on the right track, he remained silent. He spoke up only when he thought somebody was going to make a mistake.

When he had begun working at Kellex, Hobbs did not have a specifically defined assignment. He roamed from room to room, peering over the shoulders of the engineers, sticking his nose into everything. If he disliked something, he didn't hesitate to say so, frankly and bluntly. One thing he did not like was the type of valves Kellex intended to use.

The Oak Ridge plant would need thousands of valves of different sizes and shapes — leakproof valves that had to operate despite highly corrosive gas. No valve in existence was even remotely adequate. Lubrication was another apparently insurmountable difficulty, because uranium gas became explosive on contact with any greasy substance. This ruled out the use of any lubricant containing oil. But some valves, even if imperfect, had to be built immediately: the gigantic construction work going on at Oak Ridge could not be held up for lack of valves.

The contract for making them had been given to the Crane Company in Chicago, but nobody was happy about the first models produced. J. C. Hobbs took a trip to Chicago for a close look at them, then took part in a two-day conference that Kellex was holding with the Crane people. Sitting silently in his corner, J.C. listened to all the suggestions with an expression of growing pain on his face. The meeting did not produce any satisfactory solution, but there was no time to waste, and another forty thousand dollars was appropriated for new machines to make small four-inch valves. These were tapered plug valves with a hole drilled through them and seated in a case of exactly the same taper.

Hobbs had a high reputation as a valve expert, for he had developed some ingenious ones in the past. "What do you think of these, J.C.?" he was asked at the end of the meeting.

Unsmiling, Hobbs looked around and pronounced a one-word verdict: "Monstrosities!" Then, after a short pause, he went on, "They'll never work, your plug cocks! You're going to have to pull off two major miracles, and that doesn't happen often, see? First, the surface has got to be absolutely perfect — to the millionth of an inch — and there's never been such a thing. Usually we seal any machining irregularities by putting a lubricant on them. But here we can't use any lubrication."

Hobbs paused to let his words sink in, then continued. "Secondly, what makes you think the taper of the valves will remain unchanged once you get pipes on the other end that are straining and pulling like mad? Of course it won't stay the same! I'm telling you there is contraction and expansion going on in all valves — sometimes there's a one-hundred-degree difference in temperature between the top and the bottom of the same valve. You can't make it perfect — the metal is expanding and contracting all the time. Seven years ago, when I did a job involving one-thousand-degree temperatures, the one-hundred-foot-long pipes expanded up to seven inches! In this job here, with all the strain and vibration, how do you expect the valves to remain fitting perfectly?"

Crane was the biggest valve company in the world. If they couldn't do it, who could? The company superintendent, George Larsen, a practical-minded man, knew that the valves were not perfect, but there was a deadline to meet and nobody had come up with a better idea. Kellogg had tried for several months; Kellex had also struggled for a long time; all the valve companies had been consulted. Everything had failed. Construction of the huge plant could not continue because nobody knew where or how to put in the foundations for the still-to-be invented valves.

"I agree with some of the things you say, J.C.," George Larsen said, "but that doesn't help us. Where do we go from here? How do you fight expansion, how do you fight vibration?"

Hobbs had his own philosophy about that. "I think that we're wrong in fighting those things — you just can't. That's nature. And if we 'can't lick 'em, jine 'em!' "

It was a depressing meeting. Everything looked very gloomy at the Crane Company that Friday evening.

After the discouraging conference Hobbs took a taxi to the railroad station. He had been expected home in Ohio since Wednesday but had had to postpone his trip in order to investigate the trouble at Crane. "No good, those valves," he thought on the way to the station. "No good. And the eight-inch ones made out of solid alloy — they must weigh close to a ton! It would take a big crane to handle 'em. They weigh so darned much that special foundations are going to be needed. And construction at Oak Ridge is being held up because nobody knows how much steel to put in to support the big valves. . . . And what happens when you put a long pipe there? What does the weight and the vibration do to it?"

Hobbs's mind was working at top speed. He was really excited, for valves were, after all, among his main hobbies. All his life he had invented valves, admired them — even collected them. Over the years, it had become a passion, like stamp-collecting or crossword puzzles for other people. For Hobbs the really stimulating moments in life were, as he often expressed it, "when you suddenly have an idea — and put some metal around your idea."

All of a sudden, Hobbs changed his mind about going home to Ohio that day. "Driver, never mind the station! I'll go to my hotel!"

It was 6 P.M. At seven o'clock the next morning, exhausted but jubilant, Hobbs, who had been up most of the night, gave the last touch to a pile of colored drawings and blueprints (he was known by engineers all over the country for his pencil drawings in different colors). Then he called George Larsen on the telephone. "Look, on your way to the plant, you pass by my hotel, don't you? I'll eat breakfast quickly and wait to ride out with you."

George Larsen, an early riser, picked up Hobbs at seven-thirty. As the car approached the special "secret" building at the corner of the Crane plant that was well away from the other buildings, Hobbs told Larsen about his new invention.

"Here is my idea, George," he said excitedly. "Don't fight expansion of the metal, but recognize it! Let the valve expand, let it contract, let it vibrate! But don't let any surface slide on another surface — that would scratch the surfaces, and a scratch would be fatal, see? I think I can make a valve that would have a round tubular seat, *not* attached to the body, so it could move around any way it wants to. The valve itself would be a symmetrical piece of metal that would not be affected by varying temperatures. It will be thin enough not to block the degrees of heat, and it will be pivoted — suspended sort of in the middle, see? — so it can wiggle any way the seat wants to."

They were both very excited when they went in to consult Crane's head draftsman. Hobbs asked that he take the rough sketch made the night before and put it to scale on a ten-inch drawing. "I like to work from a ten-inch-scale — it's easier, you don't have to divide. . . ."

Since it was Saturday morning, the draftsman only worked until noon — about four hours, not enough to design a whole valve. Hobbs asked the draftsman to design only certain key features, the heart of the invention. Then he left and took his train to Ohio, asking the Crane people to make a print of what they had and send it to him special delivery.

On Sunday morning Hobbs received the letter. It was a long explanation of why the invention wouldn't work. Hobbs hit the ceiling; clearly the most expert valve manufacturers in the world still couldn't understand! But it didn't surprise Hobbs — in thirty years in the field, he hadn't encountered a single company that, to his mind, made a decent valve; he had always had to redesign everything himself!

After simmering down a bit, Hobbs sent a special-delivery letter to Chicago, and the Crane draftsman, who had left the plant at noon on Saturday, found all the solutions waiting on his desk Monday morning. After receiving the quick approval of the Army and Kellex, Crane soon afterwards started production of the new valves.

It was a revolutionary model, one different from all valves known at that time in industry. Hobbs's new valve was much simpler; made of nickel-plated ordinary steel, it was not only one-quarter the weight of a standard valve, but it also cost 25 percent less. No lubricant was used — none was necessary, for Hobbs had used guides made of bronze. He had remembered seeing a demonstration of specially leaded bronze bearings long ago in Grand Central Palace in New York; visitors had been able to light their cigarettes on the red-hot bronze.

In New York, J.C. lived in Manhattan's Downtown Athletic Club quite near his office, and spent the weekends with his family in Ohio. Now, as tooling up for the valves moved ahead at full speed at Crane, Hobbs had to go back and forth to Chicago in order to supervise actual manufacture of the valves — thousands of them, in sixty-five different sizes and shapes. As he commuted ceaselessly from New York to Ohio to Chicago, Hobbs often chuckled over the fact that Kellex had employed him only on a "part-time" basis!

At Oak Ridge, construction of the incredible K–25 plant was progressing rapidly, but the problem of the intricate piping system assumed colossal proportions. It would have been even more complicated if J. C. Hobbs had not introduced some drastic modifications — for which he often had to step on a lot of people's toes. There was the problem of the piping joints, for instance. They were big, heavy bolts and flanges called Sargol joints — the pipes were flanged out and welded on the edge that held them together. Hobbs estimated that millions of such pipe joints would be required and yet they could never be made airtight. He realized that such a joint, when under pressure and with the vacuum inside, would become a "pull" unit, that is, it would tend to pull apart. So he sat down and invented a joint that took into account the expansion and contraction of the pipes and prevented any leakage.

"I want a new layout," Hobbs told the chief engineer. "I don't want those elbows that you've put everywhere. Why do we need elbows? You tell me that's the custom — all right, but it's a silly custom! Pipe is only a necessary *nuisance;* pipe doesn't produce anything, and the less of it, the better. That's my philosophy: eliminate problems — eliminate every darned thing that you can which isn't necessary!"

J.C.'s philosophy was well known around Kellex, and Keith was often amused by the peculiar pearls of wisdom that Hobbs frequently dropped. "In mechanics it's like life," he used to say. "When something begins to bother you too much, and you can't solve it, don't try to find solutions — just drop the whole darned thing and try to do without it! Sometimes the best cure for problems is not to solve them, but just to drop them!"

Applying his philosophy to pipes at Oak Ridge, Hobbs eliminated most pipe elbows. "Run the pipe in a straight line from where the gas comes from and directly to where you want to use it," he told the engineers. "And remember, the less pipe the better; in fact, zero is what I want. A straight line and zero piping — that would be ideal!"

Running his grease pencil over the beautifully designed drawings, Hobbs butted lines, crossed out elbows, and thus threw away miles of piping. From time to time he would turn to the younger engineers and say, "If a feature of equipment gives you trouble, throw it out and design something *without* that feature!

"And make everything simpler!" he continued. "Look, you can cut out half your piping by pushing these two lines together — you don't have to have an alley for repair work between them. This place will be so radioactive that no operator can go in there anyway. Once it's built and sealed up it has to run for one whole year at least without anyone ever having to go near it. So just cut out the repair alley! Always remember to simplify."

The engineers who worked under J. C. Hobbs soon got the idea.

44

"WE, THE BARBERS of Richland, should feel proud of the wonderful new building entrusted to our care," read the pamphlet which had been put out for the barbers who would assume responsibility for the thousands of workers at the Hanford Engineering Works, twenty-three miles away. "And it is our aim to give this city the very highest-class barber service obtainable."

It was much more easily said than done, however: the forty-five thousand heads of hair at the Hanford plant proved to be too much for the loyal company of barbers and, though their shop operated day and night, the time allotted each customer had to be limited to a bare five minutes. The barbers were really trying to do their best; the same pamphlet gave some Emily Post–like advice in an effort to teach them the rules of savoir faire:

"Every patron is a 'gentleman,' not a 'guy,' 'old duffer,' or some other unflattering term," said the tip sheet. "Every man is entitled to respect and courtesy; recognize their rank: 'Doctor,' not 'Doc'; 'Captain,' not 'Cap'; 'Sergeant,' not 'Sarge.' Many innocent and honorable men have suffered the loss of friends just through personal kidding such as, 'Boy, were you plastered last night!' It means the loss of a customer."

The barbers' familiarity was actually among the lesser sources of irritation and discontent for the growing population of Hanford, Washington. Life was not easy in Plutonium City, especially during the first year when the most elementary facilities were lacking. The main complaints were about the housing shortage, the distance from any city, and the feeling that the Project was not vital to the war effort. The nearly continuous dust storms, with the strong winds sweeping across the sagebrush and the sand stinging the workers' eyes, filling their mouths and covering food and clothes with fine dust — these discomforts led many men to terminate their contracts in disgust. After one violent sandstorm, five hundred workers quit.

The Hanford population resembled that of a wide-open town of the Old West. Drinking, gambling and fighting were favorite pastimes of many of the inhabitants, who were described by one of the construction camp's patrolmen as "very rough hombres with no respect for the law, themselves or God Almighty." Beer consumption at Hanford was higher than in Seattle. The bar had windows that could be thrown up quickly so that tear gas could be squirted inside to stop barroom brawls. The patrolmen had a busy time in the evening. Intoxicated workers were loaded into a paddy wagon and locked up in the small Hanford jail until they sobered up enough to go back to work. The overriding concern was to keep every worker on the job and to fight absenteeism.

Colonel Matthias and Du Pont had to deal daily with hundreds of complaints. Discontent found an outlet in unprintable jokes about Hanford, or poems like the interminable one about a Dantesque dream of a Hanfordite begging the Devil to admit him into Hell, and crying with disappointment when he wakes up in Hanford:

> *What town has bachelors galore?*
> *It's Hanford.*
> *Unmarried maidens, three or four?*
> *It's Hanford.*
> *What town with lovely dames is rife,*
> *More than you've seen in all your life,*
> *But each is someone else's wife,*
> *In Hanford.*
>
> *What town has excellent police?*
> *It's Hanford.*
> *And still cannot maintain its peace?*
> *It's Hanford.*
> *There's knifings, shootings, stickups, rum,*
> *And every kind of crook and bum.*
> *They chase them out, but more still come,*
> *To Hanford.*

But there were several good things to be said about life at Hanford. "Life here is a little on the rough side," admitted the recruiters' booklets; but it had such advantages as "good hearty food for family men," famous mess hall pies and rent of $1.40 per week for cabins or barracks, including janitor service. In spite of food rationing, meat was served in copious quantity at each meal. Recreational activities were plentiful, including hillbilly dancing at the huge, four-thousand-capacity dance hall, baseball, movies, visiting bands such as Kay Kyser, shows with hula girls, and exhibition basketball games by the Harlem Globetrotters.

Relations between Du Pont and the military were generally good.

Colonel Matthias dealt mostly with Gil Church, the construction manager, and his boss Slim Read, and later with the operations head Walter Simon and his superior Roger Williams. In principle, Fritz Matthias was supposed to report to Colonel Nichols. But Nichols was becoming more and more involved in operations at Oak Ridge; moreover, he was not a man to stick to chain-of-command formalities if a job could be performed better in another way. Thus, in practice, for many of the problems concerning Hanford, Matthias reported directly to General Groves, with Nichols's full assent. Groves had given him authority to sign contracts up to ten million dollars without having to ask any higher authority. On several occasions, Matthias had arguments with his friend Gil Church; but when this was reported to Groves, the general's only comment was, "Well, if those two guys don't argue sometimes, they're both no good."

The general used to come often to inspect the progress of work until the day that Slim Read, the big, outspoken Du Pont engineer, called his attention to the effect of his visits. "You know, General, if you really wanted to speed this business up, you would curtail the visits of your people until we told you that the reactors were producing."

"Why?" Groves asked.

"Look, General, too much of the time of our top people is taken up with these visits — preparing charts and assembling data, so as to make sure that things will be perfectly clear for your inspection. And our basic work has consequently been slowed down."

For a moment Groves was silent. Then, looking Read straight in the eye, he said, "Can you guarantee that they won't be bothered by any Du Pont executives coming out here either? I mean, if I keep myself and my crew out of your hair, can you guarantee that you will keep your own Du Pont representatives out of this place?"

"Yes," came the prompt reply.

Groves turned to Norman Hilberry. "And can you keep those Chicago scientists out of here?" When Hilberry nodded, Groves said, "All right, Mr. Read, it's a deal! I'll wait for you to call me."

Most of the irritation with the military came from their insistence that security measures be extremely tight. Du Pont was not the least bothered by them — they had similar precautions in their own plants. But some scientists thought most of these measures exaggerated; the majority of Hanford's personnel could not understand them at all. Everything concerning the activities at Hanford was stringently classified. All mention of the quantity of supplies shipped in or out was forbidden — including the amount of ice cream or beer consumed. Badges and identification papers were required at the entrance to every area and every building.

The better-known scientists had to use a different name when they left their home laboratories. Compton, for instance, was Mr. Holly at Oak Ridge but Mr. Comas at Hanford. Enrico Fermi was Dr. Farmer in Hanford, and Eugene Wigner was Dr. Wagner. One day when Wigner forgot his identity badge, the guard at the door refused to let him enter. Fermi, who was with Wigner, offered to vouch for his colleague.

"Can you swear that this man's name is Wagner?" the guard demanded sternly.

"His name is Wagner just as sure as mine is Farmer," answered Fermi, showing his own top-clearance papers.

"Thank you, Mr. Farmer," said the guard, waving them in.

Groves, who did not want to take any chances, had assigned a bodyguard to Fermi with orders never to let him out of sight. John Baudino was a big, powerfully built Italian-American from Illinois, with a good education and a pleasant personality. The independent-minded Fermi, after protesting that it was all utterly ridiculous, ended up by taking advantage of the situation and using his bodyguard as an extra hand in his lab experiments. Though they became good friends, Baudino never learned to enjoy the lectures on nuclear physics that Fermi insisted on giving him during the long train trips to Hanford and Los Alamos. "Say, John," the scientist would say, "an intelligent fellow like you — how come you know nothing about physics?"

On the construction side, new difficulties and problems arose every day. In early 1944 a serious shortage of plumbers and pipe fitters developed; all efforts to find men with the necessary skills failed. Once more, Groves did not hesitate to use his special authority in order to get what he needed for the Manhattan Project: he swiftly arranged for highly qualified pipe fitters and plumbers to be released from the Army, placed on reserve status and sent immediately to Hanford. Within days, from some sixty Army stations around the country, uniformed plumbers and pipe fitters began to converge on Hanford. It was not compulsory duty, however; each man was given the choice of either working on the Project or returning to his command. If a man's work proved unsatisfactory, he was subject to recall to active duty. In a remarkably swift, efficient operation, two hundred and fifty specialists were delivered in less than one week, and all but twenty-five qualified for the Hanford work.

When the time came to harvest the crops, another thorny problem arose: what to do with the highly developed, irrigated orchards now owned by the Government? The proprietors had been evacuated; no civilian crop pickers could be allowed in the restricted area. Tons of cherries, apricots, peaches and asparagus would thus be condemned to waste. Fritz Matthias received a tip from the official in charge of Prison Industries, which handled all the commercial activities of Federal prisons.

After talking over the harvest problem with the warden of McNeil Island Penitentiary, near Tacoma, Matthias set up a temporary prison camp just south of the Hanford site. Hundreds of prisoners, working under penitentiary guards, began harvesting all the crops in the area and sending the fruit to the prison's canning factory. Thanks to this ingenious solution, no manpower was siphoned off from the nation's war effort, and nobody could learn what the prisoners had been seeing of top-secret installations during the day.

On a Saturday night in September 1944, Colonel Matthias drove 350 miles to go salmon fishing with friends at the mouth of the Columbia River. About noon the following day, a Coast Guard boat hailed them, saying that there was an urgent telephone call for Matthias: the plumbers on one shift had gone on strike.

Strikes were a constant anxiety, but they had rarely developed. Matthias drove back immediately and called a meeting of the strikers for 8 A.M. Monday. The 750 men who assembled in the Hanford theater that morning were in an ugly mood; many had been drinking, and the place was in an uproar when Matthias marched onto the stage.

"You are interrupting a project that could save the lives of a great many of our servicemen," he said over the microphone when the crowd quieted down. "I am sure that most of you are patriotic Americans. I wish I could find the dozen or so men responsible for this outbreak, and send them to Germany where they belong."

A wild storm of protest followed. Matthias felt that if there had been guns in the crowd, he would have been shot then and there. After a young union officer came to his rescue and succeeded in calming the audience, Matthias went on. "I know that most of you are patriotic Americans. I will see that your complaints are heard and handled promptly. Now, how about going back to work?"

There was a short moment of silence, then cheers and enthusiasm equal in volume to the protests of only a few minutes before.

"The buses will be at this door in ten minutes," Matthias continued in a firm voice. "Load from here and get back to work!" The strike was over. The few complaints of the plumbers were settled in a few days.

The three piles were the actual units for plutonium production at Hanford, but almost equally important were the separation plants which treated the slugs that had been irradiated in the piles. During 1944, three separation installations, called T, U and B plants, were constructed in two isolated and heavily guarded desert areas south of the Gable Mountains. They were some ten miles from the nearest Hanford pile and, for safety reasons, were placed well apart from each other. They were sinister-looking, windowless structures with walls six to eight feet thick; they were, in effect, huge, rectangular concrete boxes 800 feet long, 65 feet wide and 80 feet high. Each contained an underground row of 40 cells, which were 20 feet deep and about 15 feet in width and length; they were separated from each other by six feet of concrete and covered by 35-ton concrete lids. Operating galleries, on three levels, ran along the cell row. The entire area above the cells was enclosed by a single gallery, 60 feet high, called a canyon — a silent, deadly radioactive tunnel with glaring electric lamps, where no human being could survive once the operation started.

The most spectacular feature of the separation plants was that they were operated entirely by remote control. The system of remote control and optical surveillance developed by Du Pont for the Hanford operation was indeed without precedent in industrial history. Practically all the optical devices represented ingenious adaptations of instruments designed for other uses — Navy periscopes, Air Force bombing lenses, miscellaneous items from government surplus.

Dan Friel, the twenty-three-year-old chemist who was developing Du Pont's optical instruments, ran into difficulty when the lenses of his first devices turned black under the effect of radiation. After designing complicated systems in which not only the operator but the glass part of the instruments had to be shielded, he discovered that plastics were not subject to darkening; furthermore, he learned that the Navy was already using plastic lenses for its periscopes. Thus, a whole new category of lens material was developed by Du Pont, with plastics being used instead of glass in all instruments placed near uranium.

Friel and his colleagues designed about twenty different optical units for remote control. Most of the components were purchased from the Kollmorgen optical company, makers of submarine periscopes for the Navy. One of the most extraordinary units was the submarine periscope mounted on a huge, sixty-foot-long bridge crane, which had been specially devised by Du Pont. Each of the three canyons of the separation plants was served by one crane running on rails the length of the building. The operator stood in a cab shielded with lead from where he could maneuver the crane and the two periscopes, one mounted on each side of the cab, so that he got a stereoscopic view down into the highly radioactive canyon.* The bridge, with its "traveler," moved back and forth parallel to the canyon's wall, while the hooks and wrenches were moved up and down inside the canyon.

Another unprecedented item was the use of television units to look

---

* These periscopes, the world's largest, were designed jointly by the University of Chicago and Du Pont, then assembled by Du Pont in Wilmington.

behind barricades. Television was in its infancy — the quality was very poor; but it still proved useful, especially in the separation areas. By using "fly-eye" lenses originally made for B–29 bombsights, Friel also designed a device for looking into the interior of big tanks filled with water or chemicals; it permitted technicians to see everything that was going on throughout a 360-degree angle.

One stubborn problem was how to find a way of examining, microscopically, uranium slugs at the moment they emerged from the reactor and were yet so radioactive that they glowed in the water. Since their high radiation made it too dangerous to bring the slugs up to the surface, Friel had to develop microscopes that would not only work under water but also go down as deep as thirty feet.

The Du Pont man in charge of Hanford's separation plants was Raymond Genereaux, a blue-eyed, six-foot-three engineer. In 1942, Tom Gary, Du Pont's chief of design, had assigned him the job of designing the separation plants. Genereaux learned about the process in Chicago, where the resident Du Pont representative, Charles Cooper, was working with Glenn Seaborg's group. After the Chicago scientists had developed the process for chemical separation of plutonium, the Manhattan Project asked Du Pont to build installations for its industrial production. But this meant that the laboratory process would be scaled up one billion times!

Genereaux started the design work with thirty-five engineers and draftsmen in the Nemours Building in Wilmington. The design was particularly difficult because of the tremendous radioactivity of the irradiated uranium slugs. John Wheeler, a young but already well-known physicist from Princeton, was assigned to advise the Du Pont designers on the separation plant; because of his helpful, unpretentious manner, he soon became the engineers' favorite scientist in the Project.

At Oak Ridge, in the meantime, the Chicago scientists were already producing small amounts of plutonium for experimental purposes in their Clinton pile, located in the X–10 area. After a pilot plant for the separation of this plutonium was built next to it, Du Pont transferred several hundred engineers to Oak Ridge to study the operation. Even so, the scale at Hanford would be so gigantic in comparison with the X–10 pilot plants, that it looked as if all the problems would have to be solved anew.

One thing that particularly exasperated the construction people at Hanford was the extraordinary requirements for cleanliness imposed by the scientists. When the canyons were built, each wall had to be washed by hand, rubbed smooth with bricks wrapped in gunnysacks, and then covered with a special paint. Anyone entering one of the canyons had to put on white canvas slippers so as not to mar the smoothness of the floor.

Many people, including Du Pont engineers, were skeptical about the feasibility of remote control for such a large-scale plant. It did not sound realistic to expect the operators to exercise total control over an intricate process, to repair and replace the equipment, only by teleguided cranes and periscopes. Nonetheless an intensive training program was set up by Du Pont in Wilmington and also at Oak Ridge so that the operating personnel for the future separation plants could be taught how to handle pipes and bolts by remote control and the use of optical instruments.

A mock-up building with steel framework was later put up at Hanford, with cells simulating those in the actual canyons and with exactly the same equipment. For three months the crane operators had to practice assembling the equipment, setting up the vessels in which the slugs would be dissolved and making the pipe connections. A color system was used to distinguish the parts: the bails were painted yellow, for example, the hooks red; large numbers were painted on the flanges. All parts and tools were standardized; the wrenches on the crane had only one socket, which fitted the standard size of all studs and connections.

But no matter how precise the simulated conditions were, Ray Genereaux continued to worry about the training. Would the operators be able to perform with the requisite, almost perfect, precision once the canyons became poisonous and no one would be permitted to enter them? In the summer of 1944, as the time approached for placing the real equipment into the canyons, it occurred to Genereaux that the operators could get no better training in manipulation and maintenance of their machinery than by actually installing it. His idea was adopted, even though it meant doing the installation work in the hardest possible way.

In preparation, all the equipment was carefully dismantled, checked and cleaned with chemical solutions, then wrapped in cellophane paper. When it was delivered at the T canyon in September 1944, Genereaux called the trained operators together — about one hundred men — and gave a strict order: henceforth no one could enter what in the future would be a radioactive area; T canyon would be closed — just as if deadly radiation had already penetrated it. Then, step by step, the operators began the assembly by means of remote control, using cranes, teleguided tongs, hooks and periscopes to fasten bolts and connect pipes and wires.

Leading four of his men, Genereaux was the first to jump into the cab of one of the huge cranes. "Maybe you don't think you can do this," he said to the others, "but let me tell you — you'll do it! Now, who's going to try first?"

WESTFIELD MEMORIAL LIBRARY
WESTFIELD, N. J.

One operator lowered the crane, picked up a wheelbarrow and started practicing with it, under the amused eyes of his comrades. Then another operator, his eyes glued to the periscope, lifted two pipes and tried to connect them. When the two metal ends touched each other, a microphone transmitted the squeak. The amplifying of sounds was going to be an important new tool: the mechanics' experienced ears could even distinguish among various noises made by screw threads entering the grooves.*

The crowd of operators, amused at first but then fascinated, joined in the action. "It's my turn, you've played enough!" one complained impatiently. It had quickly become a game — not unlike the one people play in penny arcades with toy cranes that pick up rings and candy.

Deeply involved in the painstaking game, the men gained confidence; soon they attempted increasingly difficult jobs, directing the hooks and wrenches of the clumsy-looking cranes in operations of minute precision. The key tool was a special remote-control wrench designed for connecting pipes and wires. Called the "jumper," it performed beautifully. All the intricate piping and wiring was connected by means of this tool — and without any worker ever coming near the equipment. By watching through the special optical instruments and correcting their connection maneuvers by the sounds coming over a microphone, the operators worked somewhat after the fashion of an expert safecracker, listening to the sound of tumblers falling in a combination lock.

The experience gained from this unorthodox way of installing the plant's machinery was invaluable. Once the separation canyons were in operation, no other control, maintenance or replacement of parts was possible except by remote control. The irradiated slugs, containing some newly formed plutonium, would be ejected from the pile and lowered into deep pools of water for cooling. Then they would be automatically placed in square, heavily shielded casks, or buckets, after which they were put, still by remote control, on special railroad cars for transportation to storage areas. At the storage areas, which were located five miles away from the pile, the casks would then be immersed in water inside a concrete bunker.

After waiting for some days, until part of the tremendous radioactivity had cooled down, technicians would reload the casks onto rail flatcars which transported them to the first canyon. The canyon doors would slide open to receive them and the flatcars would be automatically uncoupled. The crane operator, already in his cab, would remove the three heavy

* In addition to the periscopes, the assembly operation could also be watched on the television screen in the control room. But since the quality of the newly invented gadget was still very poor, the image came blurred.

concrete blocks forming the roof of the first cell of the canyon, in order to be able to operate inside. He would take off the cask's cover and tilt the cask at a certain angle so that the slugs slid into the container filled with dissolving chemicals. The empty cask would then be replaced on the flatcar, which would be coupled to others and pulled away. At the same time, the roof of the cell would be fitted back into place.

Once the irradiated slugs had dissolved, the operators on the control floor would move the liquid through pipes into the adjoining cells. The radioactive liquid, containing some still-unseparated plutonium, would be treated consecutively in the canyons, going through three successive steps that formed the separation process: solution, precipitation and removal of the precipitate by centrifuge. At each step, the material would become less radioactive. Performing the entire operation by remote control, the operators had to be able to visualize exactly what was going on behind the thick concrete walls, and to diagnose and repair, through the maze of piping and instruments, any malfunction that might occur.

Of the many other revolutionary innovations developed for the first time in industrial history, one of the most dramatic occurred in the so-called "300 Area." For weeks the Du Pont progress reports sent back to Wilmington had been identical: "Good progress in all areas except for unchanged situation in 300 Area. We continue to push." Week after week Colonel Matthias had had to give the same answer to an increasingly impatient General Groves: "Still no success in 300 Area, General."

The 300 Area was where uranium slugs were canned. Several months had elapsed since the first unsuccessful attempts in Chicago and Wilmington to find a perfect way to wrap the uranium bars in protective jackets and thus prevent any direct contact with the cooling water. To speed up work on the problem, some of Du Pont's laboratories were moved to Hanford; but still no solution could be found, and the entire Project was now being jeopardized by the delay.

At first sight the problem did not look particularly difficult—uranium simply had to be encased in an aluminum tube — "like the casing on a frankfurter," as one engineer described it. But nothing less than an absolutely perfect fit was acceptable: the slightest leak or air pocket in even one of the thousands of slugs could have the disastrous effect of contaminating the whole area and shutting down the pile as well. The canning technique called for uniform heating of the entire surface of the uranium slug, then slipping it into an aluminum can, which likewise had to be heated uniformly, and then welding the two together. The welding of aluminum that was only a few thousandths of an inch thick presented yet another difficulty. The bond between the uranium and the aluminum casing had to be perfect; even slugs showing 90 or 95 percent quality at the test inspection were rejected.

Du Pont mobilized a special group at the 300 Area to find a good canning technique. Three university laboratories — Chicago, Iowa State and Brown — were asked to help, and the country's foremost metallurgists were consulted. Complicated methods and equipment were tried, but the ideal bond between slug and casing seemed impossible to achieve. The visits of Du Pont's Crawford Greenewalt to the 300 Area became more and more frequent, and the goading from all sides was intense. Kelyth Jones, Ward Meyers, Raymond Grills and the rest of the canning research personnel developed a deep guilt complex, confronted as they were daily by dozens of impatient officers and engineers, all asking the same question: "What the hell is taking you so long down there at the 300 Area? Where are the slugs? Don't you realize that nothing can progress any further until you do the damned canning?"

45

LIKE ALL his colleagues, Dr. Raymond Grills was doing his utmost to lick the problem. A twenty-six-year-old chemist from Illinois, he had been assigned by Du Pont some months before to study all possible methods of uranium canning and had done research in Chicago and Wilmington before coming out to Hanford. Though Grills had been told that the reactors would produce plutonium, he was at first unaware of the ultimate purpose of the production, and never learned what work was being done in other laboratories. He knew little about metallurgy and even less about uranium, whose properties were still largely unknown.

Grills was never to forget the day when he took a uranium slug to a commercial machine shop in the northern section of Chicago to have it sandblasted. Uranium oxidizes very fast and turns black, and it cannot be coated until the oxidation is removed, either by washing in acid or by scrubbing by hand. So someone at the university had suggested, "Why don't we sandblast this thing and see what will happen?"

When the slug was taken to the shop, the machinist said confidently, "Oh, sure we can do it. We can blast any material you want." He put it inside the sandblaster and pressed the button. When the sand hit the uranium, a tremendous shower of sparks filled the room — a veritable Fourth of July fireworks display. The operator nearly fainted. "My God! What's going on here?" he gasped, trembling from shock.

Grills, however, could not tell him what the slug was made of. "Just keep blasting!" he commanded. "It's all right! Nothing is going to happen!"

Another time Grills had had to take a few slugs from Cleveland to Chicago. The uranium had been placed in two rectangular boxes the size of a small suitcase. But the metal proved so heavy that he had great trouble carrying the boxes up the long stairs in the station. A porter, seeing a young man sweating and puffing from carrying just two small packages, thought that Grills was sick and offered to help him. Grills usually never let anyone else handle the uranium entrusted to his care; but after a few more steps, he was so worn out that he put the boxes down and said, "Fine!"

The porter bent to pick them up — and was almost jerked off his feet. His broad smile disappeared and he looked at Grills in awestruck surprise. "What in the world are you carrying around?" he whispered. "I've been a porter going on thirty years, but I've never come on anything like this before!"

After working on the canning problem for nearly two years, Grills, like the others in his group at Hanford, was beginning to feel discouraged. Just when all techniques seemed to have failed, a solution finally came. Its simplicity was hardly believable. Grills had noted earlier that the unusually fast oxidation of the uranium slugs prevented a perfectly even coating, no matter how quick the canning. One evening he decided to try the whole canning operation in a solder bath, working beneath the surface of the molten solder. This way no air could get in, he reasoned, and all sides of the slug would thus be uniformly exposed to the coating liquid. Working with an associate, Ed Smith, Grills submerged the slug in one of the four-foot-deep, round tanks and tried to can it beneath the surface. They did it manually, using long tongs and ignoring all the sophisticated high-power tools, heating devices and dipping arrangements that they had been using previously. Surprisingly, they obtained perfectly good, uniform heat transfer.

But then the two chemists discovered that they had burned a hole through the aluminum tube. Apparently the temperature of the liquid in the bath was so high that it melted the aluminum; in the future, the casing operation would have to be done more swiftly. They tried again, working faster this time; the second slug looked good. Experimenting late into the night, they came to the conclusion that their new coating method seemed better than anything else tried before.

Highly excited by their success, Grills and Smith postponed putting the slugs through the special testing device until the next day and they agreed to tell no one of their discovery until after the final test. The next evening they studied the results — the slugs had coated perfectly! Exhilarated, they ran to Kelyth Jones, Grills's boss, to announce the good news. The word spread rapidly to everyone entitled to know. After several more tests and experiments, no doubt remained: a canning technique had been found that assured 100 percent perfection!

Hanford's first pile was almost completed when fears arose that the cooling water, pumped from the Columbia River, would not be pure enough and might therefore contaminate the reactors. Some scientists swore that this would not develop. Others strongly advised the immediate construction of a de-ionizing plant that would distill the water. The fact was, nobody really knew.

General Groves was discussing the problem with Slim Read one night at Hanford when Dr. Hilberry entered the room. When Groves asked his opinion, Hilberry thought for a minute, then said, "I don't believe such a plant is needed. However, if I'm wrong and we *do* need it, we could not do without it." Groves reacted characteristically. Turning to Read, he gave the order: "Go ahead and build it."

"What would it cost?" asked Hilberry.

"Between six and ten million dollars," answered the general calmly. (Until 1944, the monthly pay of General Groves, who was signing checks for hundreds of millions of dollars nearly every month, was only $663.40, including all allowances. Toward the end of the war, his total pay rose to $828.67 a month.)

The scientist's eyes opened wide. "Well, I'm glad I didn't know *that* when I gave my opinion."*

By August, construction at Hanford was nearing completion, and Du Pont's production arm began to take over, under the first plant manager, Walter O. Simon. The company's engineers had performed a remarkable job, carrying out a crash program wherein basic research, development and engineering had to be pushed forward simultaneously. In two short years the gigantic Hanford Engineering Works had become a reality. From what had been a sagebrush wasteland had arisen a sprawling complex spread over some six hundred square miles: a new city, Richland, three huge reactors, two chemical-separation plants, an administrative headquarters and innumerable buildings for service facilities required in the complicated manufacturing process. Plans and designs had had to be changed constantly during construction. The helium-cooled model reactor was abandoned in February 1943 and replaced by the water-cooled pile. Though original plans had called for five reactors, only three were built; and of the eight separation plants originally considered necessary, only three were erected, one to serve as a reserve.

In early September 1944, Groves called Colonel Matthias from Washington and heard the good news: Hanford's first reactor was ready to be tried without delay. As the great day approached, tension mounted. Scientists, army and civilian engineers realized that the whole fate of the plutonium project was in the balance: no matter how thorough the preparation for them, no preliminary experiments had been able to demonstrate definitely how the huge reactors would work. Would they

---

* It later turned out that the de-ionizing plant was never needed. But in Groves's opinion, the Manhattan Project could not run the risk of not having such a plant ready if the need ever developed.

behave like the small Oak Ridge pile? And what would happen when the designed power peak of 250,000 kilowatts was reached? What if some unforeseen event occurred? Everybody was on edge. If the reactor failed, there would probably be no second chance.

"Colonel," Groves had said to Matthias on the telephone from Washington, "I'd advise you of one thing. You'd better be out there when they start running that plant. And if it blows up, you just jump right in the middle of it — it will save you such a heck of a lot of trouble!"

Matthias was there when the loading of "B" pile started in the afternoon of Wednesday, September 13. Tense and nervous, Arthur Compton and Enrico Fermi, accompanied by Du Pont's Roger Williams and Crawford Greenewalt, joined the operating personnel. The last construction worker had been evacuated that morning. Now there was only a trained crew proceeding with final inspection of the instruments. Soon, once "criticality" — the critical mass — was reached, the whole reactor within the thick protective concrete walls would become deadly radioactive.

At 5:43 P.M. Fermi stepped forward to insert the first slug into the reactor. It was only fitting that he should do it, as he had for the first pile in Chicago, at Stagg Field's racquets court, nearly two years earlier. Everyone present recognized that the Italian-born atomic genius should have the honor of directing operations. But the loading this time was going to be a very long process taking several days to do — thousands of uranium slugs had to be inserted and numerous tests carried out.

The operating crews worked through Wednesday night and all of Thursday. Early Friday morning, criticality seemed near, though the pile was still operating without water in its cooling system. The control rods were inserted, then Fermi, using his battered, old slide rule, swiftly calculated how much uranium should be added to make the pile critical while the cooling water flowed through the maze of pipes. At each phase of the loading, measurements were taken — always confirming the maestro's slide-rule prediction within a margin of only one-tenth of one percent. By Monday the pile was generating heat, and the operators prepared the cooling system for action. The build-up of power was raised by slow increments of about 5000 kilowatts each.

On September 27, 1944, only a few minutes after midnight — and two weeks after Fermi had started the loading of B pile — the long-awaited great event occurred. The control rods were withdrawn, the power rose gradually, and a chain reaction began to take place. After an hour at that level, the operators were signaled to raise the power slightly higher. By two o'clock the power had exceeded that of any previous chain reaction; and it was still only a small fraction of the reactor's capacity.

Then, at three o'clock in the morning, something peculiar — and totally unexpected — happened. The power level suddenly began to decrease, slowly at first, then faster and faster as time went on. By 4 A.M. power had sunk to half its original level. The operators, puzzled and alarmed, checked and rechecked each instrument, each dial on their control panels. The chain reaction was slowly dying off. At 6:30 A.M. the failure was total; the pile had shut down completely — by itself.

No one could understand what had happened, or why. Scientists and engineers, with disaster written on their faces, rushed to examine B pile. Different hypotheses were advanced to account for the failure. There was, of course, always the possibility of sabotage. One theory, too, was that there might have been leaks in the pipes, which would have admitted water into the graphite. Another theory was that the water of the Columbia River, which contained boron, had left a scalelike deposit on the tubes, thus absorbing the all-important neutrons necessary for a chain reaction. Still another hypothesis incriminated the nitrogen in the air: it had gotten into the pores of the graphite and "swallowed" neutrons. Another scientist suspected that mortar might have leaked.

But none of these hypotheses was able to explain the failure. Morale at Hanford plummeted. This was more than a failure; it looked like total disaster. After two years of superhuman effort, Hanford suddenly began to look like a $350-million fiasco.

46

THE FAILURE of Hanford's B pile was a bitter disappointment, and there was also something extremely mysterious about it. On the evening of September 27, crews were still trying desperately to revive the reactor. Since the prevailing theory attributed the failure to water leakage, hot helium was first circulated through the pile in order to dry it out; but it soon appeared that the amount of water was too insignificant to have caused the trouble. Then, abruptly and without any apparent cause, the reactor became critical again, like a dead monster coming suddenly to life and starting to breathe.

By 1 A.M. the pile had been brought up to 200 kilowatts, and by four o'clock the next afternoon, it was raised again to 9000 kilowatts, the same level reached on the previous day. But before the operating crew could show any jubilation, the neutron multiplication again began to decrease and the chain reaction died off. It was an exact duplication of what had happened the day before.

What was wrong? Alarmed men rushed to the telephones to consult Chicago and Oak Ridge. Engineers scrutinized every chart, rechecked every instrument. Groves's reaction was immediate. No one was to go to Hanford, he ordered, unless specially asked; telephone calls were to be severely limited. He himself remained in Washington. "It's Hanford's baby," he said. "Let them solve the problem alone!" Scientists were brought in from all over the Hanford area like doctors to the bedside of a dying patient. Enrico Fermi was the great authority whose diagnosis was eagerly awaited. At the same time emissaries were sent to the 300 Area, some twenty-five miles away, to the laboratory of a young specialist in reactor "diseases."

John A. Wheeler, a thirty-one-year-old physicist from Princeton, had been studying the problems of "poisoning" in atomic piles for nearly three years. After leaving Princeton to work on the Project for Du Pont, he was given great encouragement to continue his own research. His immediate superior, George Graves, had first said, "Who in the hell told people to worry about radioactivity?" But soon Graves was paying great attention to Wheeler's memos about possible bugs in the future reactors and himself prodded the scientists in Chicago to experiment more on possible weak points. While Wheeler worried about the possibility of fission products' having a poisoning effect on the reactor, Graves kept a book in which every conceivable crisis situation was catalogued.

When John Wheeler first came in contact with the atomic project, he thought that the job would take him away only temporarily from other fields of physics where his real interests lay. He even refused to join when he was asked at the beginning of the war; he was unwilling to take the pledge of secrecy without knowing what the work was all about. At the time, he did not believe that the war in Europe would affect the United States in a major way and he was quite content to pursue his studies of the nature of matter and energy, of space and time. Trying to understand how the world was put together had been Wheeler's passion since childhood, and, strangely enough, he did not think that nuclear physics would help him in finding the answers.

As a boy, John Wheeler had never really had a home town. His father was a librarian and the family frequently moved from one post to another. Born in Florida, John lived there only six months before the family moved to California, where they stayed for three years; then they went to Ohio for seven years, to Vermont for two and to Baltimore for eight. At the age of twenty-one, the precocious youth had already received his doctor's degree from Johns Hopkins University. His family was proud but hardly surprised: at the age of three he had already begun to ask his mother about the world of nature. By the time he was ten, his passionate interest in scientific experiments had nearly led to a fatal tragedy when, after reading a book on explosives, he obtained some dynamite for an experiment — and promptly blew off one of his fingertips.

The hero of his student years was the great Danish physicist Niels Bohr, principally because of Bohr's deep interest in philosophical theories of the nature of the universe. To Wheeler the Dane was essentially a philosopher, one who looked upon physics as a proving ground for philosophy rather than as merely a method of investigating the substance and mechanism of nature. Wheeler himself was fascinated by problems of cosmology — such ultimate questions as what might happen in a billion years when, according to one of the main theories, the universe will stop expanding and start contracting. He was amazed by Bohr's theory concerning the effect that an observer exerts on the object he observes: according to his theory (which was vehemently attacked by Einstein), it is impossible to observe something without affecting it.

Wheeler was so fascinated by Bohr's thinking that, after receiving his Ph.D., the first thing he did was to write to Denmark to apply for work with the man he thought could best comprehend the nature of the universe. Accepted by Bohr, Wheeler stayed for one year, working as a purely theoretical physicist. It was an exciting time, in 1934 and 1935, when Fermi's experiments in neutron physics were electrifying the scientific world. It was also the period when Bohr rejected the prevalent hypothesis that the atomic nucleus was similar to a miniature solar system, and proposed his own theory of the nucleus as being like a drop of liquid. Wheeler then returned to the United States to teach, first at the University of North Carolina, then at Princeton.

When Niels Bohr arrived in New York in January 1939, carrying the first news of the splitting of the uranium atom in Germany, Wheeler was at the pier to meet him. Dying to discuss the event with a fellow scientist after the long days aboard ship, Bohr exuberantly unloaded all his thoughts right there on the pier. Wheeler was so excited that he immediately canceled all his other activities in order to work with the Dane. The first thing they did was to rush to Princeton's Fine Hall Library to study the collected papers of Lord Rayleigh, who had worked on liquid droplets, in order to adapt his formulas to Bohr's liquid-droplet model of the nucleus. During the four months Bohr stayed at Princeton, Wheeler had the opportunity of sitting in on most of the fascinating discussions that Bohr had with Fermi, Szilard and, later, with Wigner. It was during this period that Bohr first propounded the idea that U–235, and not U–238, was responsible for nuclear fission. Bohr and Wheeler prepared a paper on the mechanism of nuclear fission — what went on and why and what one could expect in the future. The paper was received with enormous interest at a meeting of the American Physical Society in Washington on April 25, 1939.

Bohr went back to Europe and, after the invasion of Denmark in April 1940, temporarily lost contact with America. Wheeler returned to his more philosophical interests but soon became deeply involved with scientists working on fission theory. Szilard and, especially, Wigner were engrossed in the problem of how to prevent the "capture" of neutrons, a phenomenon that would slow down a chain reaction. When Arthur Compton came to Princeton after Pearl Harbor to invite physicists to join his Metallurgical Laboratory, both Wigner and Wheeler accepted.

In Chicago, Wheeler worked mostly on "the bugs under the table" — the things that might go wrong. The danger of poisons affecting the chain reaction was high on his list. He went to Wilmington to conduct courses for the Du Pont engineers, explaining atomic fission and working with them on the design of the plants. He was one of the few Chicago scientists willing to do this. Most of Wheeler's colleagues were at first unhappy about the engineers' taking over responsibility for the Project, but

Wheeler himself had no strong feelings one way or another, probably because fission alone did not particularly attract him as the subject for his life work.

Despite criticism by some of his academic colleagues, Johnny Wheeler gladly gave the engineers all the assistance he could with nuclear physics. He became, so to speak, their favorite scientist, and in designing the pile, Du Pont engineers took into consideration many of his suggestions, including his warnings about possible reactor poisoning. All this led up to the reason why Wheeler, who had permanently moved to Hanford in July 1944, was among the first persons to be consulted when the B pile stopped functioning.

Since Wheeler had not been present when the reactor failure occurred, he first asked for the readings of the control-rod positions and carefully examined the curve of the pile's reactivity during the start-up. There was no doubt in his mind: the shape of the curve indicated that a short-lived fission product was causing the trouble. The poisoning he had feared for so long had finally occurred. The fact that the chain reaction stopped after a few hours, only to start up again later by itself, proved that some unpredicted substance was being formed during the fission and absorbing so many neutrons that the chain reaction died. This product being short-lived, the difficulty cleared itself up after the reactor was turned off — the poison disappeared after a certain number of hours. The mysterious poison was thus not a permanent but a short-lived, radioactive one.

It took Enrico Fermi only one look to recognize the validity of Wheeler's diagnosis, and the two men proceeded immediately to identify the cause. By studying the charts, they knew exactly how many hours and minutes the effect of the unknown poison lasted, and they started looking for a radioactive gas whose rate of decay — or "half-life" — would fit the description. The scientists proceeded in much the same way that the police identify a criminal by an artist's composite picture. It did not take long before the first disease in reactor technology was discovered. It was called xenon–135, a gas with a half-life of 9.4 hours.

No such poisoning had been reported before at the experimental piles run by the University of Chicago. Greenewalt telephoned Allison in Chicago, explained in coded language what had happened and asked him to check with Walter Zinn at Argonne and Richard Doan at Oak Ridge to see whether they had noticed similar effects. So far they had not, but they began running their piles at full power. Argonne's heavy-water pile, called CP–3, after running for twelve hours started producing a poison that Zinn easily identified as xenon–135.

General Groves was seething with anger when Arthur Compton told him this at a meeting in Chicago on October 3. He had given explicit orders to run Argonne's CP–3 at full power around the clock, and his orders had been disregarded. If the scientists had followed his instructions, they would have found out about the xenon poisoning much earlier. The scientists replied that since CP–3 was a research pile, they could not perform experiments with it if it were operating at full capacity all the time. In Groves's opinion, it was just extreme naïveté and lack of common sense that had led them to disregard his clear-cut instructions. Compton admitted that they had made a mistake, but assured the general it was still not too late to correct it, and flew out at once to Hanford.

On his arrival Compton was told by Hilberry and Greenewalt that steps had already been taken to repair the failure. With no time to wait for definite proof of the correctness of the xenon explanation, Fermi accepted it tentatively as a working hypothesis and started looking for a cure. His calculations led him to the conclusion that the way to compensate for the lost neutrons, which were absorbed by the xenon poison, was to boost the capacity of the reactor. This could be done only by adding more uranium tubes: Fermi's figures indicated a need for at least a 25 percent increase over the current level of 1500 tubes.

If the reactor had been built strictly according to the scientists' design, such a modification would have been impossible. There would not have been enough space or holes in the graphite pile for the hundreds of additional tubes required. Furthermore, the plutonium program at that late stage could not afford abandonment of the completed reactors and the construction of new ones.

Once more, however, the Project was miraculously saved, this time thanks largely to the stubborn insistence of Du Pont's engineers. They had allowed large margins and left extra space in the pile, despite the disagreement of scientists who thought such precautions were completely unnecessary and served only to slow the completion of construction.

The most obstinate of the Du Pont men was George Graves, who had long been impressed by John Wheeler's obsession with reactor poisoning. One year before the start-up, Wheeler had written a memo recommending serious design changes in the reactor, including the addition of 504 uranium-bearing tubes. His concern made Du Pont act even more cautiously than usual. It seemed to be too late for major changes: the massive steel and pressed-wood shield blocks for the reactor had already been built and were to be shipped to Hanford within a few days. Wheeler's modifications required that all holes be enlarged and additional ones bored in the shield blocks. But Graves and Du Pont's management reacted promptly and vigorously, and imposed the changes over the scientists' opposition.

Now everybody was only too happy that conservative Du Pont had played safe and generously allowed extra room in the reactor. George Graves became the hero of the day, and someone even wrote a ballad in his praise:

> *We'd called up a tight design*
> *Hewn strictly to the longhairs' line.*
> *To us, it looked almighty fine —*
> *A honey, we'd insist.*
>
> *But Old Marse George, with baleful glare*
> *And with a roar that shook the air,*
> *Cried, "Dammit, give it stuff to spare —*
> *The longhairs may have missed."*

Additional uranium was gradually loaded and, as Fermi made calculations at each new level, the entire control system was readjusted to the higher power. Finally, when the number of tubes reached 2004, the reactivity completely overcame the effect of the xenon.

On Christmas Day 1944, several tons of irradiated slugs were turned out by the B pile at Hanford. Three days later it operated with a full loading. In the meantime D pile had begun running, and in January F pile also started production.

Extraordinary safety measures were taken to prevent accidents in the piles. The reaction could be controlled by insertion of boron rods (boron soaks up neutrons like a sponge); there was a second set of emergency control rods that could drop from above; and if the reaction ran out of hand the pile could be flooded with a boron solution. The big worry was the interruption of cooling water; according to the scientists, even a fraction of a second without cooling would cause such tremendous build-up of heat in the reactor that it would collapse or explode.

This danger made Du Pont gear all safety devices to the pumps in the cooling system; the instant that there was an interruption of electrical power, the emergency rods would drop in, soak up the flux of neutrons and stop the reaction dead. If the rods were not sufficient, the boron solution would be poured in automatically. These devices were tested before the pile was radioactive, but once it was operating, the engineers never had the courage to test them by shutting off the power.

One day a mysterious power failure occurred somewhere in the current, immediately triggering the safety controls of the reactors. In a fraction of a second the whole plant was shut down cold. Hanford Engineering Works had installed special safeguards in the line so it could receive power from either Bonneville or Grand Coulee even if the whole Northwest was out of power. Thus the current was reestablished automatically after a lapse of only one-fifth of a second. That split-second interruption, however, necessitated three days of work to get the piles back to full capacity again.

What had happened? Was it sabotage? Colonel Matthias's security men swarmed into the area and imposed the strictest secrecy on all information concerning the power failure. Only the top Du Pont people were informed confidentially about the cause of the trouble: a Japanese balloon.

It was not known to the general public that during the war the Japanese were attempting to use fire balloons against the West Coast of the United States. They were sending them with the winds. The balloons were designed to operate at an altitude of forty thousand feet, where they caught the jet stream flowing from west to east. The balloons, made of brownish rice paper, measured thirty-three feet in diameter, carried fire bombs and had a system of weights and altimeters that automatically kept them at the right altitude. When a fire bomb reached an approximate target zone, it was released automatically.

About nine thousand "Fugo" balloons were launched, but, flying without control once they got up into the air, they were inefficient. The first two to be seen in the United States fell in Montana and North Dakota and were reported in the Japanese press a week later. Since only local American newspapers had mentioned the incidents, Japanese spies were obviously reading the smallest country publications. After that any mention of the balloons in American papers was censored out.

At least two Japanese balloons fell in the Hanford area, and one of them dropped on the power line between Bonneville and Grand Coulee, thus interrupting electric current and thereby triggering the safety mechanism of the reactors. The incident was in fact welcome at Hanford: it proved that all safety arrangements, never before tested in an actual crisis, were working beautifully. From that moment on, everybody felt more confident about the piles.

In the meantime, construction of Hanford's separation plants had been completed, and three marvels of remote control, the canyons, were ready to process the irradiated slugs. The first of them, the T separation plant, was turned over to the operating personnel on October 9, 1944. Test runs with the dissolver started in November, and on December 26 the first slug irradiated in the B pile was dissolved. Before the end of January

1945, Hanford's scientists had entirely processed the first material and separated plutonium.

The shipment of plutonium from Hanford to Los Alamos required meticulous preparation. The bomb material was sent by auto convoy in the form of a thick solution, almost a jelly, and the container was suspended in the center of a wooden box about two feet high and a foot and a half in length and width. There were several boxes, but none contained more than a minimum amount of plutonium, so that a critical mass could not develop under any situation. The boxes were shielded inside, but there was very little external radioactivity and they could be handled without any hazard.

Colonel Matthias had to make sure that no danger existed in case the boxes were wrecked or destroyed during shipment, and that their transportation did not attract attention. Army ambulances were finally selected as the vehicles to carry the plutonium; they were frequently seen all over the country and caused no suspicion. The convoy consisted of an ambulance between two radio-equipped military police cars in which armed guards rode. They wore uniforms, so the convoy looked like a normal military operation. Except for an officer riding in the ambulance, none of the drivers or soldiers knew what they were transporting. Matthias insisted on the convoys' taking different routes and never stopping at the same place to eat. Occasionally he would send a counterintelligence officer in another military police car to spot-check on whether the drivers were developing habits that might imperil the secrecy of the operation.

A special military police group was set up at Hanford and another one in Los Alamos. Fort Douglas in Utah was chosen as a transfer point where the Hanford drivers would deposit the boxes with an officer, stay overnight and drive back, without ever seeing the Los Alamos ambulance that picked up the plutonium from Fort Douglas. There were usually two trips a week.

The first bit of plutonium for Los Alamos left Hanford carried by Colonel Matthias personally. Oppenheimer's laboratory was waiting for it with desperate urgency, so Matthias decided to rush it there by train. Carrying the precious metal in the square wooden box, he drove to Portland and took the train to Los Angeles, where he was met at the railroad station by a Los Alamos officer. The officer did not know what he was supposed to pick up. "You have a bedroom back to Los Alamos on the train, I hope?" asked Matthias.

"No, I couldn't get a bedroom, sir," answered the officer. "I have an upper berth."

"Do you realize that what you're going to carry is pretty valuable?" shouted Matthias.

"What do you mean, valuable, sir?"

"I mean that it cost three hundred million dollars to make it!"

The flabbergasted junior officer rushed back into the station and, by alternately begging and threatening, finally managed to get a roomette on the Albuquerque train.

The first small sample of plutonium reached Los Alamos on February 2, 1945. Production of bomb material at the Hanford plants was, at long last, going full speed.

47

In the spring of 1944, despite some spectacular technological breakthroughs, the situation at Oak Ridge was still critical: no uranium–235 had yet been produced. The extremely costly electromagnetic plants seemed too slow to separate enough bomb material in time. The gaseous-diffusion process was still plagued by the barrier problem, and unless it was solved quickly, the K–25 plant — the world's largest plant — would be nothing but a lifeless monster in the Oak Ridge woods, a breathtaking technological marvel but one that had never served any purpose.

Los Alamos was frantically designing uranium bombs, model after model. Yet there was still not enough fissionable uranium. Separation of isotope–235, the only uranium usable for bomb purposes, was still the Manhattan Project's major problem. The question arose in many minds whether the whole uranium project should perhaps be abandoned so that total effort could be concentrated on the plutonium weapon. Then, suddenly, an unexpected suggestion brought new hope to the uranium program. Oppenheimer wrote to General Groves and asked: Couldn't Oak Ridge try another separation method, the so-called "thermal diffusion" method?

The idea came as a revelation. "Why haven't we thought of it before?" Groves exlaimed, suddenly agitated. "That's the thing to do, of course!"

Why wasn't the Manhattan Project already using the method known as thermal diffusion, which the Navy had been developing for over three years? The S–1 Committee knew very well that this method existed, and so did the Manhattan District. In this case, however, Groves could not explode with anger and angrily blame the oversight on absent-minded scientists or subordinates. He could not say that he did not know about the existence of the Navy program. Quite the contrary, for the very first nuclear laboratory that Groves had visited, in the week following his appointment in September 1942, was the Naval Research Laboratory on the Potomac River. There, under the direction of Dr. Ross Gunn, a young physicist named Philip H. Abelson was trying to separate uranium isotopes by a process different from those proposed by the S–1 Committee and later adopted by the Manhattan Project.

The Navy's research on thermal diffusion was an independent venture unconnected with Vannevar Bush's Office of Scientific Research and Development. The Naval Research Laboratory was not working on an atomic bomb but was trying to find a better means of submarine propulsion. As soon as the news of the first uranium fission in Germany was announced in 1939, Dr. Ross Gunn organized research to explore the feasibility of nuclear propulsion for submarines. Thus, with the atomic submarine in mind, the Navy developed its method for separation of uranium isotopes.

Groves's first impression of thermal diffusion had not been favorable. Philip Abelson, the intense, twenty-nine-year-old native of the state of Washington who had developed the method, seemed to be very efficient and competent. The general had been quite impressed to learn that Abelson was the co-discoverer, along with Edwin McMillan, of neptunium, the first transuranium element.* Still, in Groves's opinion, the whole thermal-diffusion process seemed of little use to the Manhattan Project.

The equipment was nevertheless ridiculously simple. All it consisted of was two long, vertical, concentric pipes, enclosed in a cylinder. The inner one was heated from the inside; the other was cooled from the outside. Uranium hexafluoride gas, in liquid form, was circulated in a narrow space between the hot and the cool pipes with the idea that the lighter isotope would tend to concentrate near the hotter surface. Surprisingly enough, and for reasons not entirely understood by the scientists, this simple method worked. Unfortunately, though, incredible amounts of steam had to be used — the quantity of coal required was fantastic. If pure U–235 were to be separated in quantity, production costs would be astronomical — some estimates even ran as high as $2 to $3 billion.

During his first visit to the Naval Research Laboratory, Groves had also realized that relations between the S–1 Committee and the head of the Navy program, Ross Gunn, were strained and collaboration would be difficult. The general got the clear impression that Gunn, a member of the original Uranium Committee (the predecessor of the S–1 Committee) but dropped during its last reorganization, had had his feelings hurt by Bush and Conant and now preferred to keep his work independent of them. Bush and Conant, for their part, were skeptical about the Navy's separation process.

---

* Transuranic elements: Up until 1940, there were ninety-two recognized elements, the heaviest one — and the last discovered — being uranium. The elements discovered since then are therefore called transuranic (beyond uranium). Neptunium was the first, and it was followed by plutonium. At the present time there are eleven transuranic elements, all radioactive and all produced artificially. Several have been given the names of individuals or laboratories connected with the Manhattan Project: lawrencium, fermium, berkelium.

As a result of his visit to Gunn's laboratory, Groves appointed a special Reviewing Committee of eminent scientists whose verdict was definitely negative. The general agreed, and recommended that the thermal-diffusion method not be considered for the Manhattan Project. Later, critics insinuated that the old Army-Navy rivalry was a factor in Groves's decision. "Nonsense!" answered the general scornfully. "This so-called rivalry doesn't go much farther than the annual Army-Navy football game." Anyway, all members of the S–1 Committee fully agreed with him — they considered the thermal-diffusion method an impractical, exorbitantly expensive and, in the final analysis, probably unfeasible process.

By the spring of 1944, however, the situation was different. What the Manhattan Project desperately needed was not necessarily *pure* uranium–235, which thermal diffusion was incapable of separating anyway, but uranium of *any* degree of enrichment. It had been found that the efficiency of the electromagnetic plants — the Y–12 complex at Oak Ridge — soared tremendously when fed with even slightly enriched material. In other words, the Y–12 plants could separate pure bomb material in shorter time if fed not with natural uranium (which contained only 0.7 percent of the isotope–235) but with enriched material containing a higher percentage of the precious U–235. With the gaseous-diffusion process still inoperable, the problem was now clear-cut: how to find ways of mass-producing enriched — however modestly — feed material for the electromagnetic setup.

Oppenheimer's tip about the Navy's thermal-diffusion method came originally from Philip Abelson in an indirect fashion. The information had filtered through a loophole in the security system. Like many American physicists and chemists who were not supposed to know about Oak Ridge and Los Alamos, Abelson was nevertheless in constant touch with colleagues and laboratories throughout the country and knew that an atomic weapon was being built.[*] Moreover, after his discovery with McMillan of the new element neptunium, he served as technical adviser in Washington to Lyman Briggs, chairman of the Uranium Committee. Then the versatile Abelson also became the first scientist in the country to produce several hundred pounds of uranium hexafluoride, which was sent to Columbia University for its research program.

It was through his contacts with various Columbia scientists that Abelson learned that they were worried about progress in uranium separation,

---

[*] He was intimately acquainted, for instance, with everyone on Lawrence's team, for he had worked at Berkeley's Radiation Laboratory as a graduate student and then after getting his Ph.D.

particularly by gaseous diffusion. He had already obtained encouraging results with his thermal-diffusion method, and had written a report to that effect for the Navy. In the late spring of 1944 he saw to it that Edward Teller, who was working at Los Alamos, received the gist of the report. Teller discussed it with Oppenheimer, who immediately saw the possibilities that thermal diffusion offered for producing enriched feed material for the electromagnetic plants. He telephoned Groves, who acted at once. Reversing the decision that he had taken twenty months earlier did not bother Groves in the least. It was the nearest that he was ever to come in admitting that he had not guessed right. He was not a man to meditate over past errors or to defend previous decisions that had been proven wrong. The important thing was to move ahead, and move fast. His first action was to secure the full support of Admiral Ernest King, who instantly issued the necessary instructions.

On June 25, 1944, Groves received in his office Mrs. H. K. Ferguson, a tall, handsome woman in her forties. Since her husband's death six months earlier, she had been the president of the H. K. Ferguson Company, an engineering firm in Cleveland. She was accompanied by the company's chief engineer, Wells N. Thompson. After briefly describing his plans for building a thermal-diffusion plant, Groves asked his visitors to submit a bid.

The next morning the two Ferguson executives presented their bid and Groves, emphasizing the extreme urgency of the job, gave them the contract. Then he arranged a meeting for the same afternoon at the Anacostia Naval Air Station, where he introduced the Ferguson people to Dr. Abelson and Lieutenant Colonel Mark C. Fox, Groves's representative on the new project. By evening Fox was already issuing priority orders to several companies for strategic materials. Engineering studies at Ferguson's Cleveland Office began immediately and, within three weeks, Groves cut the original six-month construction schedule down to four months, to the consternation of the Ferguson engineers.

By summer the Navy had almost completed its pilot plant for thermal diffusion at the Philadelphia Navy Yard. In order to save time, Groves asked the Ferguson Company to copy the Navy installations down to the last detail, rather than making their own new design, and then to build plants for full-scale production. There was no time for improvements on the rather primitive Abelson design, which had many of the imperfections of a homemade job executed without the help of specialized engineers. By order of Admiral King, Navy blueprints were immediately sent to the Ferguson Company.

Abelson's installations at the Philadelphia Navy Yard were a bit primitive. They consisted of one hundred vertical columns resembling a gigantic church organ with pipes forty-eight feet high. Each column was composed of a thin nickel pipe, less than two inches in diameter, within a copper pipe. These two pipes, in turn, were encased in a third one, only four inches in diameter, made of galvanized iron. The nickel pipe was heated to 280 degrees centigrade by running steam inside it. The copper pipe was cooled to 70 degrees centigrade by water which ran on the outside and was contained by the iron casing.

The principle of the separation was simple: when uranium hexafluoride was made to pass between the nickel and copper pipes, the lighter isotope tended to concentrate near the hot nickel wall and then move upward, while the heavier molecules moved in a downward flow along the cold copper wall. Each column formed an individual unit, but a group of columns were usually operated simultaneously. U–235 molecules diffused toward the hot inside wall and were carried upward by convection currents. The uranium compound that had been enriched in the 235–isotope was then skimmed off at the top, while the depleted uranium compound was siphoned off at the bottom.

The process was efficient only in providing a slightly enriched product. In his small Washington plant Abelson and his assistant, John Hoover, had already doubled the enrichment from 0.7 percent of pure U–235 to 1.4 percent on a very limited amount. It was, of course, far from sufficient for bomb purposes. But it was excellent as feed material for the electromagnetic plants.

The building of a huge thermal-diffusion complex would be a major undertaking. Where could the tremendous amounts of hot steam be produced? Groves thought of the power plant at Oak Ridge, which would be completed in a few weeks to serve K–25, the gaseous-diffusion plant, which was still far from being ready. Why not use this powerhouse to produce steam for the new process, while waiting for K–25 to be completed? The decision was therefore taken to build the thermal-diffusion complex at Oak Ridge, next to the K–25 power plant. It was given the code name S–50.

The Navy pilot plant in Philadelphia had one hundred columns. The Ferguson Company was instructed to make an exact copy of the columns — and multiply the installation twenty-one times. S–50 was to consist of three groups, each containing seven "racks" of 102 columns each. It represented a total of 2142 uniform columns, each forty-eight feet high, with tubes built with the highest possible degree of perfection. The manufacturing problems were staggering. Twenty-one firms turned down the assignment after seeing the specifications: a nearly perfect roundness, with tolerance of only 0.002 inch, for the copper and nickel pipes.

Furthermore, in the opinion of nearly all experts in the field, piping could not be drawn out to forty-eight-foot lengths.

Finally, two contractors accepted the challenge: the Mehring and Hanson Company of Washington, D.C., and the Grinnell Company of Providence, Rhode Island. They devised methods of welding and soldering shorter lengths of nickel and copper tubing, and also of overcoming the difficulties of fastening together hot nickel and cold copper tubes.

On July 9, 1944, Ferguson began clearing the S–50 site on the banks of the Clinch River at Oak Ridge. By the end of the month the foundations had been dug. Plant construction started at a mad tempo, as though the builders were determined to break all speed records for plant building. Groves pushed them mercilessly. Now he declared that even the four-month deadline was much too late. "It should be in operation within ninety days!" he insisted. Even though the Ferguson people were still in a state of dazed shock after this decision, Groves wrote his representative, Lieutenant Colonel Fox, a few days later: "After considering the various factors involved, I feel that my statement to you as to the schedule of completion of the work under your charge is reasonable. . . . I think you can beat it."

The main S–50 building – a huge black structure 525 feet long, 82 feet wide and 75 feet high – rose from the ground with extraordinary speed. In September battalions of pipe fitters, electricians and welders invaded the place. The Ferguson technicians were already installing the heating system, working in the midst of deafening noise and white clouds of escaping steam. Abelson moved to Oak Ridge to instruct the Ferguson people and to advise Colonels Nichols and Fox.

In the meantime, the Ferguson Company had formed a special new subsidiary, the Fercleve Corporation, to operate the plant. The operators, being completely inexperienced, had to learn their job at the same time as the S–50 plant began operation. Many errors were inevitable; one accident at Philadelphia cost the lives of two operators and several other men were severely injured. The situation did not look very bright; there was room for serious worry and skepticism. But Groves and Nichols would not hear of postponement or delay. Lieutenant Colonel Fox was also not the kind of man to give the constructors and the operators time to catch their breath between jobs.

So he was not too surprised, the day he asked Groves for a free weekend to get married, when the general replied, "OK, if you take from Saturday evening, after work, and report to work first thing on Monday morning." On Saturday afternoon, at four-fifteen, Groves called the office. "Colonel Fox is not here," answered the secretary.

"Where is he?"

"But, General, he's getting married!"

"I know, I know," grumbled Groves. "But why did he have to leave so early?"

On September 16, with 320 columns ready out of 2142 and the process building only one-third completed, operations started in Rack 21. Ferguson Company and Lieutenant Colonel Fox proudly announced that they had beaten even the impossible ninety-day deadline set by General Groves. It had taken them only sixty-nine days from the time the construction order went out.

48

THE EXPLOSIONS heard by Los Alamos residents on their first Fourth of July on the mesa were not fireworks. The sounds came from the canyon near Anchor Ranch, where a half-dozen men were playing a noisy and extremely dangerous "game": they were placing boxes of TNT around large steel pipes, then detonating them. The pipes were thus transformed into compressed, solid blocks of metal. This was what Seth Neddermeyer, the leader of the small group, called implosion. But Captain William S. ("Deak") Parsons, for whose benefit the demonstrations were being made, remained as unconvinced as ever.

As employed by Neddermeyer, the term implosion was new. Before the demonstrations, even its underlying principle had been entirely unknown. When he first advanced the idea, it sounded more like an exercise in theoretical thinking than a feasible technique. Neddermeyer believed that pieces of plutonium could be blown together into a small ball if explosives pushed them from the outside toward the center. According to his theory, a sphere of plutonium could thus be assembled — by implosion — in millionths of a second.

Oppenheimer was skeptical about the idea and so were most of the division leaders, including Bethe and Bacher. As for Captain Parsons, head of the Ordnance Division, he was outspokenly against it. The other scientists, realizing that the problems created by implosion might be stupendous, preferred to stay with the proven gun method; Parsons, a Regular Navy officer with great knowledge of artillery and ballistics, was naturally in favor of what was called the "good old gun." For him, too, it was a matter of priorities: with men and supplies so badly needed everywhere in the war effort, any deviation from tried-and-true methods in favor of fantastic, unproven ideas was, in his opinion, utter folly.

Neddermeyer, however, staunchly backed by the small group of scientists who believed in his idea, pushed forward with his experiments. But the results had a disappointing sameness. The implosions were too ragged, too asymmetrical — one point of the sphere would sink in very fast, while another would not sink in at all. No uniformity could be achieved. The shortcomings of the implosion method loomed ever larger.

Most scientists at Los Alamos paid no further attention to Neddermeyer's group and concentrated all their energy on the gun-assembly method. Then the bad news suddenly came: the gun-assembly method, considered so tried-and-true, could *not* be used with plutonium. An unsuspected isotope, capable of spontaneous fission, had been discovered in the first samples from the small reactor at Oak Ridge. This meant that, with neutrons being constantly released by the isotope, a gun-type assembly would be much too slow to block a possible premature reaction. The plutonium bomb was therefore an impossibility — unless some fantastically fast way of assembly could be discovered. Morale at Los Alamos sank to its lowest point.

The only other way, then, was implosion. But could this be accomplished with precision? Precision had to be absolute, with a uniformity and simultaneity that all earlier tests had failed to achieve. The Theoretical Division calculated that if one point of the sphere were detonated more than one-millionth of a second later than another point, implosion would simply not work. The job seemed impossible. Then the whole concept of implosion was changed by two men: John von Neumann and Robert F. Christy.

At forty, mathematician Johnny von Neumann was one of the original members, together with Albert Einstein, of Princeton's Institute for Advanced Study. In his capacity as consultant to the Manhattan Project, he visited Los Alamos periodically. He was a Hungarian from Budapest who had studied in Berlin, Zurich and Göttingen and had become an American citizen in 1937.* Von Neumann, already renowned for his mathematical theory of games, was an extremely warm, friendly person. His phenomenal mind could perform such extraordinary computations that a dazzled colleague was moved to say, "Johnny wasn't really human at birth. But after living with humans for this long, he has learned how to do a remarkable imitation of one." Within the highly critical scientific fraternity, the title of "genius" was as sparingly bestowed as canonization in the Catholic Church. But there was unanimous agreement on one point: John von Neumann was recognized as an authentic genius — on a par with Enrico Fermi and Niels Bohr.

Von Neumann first came to Los Alamos in the fall of 1943 and, on hearing about the implosion concept, launched into some extremely complicated calculations that were beyond the comprehension of nearly everyone else. Then one day he told the laboratory's governing board about the similarities he saw between Neddermeyer's principle and some

---

* Not only Von Neumann, but Wigner, Szilard and Teller were Hungarian-born. It was remarkable how many top atomic scientists tiny Hungary contributed, a number proportionally unmatched by any other country.

work being done on armor penetration at the Aberdeen Ballistics Laboratory in Maryland, where materials were being accelerated to very high speeds by hitting them with explosives. Von Neumann not only believed implosion was feasible, he recommended it as the *only* way that plutonium should be assembled.

This time somebody listened. Oppenheimer was convinced by Von Neumann, whom he had known and highly respected from their acquaintance as graduate students in Germany. Soon most laboratory groups were instructed to switch to the study of implosion.

The other factor in Oppenheimer's change of mind was the discovery of the "Christy gadget." Dr. Robert F. Christy of the Theoretical Division calculated that implosion of a subcritical mass would cause such compression that plutonium would thus become critical. Christy's gadget aimed at achieving "criticality" by extra compression instead of extra size. "This remarkable phenomenon — the compression of 'incompressible' solid matter under extreme pressures of implosion — was too far from the course of ordinary terrestrial experience to be grasped immediately or easily," noted David Hawkins, a member of the laboratory.

By February 1944 the Christy principle had been adopted, and priority was given to studies of spheres. But friction developed in the Ordnance Division, to which the implosion group belonged. Captain Parsons and Dr. Neddermeyer had not gotten along together ever since the Navy officer had shown his hostility to the implosion idea. Neddermeyer, a lone-wolf type of physicist, believed that work on implosion should be done by a limited group of top scientists; he was not happy under Parsons' disciplined leadership. Parsons, on the other hand, considered that implosion, now that it had been adopted as the preferred method, became an ordnance problem that called for the mobilization of all the manpower and resources of his division.

When the Parsons-Neddermeyer conflict worsened, Oppenheimer brought in George Kistiakowsky, a spirited, Russian-born chemist, to act as a buffer between the two men. Gradually, Parsons's responsibility for turning atomic devices into combat weapons absorbed his attention more and more, and the implosion work in his division was left to Kistiakowsky. Neddermeyer switched his attention to other fields and ceased his participation in the implosion development. With the reorganization in the summer of 1944, Oppenheimer made implosion the responsibility of Kistiakowsky and Bacher, heading the Explosives and "Gadget" Divisions.

The outspoken "Kisty" was one of the very few experts in the science of explosives in the United States. Before the war, amazingly little was known about the theory of explosives and the behavior of detonation waves. Asked by Conant to study these problems for the National Defense Research Committee at the beginning of the war, Kistiakowsky had become one of the pioneers in the field.

Born in Kiev in 1900, Kistiakowsky never finished high school in Moscow because he left to join the White Russian armies led by Denikin and Wrangel in the fight against the Bolsheviks. After the defeat of the White Russian forces, he escaped through Turkey to Berlin, where, as a penniless student, he managed to obtain his university degree. "In Germany you'll always be called the Russian," one of his professors told him. "Why don't you go to America?" He did, in 1925, and after the first few days at Princeton, the thin, sharp-featured chemist decided that it was the country for him.

In one year the number of people working on implosion had jumped from only a score to over six hundred. In theory, at least, the method now appeared feasible. But was it possible to design and build such a monster of precision and symmetry, to coordinate — to the millionth of a second — incredibly complicated systems of detonators, explosives and neutron sources?*

The core of the implosion bomb was a plutonium globe of a size just below the critical mass. Made of two hemispheres, it was placed in the center of a larger sphere of explosives, like the pit in a peach. Several detonators, arranged symmetrically on the outside surface and triggered simultaneously by an electric circuit, were to set off the blast. The pressure was expected to go *inward* and squash the core into a compressed critical mass. The fission would start a fantastically fast chain reaction, splitting the billions of plutonium nuclei and thus releasing destructive energy never matched before. On paper, that was how it was supposed to work. But to make an actual bomb, tremendous difficulties had to be surmounted, and complicated gadgets and ingenious techniques had to be devised.

The core itself was designed in the Gadget Division, which was organized in August 1944 under Robert Bacher in order to centralize all work on weapon physics. The most secret and dangerous work was done by night in remote Omega Canyon by the Gadget Division's assembly ex-

---

* The solution of the design and engineering problems constituted one of the top secrets of the war. Even now, more than two decades later, it has not yet been released to the general public. But though it is still highly classified, the information is scarcely very secret today: it was all undoubtedly transmitted to the Soviet Government by one of the brightest young members of the Implosion Group, Klaus Fuchs, regarded as an unusually hard worker by his colleagues. Before coming to Los Alamos the British scientist had also familiarized himself with the secrets of the K–25 gaseous-diffusion plant at Oak Ridge. His description of the bomb's mechanisms, given to the Russians at the end of the war, contributed considerably to the postwar change in the balance of power.

perts. A fearless thirty-three-year-old Canadian, Louis Slotin, operated a strange machine there called the "Guillotine." A small piece of fissionable metal was dropped from the top of the Guillotine through the center of an almost critical assembly. At the moment it passed through, the assembly became critical, and the resulting short-lived chain reaction was recorded and measured. In successive experiments larger and larger slugs were used, and the instruments recorded stronger and stronger reactivity, to the point when "tickling the dragon's tail," as Slotin's activity was called, became a very hazardous enterprise.*

The plutonium hemispheres were produced by Los Alamos metal-lurgists in the Chemistry Division headed by Joe Kennedy, still in his twenties, and by Dr. Cyril S. Smith, an Englishman who had come from the War Metallurgy Committee in Washington. The work of the two hundred people in their department was a combination of heroic struggle with the most exotic metals and shapes any metallurgist had ever seen and, on the other hand, comical ignorance of the new material they were handling. Not one of them had ever seen plutonium. For many months Smith and Kennedy regularly visited Chicago, where Seaborg, Chipman and their colleagues taught them the little they themselves knew about the bizarre metal. Chicago's job was to do all the microchemical work, while Los Alamos was to take over after the first gram quantities had been produced.

The plutonium arrived from Hanford as a syrup-like nitrate and had to be purified and turned into a metal at Los Alamos. The purity require-ments were fantastic, unheard of in industrial history, but the metal-lurgists, led by Eric R. Jette, Arthur M. Wahl, Iral B. Johns and Richard D. Baker, finally succeeded in producing a metal of a degree of purity never before attained on a large scale.

Every step in production presented new surprises, new difficulties. Because of plutonium's deadly toxicity, metallurgists had to be specially trained to handle it. They wore rubber gloves, worked behind protective shielding, and manipulated the plutonium with long tongs. Not only was the air in Building D filtered and ventilated, but a microscopist from the Smithsonian Institution was hired to analyze regularly the dust that it contained.

Another problem that preoccupied the laboratory for nearly a year was finding the proper crucible for melting plutonium. No container seemed to resist the corrosive action of the metal, and though one material after

---

* Shortly after the war, Louis Slotin died in an accident which occurred when the screwdriver slipped in his hand during an experiment. In order to protect his col-leagues in the room, Slotin disconnected the deadly device with his bare hands, thus absorbing a lethal amount of gamma rays.

another was tried, nothing worked. The situation looked bleak. Fortunately, a scientist at Berkeley, Professor Erman D. Eastman, had been experimenting with some very exotic materials, and one of them, cerium sulfide, was used provisionally for the first crucibles. In the meantime, John Manley, going against prevailing theories, attempted to use a crucible made out of magnesium oxide. Strangely enough, in spite of the rules of thermodynamics, it worked and was adopted.

Plutonium's density was so completely unknown that Joe Kennedy and John Chipman, after a heated discussion, made a ten-dollar bet on whether its density was fourteen or twenty. To the stupefaction of everyone, it turned out that both of them were right! At different temperatures the weird metal assumed five different states, behaving like five *different* metals. This was an extraordinary phenomenon that no one could have predicted. Another surprise was the melting point, which turned out to be much lower than expected. To shape two perfect hemispheres weighing several pounds each out of this strange, difficult and lethal material was a fabulous performance that pushed metallurgy several years ahead in development.

However, the plutonium sphere by itself, no matter how perfect, was not enough for a sustained nuclear reaction. When the fission began, most neutrons coming near the edge of the bomb would fly away without hitting a nucleus, and the chain reaction would die. Some device was needed to prevent the neutrons' escape from the core's surface, or at least to reduce the waste. The idea of the "tamper" was thus conceived: wrap the bomb material in a shell that would reflect the escaping neutrons back into the sphere. Early calculations indicated that a good tamper would permit substantial reduction in the size of the critical mass that would be needed. Serber predicted by rough guesses (which later proved amazingly close to the truth) that with the use of tampers, the critical mass for uranium–235 would be fifteen kilograms; for plutonium, it would be only five kilograms.

An intensive search began for reflecting materials that should also serve the second purpose of the tamper — to contain, for a small fraction of a second, the disintegration of the exploding bomb and thus obtain maximum efficiency. The tamper had to be heavy so that its inertia would hold together the active material during the explosion.

A lack of knowledge, plus the extreme urgency of the program, forced the scientists to have recourse once more to what had become the characteristic working method of the Manhattan Project: exploring all possible avenues of investigation at the same time and at top speed. Every element in the periodic table was tested. The special group under John

Manley worked closely with Hans Bethe's Theoretical Division and with Niels Bohr, who contributed enormously to the understanding of the nuclear properties of the tamper. The Metallurgical Division was flooded with orders for the most unusual materials in the most peculiar shapes. Experiments were made with lead, iron, gold, platinum, tungsten — everything had to be tried regardless of cost. Fort Knox even provided enough pure gold for two hemispheres twelve inches in diameter; but gold did not prove able to reflect neutrons.

Then the procurement people received an unusual order to supply enough solid platinum for a disc one inch thick and twelve inches in diameter! They found the precious metal in New York and the metallurgists made what was probably the biggest platinum object ever known! For security reasons, the gold was called "brass," and the platinum "zinc" — but their huge price looked so trivial compared to the fantastic cost of uranium–235 and plutonium that after a few days no one paid any attention.*

Requests for plutonium and gold were routine compared with those for materials like osmium, an extremely dense metal. And Los Alamos never did make an osmium disc: the amount requested turned out to be greater than the entire known supply in the world.

At the outset, the group working on tampers had no uranium–235 or plutonium on which to test the different materials. Most of their experiments were therefore made with the Cockcroft-Walton accelerator, which roughly simulated the expected neutron production. After the first experiments, the list of possible tamper materials was restricted to tungsten, carbon, uranium, beryllium oxide and lead. During the summer of 1944, cobalt, manganese, nickel and tantalum were included in the tests.

At the moment of implosion, neutrons were needed to ignite the plutonium reaction. Spontaneous fission was possible, but the chance of its occurring was too small to depend on. It was imperative to incorporate some neutron-making device in the bomb, but it was equally imperative *not* to release the neutrons prematurely. Somehow the weapon had to be assembled *without* neutrons, and then the neutrons had to appear suddenly, right at the microsecond of implosion. Not before, not later.

---

* Later, when the Project's official historian and also a prominent physicist, Dr. Henry D. Smyth, saw small quantities of plutonium for the first time, he exclaimed enthusiastically, "How impressive! Man has succeeded in transmuting a new element that never existed on earth before!" As he went on and on, Feynman wryly remarked, "Yes, and how fitting it is that at this dramatic moment, you are absent-mindedly kicking a doorstop made of solid gold!" Smyth looked down: in order to keep the door open for ventilation (working with plutonium being dangerous for the lungs) during the measuring of plutonium, the physicists were using, as a doorstop, the gold hemisphere that had been tried as a tamper but found unsatisfactory.

"I'm sure I could make a device that would be triggered exactly when the Gadget compresses," said Dr. Charles Critchfield one day to Oppenheimer. Critchfield, a thirty-three-year-old physicist, had worked on anti-tank projectiles in Washington and knew guns and ballistics well.

Oppenheimer was skeptical, as was Bacher, the Gadget Division's leader, but Critchfield was told to go ahead and try. The first one of the major scientists to become interested in Critchfield's idea was Niels Bohr. He convinced Bacher and Oppenheimer that Critchfield was on the right track. A top-level special committee was formed, including Bethe, Fermi, Bacher and Kistiakowsky, to supervise his work. The neutron source became one of the laboratory's major projects.

The device Critchfield and his group of about sixty people developed was as small as a nut, and its official name was "initiator." But in laboratory jargon they called it the "Urchin." It was made of beryllium and polonium, two elements that produce neutrons when put in contact with each other. The device was placed between the two hemispheres. The idea was that the implosion waves would demolish the initiator and the beryllium would mix with the polonium, producing neutrons which would ignite the nuclear reaction. Polonium, discovered by Madame Curie, is a peculiar metal, as soft as cream cheese, dangerous when inhaled and difficult to produce. Its properties were almost as unknown as those of plutonium and up to that time it had been made only in laboratory quantities. Charles A. Thomas, coordinator of all the Manhattan Project's chemical and metallurgical work on plutonium, was faced with the tough and urgent problem of producing polonium in large quantities. Wasting no time, Thomas, research director of Monsanto Chemical Company, set up a makeshift laboratory in the indoor tennis court of his mother-in-law, Mrs. Harold E. Talbott. Her big estate in Dayton, Ohio, seemed to offer ideal conditions for seclusion and secrecy, and the first quantities of the polonium, used at Los Alamos for Fat Man's initiator, were separated there in her tennis court.

Several dozen different kinds of initiators were tested with high explosives at the firing site in Sandia Canyon. Plain old ball bearings (nicknamed "screwballs") from large turbines were used for the tests. The machinists drilled a hole in a ball bearing. The Urchin or initiator was placed in the hole, which was then plugged with a screw. Then the ball was surrounded by explosives and detonated. After the explosion, the metal was recovered and taken to the laboratory, where it was examined by means of neutron counters to see how efficiently the beryllium and the polonium had mixed. But in reality this could not be a conclusive test: the future bomb assembly would require only a few microseconds, whereas the neutron counting following the Sandia Canyon experiments was carried out a whole hour later. There was no sure way of testing the initiator except in the real bomb. The final design, by Dr. Ruby Sherr, looked very promising; but not until the first nuclear explosion could the Los Alamos scientists be positive that it would work.

One of the most complicated tasks was arranging the explosives around the plutonium core. Implosion would work only if the entire surface of the sphere were compressed with perfect uniformity and simultaneity. Detonation waves of TNT, however, were spherical; some therefore would strike the surface sooner than others. The convex shape of the bomb's surface created further difficulties — some points on the surface would be struck by explosion waves before others. Although the difference might only be in millionths of a second, it would still be enough to cause failure.

Laymen could scarcely comprehend the importance of the infinitesimal units of time that were involved. But the scientists had to work with them, measure in them and study in them. When this proved not enough, they conceived the ambitious plan of photographing in them. The head of the Instrumentation Group, Professor Julian E. Mack, designed a camera that could photograph events happening in one hundred-millionth of a second! This miraculous device, called a "sweeping-image" camera, was based on the principle of the rotating mirror, developed by Professor Jesse W. Beams of the University of Virginia. Julian Mack, designing his model according to the requirements of explosives research, had it built in the laboratory's workshop from old parts and used commercial lenses. Though its performance was amazing, the sweeping-image camera was hardly impressive to look at — it was shaped like a round, one-foot-long tin can, with a long lens sticking out the top.

When the camera was assembled and Mack and Berlyn Brixner took the first pictures of explosive shock waves with it, the photos looked extremely peculiar — entirely different from what the scientists had expected. "Something's wrong with your camera," said the physicists. Mack and Brixner were confused; they had not seen many pictures of detonation waves before. How could they know what they ought to look like? But they were convinced that their new instrument was good. It operated like the cameras that took photo-finish pictures at horse races. Focused on one single line, with the film moving forward all the time, the lens saw nothing but what happened on the focus line. When a horse — or an explosion wave — crossed the line, the camera took its picture. If nothing crossed the line, no picture was taken.

An explosives expert, Walter Koski, confirmed that Mack's camera was right — and existing ideas about shock waves were wrong. He had a new flashlight technique capable of taking a single snapshot picture of anything in one ten-millionth of a second. When he photographed the implosion of a given metal, his picture showed exactly the same peculiarities as the photos produced by Mack's camera. From then on, the sweeping-image camera was adopted as an important tool for the understanding and study of implosion. Still another camera, invented by W. G. Marley, a scientist with the British mission, worked at the rate of 100,000 pictures per second; it, too, proved to be extremely useful in implosion research.

As operators and cameramen stood in a concrete bunker shielded by bullet-proof glass, the first pictures of implosion experiments were taken. They clearly showed the irregularities and lack of symmetry of the implosions. It was obvious that, owing to the lack of uniformity, the plutonium bomb could never be set off under the existing system. The eventual solution of the symmetry problem was a masterpiece of ingenuity and precision. The scientists' observation of the convex shape of the explosive shock waves brought to their minds the idea of using lenses. Would it not be possible, as in optics, to change the shape of the detonation waves? This idea was suggested by several scientists: Von Neumann and Peierls had both thought of it; James L. Tuck, of the British mission, had done some work with "shaped" explosive charges in England, and so had Kistiakowsky at the United States Navy Explosives Laboratory in Bruceton, Pennsylvania. But the real development — the first thorough application of lenses to explosives — was carried out entirely at Los Alamos.

The lenses placed in the implosive bomb changed the shape of detonation waves in the same way that glass optical lenses change the shape of light waves. They were ingenious arrangements of different kinds of explosives — arrangements that were stronger or weaker, thus producing detonation waves that moved outward at different speeds. Thanks to meticulous design and placement, the lenses combined in such a way that all the explosion waves arrived simultaneously. The lenses transformed convex waves into concave waves, thus enabling them to reach all points on the bomb's spherical surface uniformly and at the same microsecond.

The perfectly simultaneous detonation of a dozen lenses made of explosives was one of the main problems at the last moment. The detonators were triggered by electric wires, but painstakingly accurate chemical studies were required before the propagation speed of the electric impulse in each explosive could be determined. In normal explosions, the speed of detonation is one-thousandth of a second. In the plutonium bomb, however, one-millionth of a second was barely acceptable as the norm.

Few things irritated George Kistiakowsky, the Explosives Division leader, more than his colleagues' almost superstitious attitude toward explosives. Kistiakowsky was shocked by their general ignorance of this field. "There is nothing magic about explosives," he said repeatedly to them. "Nothing impossible to understand, if we study them. The risks are badly misunderstood — people usually fear the wrong dangers." Transporting the high explosives of the bomb, for instance, was much less dangerous, according to Kisty, than handling a simple case of dynamite.

But *that* idea was one his colleagues would not buy. One day, highly irritated after a discussion, Kisty stalked out of a meeting and decided that he had somehow to prove his contention. He loaded a fully charged bomb model in his car, then drove furiously over the bumpiest roads on the mesa for a half hour. When he returned to the main lab building, his ashen-faced colleagues were tensely waiting. He said nothing, but his triumphant look spoke volumes.

49

IN EARLY APRIL 1945, Oak Ridge was buzzing with preparations for a highly important visit. The order had been sent out to have each of the plants shipshape by the eleventh. Detailed and elaborate charts and graphs had to be drawn and brass buttons on all military uniforms were to be polished to perfection. Then, when new ramps appeared at various entrances, a rumor swept through the whole town that the ramps were for President Roosevelt's wheelchair.

But the rumor proved wrong. When the car arrived from Knoxville at lunchtime, General Groves stepped out, together with a tall, slightly stooped, elderly man leaning on a cane. They shook hands with Colonel Nichols, who was waiting in front of the guest house on the grounds. "Welcome on your first visit to Oak Ridge, Mr. Secretary," said Nichols, and he showed the two visitors into a private dining room.

At seventy-eight, Secretary of War Henry L. Stimson was still the extremely active and efficient head of his department. He had flown from Washington to see, at first hand, Oak Ridge — the largest of the top-secret cities of the Manhattan Project, an undertaking for whose success he, above all, was responsible. During the flight, Groves tried to take advantage of the opportunity and explain, as simply as possible, a few of the fundamentals of nuclear physics. Looking quite disinterested, the Secretary of War had nevertheless listened politely. At last he interrupted impatiently. "Doctor, don't try to tell me all this. I can't understand a word you're saying!"

Groves reddened. "Please don't call me Doctor, Mr. Secretary — especially in front of the scientists. They might resent it."

"But you *are* a scientist!" Stimson said firmly. "You're not only a general but a scientist, too — we all know it."

The only time Stimson had shown any real interest in the lecture was when Groves had pulled out a drawing representing the helium atom. "Helium?" Stimson asked. "That comes from Helios, the name of the Greek sun-god, doesn't it?" He was immensely pleased to have recognized at least one familiar word in the spate of incomprehensible scientific jargon.

WESTFIELD MEMORIAL LIBRARY
WESTFIELD, N. J.

Henry Stimson knew nothing about the atom and he did not have to. His sole concern was to make sure that the Manhattan Project would be a success; that the bomb would be produced in time to be used to win the war. All the needed resources of the nation had been made available for the Manhattan Project. President Roosevelt had given his Secretary of War full authority and responsibility for the Project, and during the past year it had been receiving more and more of Stimson's time and attention. The aging Secretary was not in very good health: he had thought of resigning the year before — had it not been for the atomic project.

"You know, General," he confided to Groves, "I want to devote all my time to this particular project — it's really the only reason I'm staying on as Secretary of War."

Groves had great admiration for the distinguished old gentleman who guided the War Department with such complete integrity and dedication. Groves had not begun to see his top superior regularly until the end of 1944, but their relationship soon became very close. Earlier, during the first two years of the Manhattan Project, they would meet only occasionally, when Groves brought to the Secretary of War the few reports he made for the information of President Roosevelt.

Normally, though, Groves's contact with the Secretary of War was conducted through Stimson's special assistant, Harvey H. Bundy, who was the very model of the brilliant, faithful and self-effacing civil servant. Bundy knew all the habits of his superior and was also his close friend. He worried about Stimson's health and knew how to handle his rare outbursts of temper. Sometimes he would say to Groves, "General, don't stay too long with the Secretary — even if he wants to keep you. He's very tired today." Or: "General, when you get in the car with Mr. Stimson, don't say a word to him. He's thinking and wants to be left alone. When he's ready to talk to you, he'll open the conversation."

In time, Stimson enjoyed his meetings with Groves. In the initial year of the Project, Stimson was equally surprised and amused when he first had a clerk telephone Groves's office to say that he wanted to talk to the Manhattan Project chief right away. Groves's reply had been unhesitating. "Tell the Secretary that I'm awfully sorry, but it's very inconvenient for me to come right now. I wish you'd make certain that it is a rush thing, because I have people in my office who've come a long distance to see me." The clerk returned a few minutes later. "The Secretary says it's perfectly all right. Can you come over this afternoon without any inconvenience?" "Yes, of course," Groves replied.

The rules for their relationship having been established, Stimson respected them thereafter — and for good reason. He knew that General Leslie Groves was doing exactly what he was expected to do: he was giving all his attention to the top-priority Manhattan Project. From that time on, Groves never received a call from Stimson's office that did not begin with: "At what time, General, is it convenient for you to come and see the Secretary?"

Only a few days before the trip to Oak Ridge, however, Groves received an urgent message from Stimson's office. "The Secretary would like to see you at once — and he doesn't care what you're doing. It's extremely important and you'd better get on over here in a hurry."

Serious trouble was beginning to boil up in Congress. Representative Albert J. Engel of Michigan had received information about a gigantic and highly secret construction project being carried out in Tennessee, outside Knoxville, and demanded details. Senator Harry S Truman of Missouri, then chairman of a special Senate committee investigating material defense programs, was also concerned by the immense amount of money given to the mysterious Manhattan Project in the past. But when Stimson gave his word of honor that an investigation would endanger national security, Senator Truman had promptly agreed to post-pone any Congressional inquiry until after the war and to keep the matter quiet until then. Subsequently, Stimson, Vannevar Bush and General George C. Marshall, Army Chief of Staff, had gone to Capitol Hill and explained the purpose of the Manhattan Project in a secret session with the leaders of the House of Representatives: Speaker Sam Rayburn, Majority Leader John McCormack and Minority Leader Joseph Martin. After learning of the importance of the Manhattan Project, all three House leaders promised to cooperate in the appropriation of funds without publicity. Later, a similar meeting was held with Senate leaders. But in spite of the intervention of the Congressional leaders, Representa-tive Engel was still insisting upon an investigation. Suspecting a scan-dalous waste of taxpayers' money, he objected strongly to the huge new transfer of War Department funds, amounting to millions of dollars, ear-marked for something vaguely called "Expediting Production" — which was one of the concealed sources of money for the Manhattan Project.

There was no way to placate Engel any longer, or some of his suspi-cious colleagues, except by showing them Oak Ridge and appealing to their patriotism. But before that, Secretary Stimson felt that he himself should see the Tennessee plants that had cost a staggering $1 billion to build.

After a late luncheon at Oak Ridge's guest house, Stimson, escorted by Groves and Nichols, was driven to K–25, the gaseous-diffusion plant. The Secretary had been kept regularly informed about the progress of the various Manhattan Project installations and he was acutely aware of the tremendous size — and astronomical cost — of the K–25 plant, the biggest and most difficult of them all to build. But the sight that confronted them from the ridge, when their motorcade, after a thirteen-mile ride, reached the edge of some isolated woods, was so unexpected that even the usually self-contained Stimson gasped in awe.

Here, where there had been only wilderness less than two years before, had emerged the largest building ever constructed. Spread over an area of two million square feet, the incredible U-shaped structure was almost a half-mile long and four hundred feet wide on each side. It looked like a sinister fortress, with small windows only on the top floor, high up on the tall gray walls. K–25 was in full operation, and a continuous humming — a high-pitched sound resembling the buzzing of a bee swarm — came from the plant, mixing weirdly with the springtime sounds of the woods.

Though the gaseous-diffusion process itself was fully automated, the first large-scale automation in history, nine thousand Union Carbide people, working in three shifts, were nonetheless needed to operate the plant. The complexity and size of the plant were without precedent in industrial history.

The building had three floors and a basement, which was taken up by coolers and a maze of water and air pipes. The diffusion process took place on the first floor, where uranium gas was recycled through many thousand cascade stages. It did not look at all like a factory — the forty-four-acre floor area was deserted: no one worked around the hermetically sealed equipment.

Even with all the tests and precautions taken to insure tightness and absolute precision, many pieces of equipment were in addition wrapped in vacuum-tight containers and put under nitrogen pressure, so that no oxygen could ever leak into the vacuum-chamber system. The only human beings involved were members of inspection crews, who descended periodically to check the dials and gauges of all the installations, which looked like huge sealed metal boxes.

On the second floor, too, no workers could be seen except for the inspection crews. Here were located the cascade's several miles of piping and wiring, as well as thousands of valves. On both floors, inspection personnel had to observe extraordinary cleanliness measures: the men wore white cotton coveralls and had to change their clothes each time they entered. There was an obsessive fear of any grease at K–25 — oils react violently with the gas — and no piece of equipment was therefore ever touched by the bare human hand; special gloves that left no lint were used by all personnel. The air was also constantly filtered, for no dust could be tolerated in the surgically clean plant.

K–25 was actually operated from the third floor, where thousands of men worked in silence under the bright fluorescent lights around instrument panels, dials, pressure gauges and thermometers located along the endless corridors. Indeed, the corridors were so long that inspectors had to move about on bicycles; seeing the light from a small window, often a half-mile farther along a corridor, was a reassuring experience for the solitary cyclist making his rounds.

K–25 had begun operation on January 20, when the first stages were charged with uranium hexafluoride gas and the recycling of the gas was set in motion. After some last-minute trouble with the pumps, additional stages were charged by the end of February and the slow separation of uranium–235 finally went into gear. Kellex, the designer and builder of the gigantic installation, bowed out, and the operating company, Union Carbide, took over.

Large operating crews had been selected and trained for over a year by a sturdy, outspoken, forty-year-old engineer from Ohio, Clark E. Center, one of Felbeck's closest assistants. Because of his extensive experience with gas separation in Carbide plants, and because of his skill in dealing with people, Center was well qualified to become the first superintendent of the huge K–25 operation.

He was staggered at first, then fascinated, by the extraordinary challenge; he became irretrievably absorbed by the job. He, as well as the other engineers at Oak Ridge, knew that a task of such gigantic proportions comes once in a lifetime. Even to a layman like Secretary Stimson, it was clear that K–25 was a masterpiece, perhaps the supreme masterpiece of American technological genius.*

After visiting the pilot plant reactor in the X–10 area, operated to secure data for Hanford, the Secretary returned to the guest house. He was tired but pleased and impressed by what he had seen. In order to spare his energy, no engineer or scientist had talked to him at the plants. The same evening, however, Colonel Nichols and his wife invited the Secretary to meet about twenty-five key people, mostly top men from Tennessee Eastman and Union Carbide.

Stimson's aide, Colonel William H. Kyle, tried to keep the frail and aged Secretary seated on a sofa, while guests were brought to him, each for only two minutes. But the charming old gentleman refused to tolerate such formality and, while sipping his old-fashioned, remained on his feet in the center of the party. Very happy and stimulated that evening by the

---

* The finest tribute to the builders of the K–25 plant is this: Despite all its unprecedented features and intricacies, the plant is now entering its twenty-third year of operation without ever having broken down or having been shut down for repairs. Started in 1945, the automated K–25 plant still performs today like a precision mechanism.

company around him, he wanted to talk to everyone. "You know, you men can be proud of getting this extraordinary thing done. But if it fails, I know who'll be responsible for the failure — *me!*" But now, after his first on-the-spot inspection of Oak Ridge, Stimson was not at all apprehensive about the heavy responsibility that he had assumed when the Manhattan Project was no more than a nebulous idea.

At six o'clock the next morning a briefing was held at the guest house on the current state of production, followed by a tour of three process buildings at the Y-12 plant. The electromagnetic method, absurdly inefficient and costly though it was, still offered the best prospect for producing enough uranium-235 on time. The other two methods — gaseous and thermal diffusion — were just beginning production; the fantastic K-25 plant was concentrating U-235 only to a richness of 1.1 percent at the time. At the outset the electromagnetic method worked incomparably better with slightly concentrated material than it did with natural uranium. The decision had therefore been taken to use K-25's products as feed material for the electromagnetic method until higher stages of the gaseous-diffusion plant could be completed. At the same time, the Y-12 plant was also fed with slightly enriched uranium that came from the S-50 plant, the thermal-diffusion installation. The overall production plan was terribly complex. It called for a gradual increase in K-25 production up to above 20 percent enrichment, combined with a decrease in production of the Alpha calutrons. These two plants, together with the thermal-diffusion one, started with natural uranium and processed it to a certain enrichment; then the enriched material was fed to the Beta tracks, which would make the final concentration. Drawn up at an early stage before anything exact was known of the plants' possibilities, the plan scarcely seemed like a sound scientific program for the outcome of the war largely to depend upon.

Coordinating the production of the various Oak Ridge plants, which had to produce constantly changing degrees of enrichment, became a vital problem. Nichols formed a special group under an Army officer, Major Arthur V. Peterson, to cope with it. Each week Peterson presented new combinations of processing time in the different plants and degree of enrichment, with curves showing the status of the plants, and then recommended a production program for the following week. Each plant naturally fought for a top priority. Ernest Lawrence pleaded with Groves for additional Alpha plants to be built near industrial cities. Dobie Keith and George Felbeck swore that if the top of the cascade were completed, their K-25 would produce bomb material before Y-12. These men were all among Groves's favorite people, but he wanted to discuss the problem with Nichols. Dobie Keith became infuriated one day when Nichols came to see him with some of Peterson's first graphs.

"Dobie, do you know Pete?" the colonel asked, referring to Major Peterson.

"Sure I know him. He's doing a swell job of coordinating."

"Well, look at these curves! They're right: they show that with the Beta plants we can do a faster job of enriching than if we build the top of K–25. We don't need a top for your plant."

Keith was incensed. "The hell we don't!" he shouted. Like a proud father, he could not take any criticism of his child, the fabulous K–25.

"I was surprised myself, Dobie," Nichols replied calmly. "The electromagnetic was to be just a stopgap until we could build the gaseous-diffusion plant. But now, honestly, I can't find anything wrong with Pete's chart."

Dobie Keith was not at all convinced. "Give me that chart! I'll get Manson Benedict on it."

The next day, a very defeated-looking Keith came to Nichols. "Nick, you're right," he said sadly. "We've missed the boat. That's the way to operate — build more Beta plants!"

General Groves was still the one who had to make the final decision. He sent out the order that, for the time being, the K–25 plant would concentrate on the lower stages of enrichment, and the building of the top of the cascade would be postponed. The electromagnetic plants would be devoted entirely to turning out the higher, more enriched, degrees of uranium. Thus, the final product — the fissionable bomb material — would first come out of Y–12's Beta tracks, which would be fed with enriched uranium from both the K–25 and S–50 plants.

In explaining the details of the production program to Stimson, both Groves and Nichols were optimistic about meeting the deadline. A few hours later the exhausted Secretary of War left Oak Ridge to catch his plane at Knoxville airport. "I feel immensely cheered and braced up," he declared before leaving. "Oak Ridge is the largest, most extraordinary scientific experiment in history."

The day after Stimson's visit to Oak Ridge, a news flash from Warm Springs, Georgia, shook the nation: President Roosevelt had died of a massive cerebral hemorrhage.

Uranium production went rapidly into high gear at Oak Ridge. By May the number of operating stages* at K–25 had doubled; in June, the K–25

---

* In the gaseous-diffusion process, uranium hexafluoride gas (UF–6) is made to pass through the barriers on several thousand successive stages, which form the complete "cascade." At each successive stage, the uranium receives a higher degree

plant started feeding the Beta tracks with 7 percent enriched material, thereby greatly increasing the output of fissionable material from the Y–12 plant. With a final push, Oak Ridge could be expected to send enough uranium–235 to Los Alamos to make at least one atomic bomb a month later.

---

of enrichment, until, finally, pure uranium–235 is obtained as the end product. To produce material of a lesser degree of enrichment, however, uranium hexafluoride gas did not have to pass through as many stages. Thus the K–25 plant was able to begin production before the final stages of the cascade were completed.

50

At 3 A.M. on Thursday, July 12, 1945, physicist Philip Morrison showed his pass to the MP's and entered the heavily guarded vault for nuclear materials at Los Alamos. He was accompanied by Paul Aebersold of the radiation-monitoring group. The two men opened the vault and cautiously pulled out two heavy hemispheres. Smooth and shiny, they were coated with nickel in order to protect the plutonium of which they were made from corrosion — and make them safe to handle. The night before, Robert Bacher, Marshall G. Holloway, Louis Slotin and Morrison had made the delicate, final adjustments on the hemispheres. The two halves of the bomb's core were now ready to be transported to the test site.

The final shaping and electroplating of the hemispheres had been carried out by the Los Alamos metallurgists only ten days earlier, when enough pure material had finally been made available. But a new and unexpected anxiety confronted the scientists at the last moment. Soon after the core had been prepared, little blisters began to develop on the nickel plating. The blisters, the result of imperfect electroplating, appeared right on the matching surfaces of the hemispheres — the worst possible place. If they were not somehow removed, there could be a premature firing of the bomb.

Had plutonium been an ordinary metal, the metallurgists could have ground the blisters down. But grinding a plutonium surface was an extremely delicate operation. Cyril Smith, the head of the Los Alamos metallurgy group, and his assistants finally came up with a solution. The blisters would be partially abraded, but without grinding completely through the nickel coat, before the hemispheres left Los Alamos. Then, at the moment of bomb assembly, a layer of gold foil would be slipped in between the two facing halves of the core. The gold foil, it was hoped, would provide a perfectly smooth surface. The only way to find out if the idea would work, however, was to try it out in the actual blast scheduled for just four days later!

With great caution, Morrison and Aebersold loaded the plutonium hemispheres into special, field carrying cases, which were then placed on the back seat of a sedan. The two scientists seated themselves, one on each side of the precious core, and a security officer took his place in the front seat of the car. When another car, filled with armed GI's, took up station ahead of the sedan, the long 210-mile drive southward to Alamogordo finally began.

Since that spring, an ever-increasing number of cars had been making the trip from Los Alamos to the secret camp of Project Trinity, located on the Alamogordo bombing range. Before leaving, every driver was given written instructions by Dana P. Mitchell, assistant director of the Laboratory. They read: "The following directions are strictly confidential, and this copy is to be read by no one but yourself. You are to turn this copy in to me personally on your return to the site. . . . Under no condition, when you are south of Albuquerque, are you to disclose that you are in any way connected with Santa Fe. If you are stopped for any reason, and you have to give out information, state that you are employed by the 'Engineers of Albuquerque.' Under no circumstances are telephone calls or stops for gasoline to be made between Albuquerque and your destination. Stop for meals at Roy's in Belen, which is on the left-hand side of the main road going south. If you leave the site at 7 A.M. you should make this stop around lunchtime."

Oppenheimer, looking more strained and emaciated than ever, had left Los Alamos the previous day and had joined Kenneth Bainbridge, head of Project Trinity, at the desert site. Navy Commander Norris Bradbury, in charge of bomb assembly, was eagerly awaiting the arrival of all components of "Fat Man" — the nickname of the plutonium weapon.

On July 5, just six days after enough plutonium had been released, Oppenheimer had sent to the Project's top consultants, Arthur Compton in Chicago and Ernest Lawrence in Berkeley, the following telegram: ANY TIME AFTER THE 15TH WOULD BE A GOOD TIME FOR OUR FISHING TRIP. BECAUSE WE ARE NOT CERTAIN OF THE WEATHER WE MAY BE DELAYED SEVERAL DAYS.

Fat Man — the result of prodigious effort, ingenuity and precision — was ready at last. It seemed to possess, beyond every expectation, all the qualities of the ultimate weapon. All, that is, except one: the certainty that it would explode. This uncertainty could mean the difference between an early termination of the war and a $2-billion fiasco. On paper, according to some of the best scientific brains, there was no reason why the bomb should not work. In the laboratories and on the proving grounds, each one of its intricate components had passed endless tests. But how would Fat Man perform as a whole, at the moment of explosion? It was impossible to hold any tests with models. There was only one way to get the answer; it was by exploding the real thing, the complete bomb — Fat Man himself.

Months before enough plutonium was available, and before the problems of implosion were solved, a special group under Dr. Kenneth T. Bainbridge, a Harvard physics professor and a group leader in Kistiakowsky's division, was assigned the task of preparing the first atomic test. From a military point of view, the Trinity explosion meant the dress rehearsal for the real dropping of an atomic bomb on the enemy from the air. But historically the test was going to be, if it succeeded, a breathtaking premiere such as no human being had ever witnessed before: for a split second, man was going to re-create on earth something that had not occurred since the creation of the planet. Technically, the test could mean two "world premieres": first, no chain reaction had been achieved with *fast* neutrons before because such large quantities of plutonium had never been assembled; and second, implosion had never been attempted before.

Several sites in the nearby Southwest had been considered and inspected by a group that included Oppenheimer and Bainbridge. Finally the desert area called Jornada del Muerto (Journey of Death), part of the Alamogordo bombing range in southern New Mexico, was selected in the summer of 1944 with General Groves's approval. The arid Jornada del Muerto was as grim as its name, bringing to mind the many early Spanish pioneers who had perished there from exhaustion and thirst. The nearest towns were Socorro and Carrizozo, over twenty miles away. This barren area fitted the requirements. It was flat, unpopulated desert land. The weather was generally good, and the site, being situated about two hundred miles south of Los Alamos, was not too far for the scientists to travel to, and yet not so near as to make it seem conected with their real work. In September 1944, Groves made arrangements with General Uzal Girard Ent, Commander of the Second Air Force, for acquisition of an 18- by 24-mile section of the northwest corner of the bombing range. The code name Trinity was chosen by Oppenheimer.

By October 1944 the plans for Trinity Camp were drawn up and two months later construction was already completed. One slight delay was caused by the Air Force's failure to procure detailed maps of the area. The maps had been requested by the laboratory through its security officer in order to avoid revealing its interest in Alamogordo. In the end, geodetic survey maps had to be used instead of the aerial mosaics.

The building of roads and communications was still in progress when a small unit of MP's under Lieutenant Harold C. Bush took up residence to guard the camp. Then the scientists in Bainbridge's group began to arrive from Los Alamos. For several months they had to live the same spartan life as the soldiers, sleep in barracks and remain confined to the area. Life at camp was monotonous. In the usual ninety-degrees-plus heat, the only places to swim were cattle-watering reservoirs at the old McDonald ranch. The Army supplied outdoor movies, and a few men tried clandestine antelope-shooting with submachine guns. But aside from these recreations, the personnel's entire time was filled with hard work — installing an intricate system of observation posts, recording instruments and communication networks in the desert. In spite of solitude and hardships, morale was high; all the men knew the purpose of their job and felt like active participants in a great historic mission.

Plutonium was so rare in 1944, and the success of the first atomic explosion was so much in doubt, that recovery of the precious fissionable material in case of failure became one of the main preoccupations. Fantastic ideas for preventing the waste of plutonium were proposed. The one that was finally adopted sounded scarcely less fantastic than any of the others: to contain the explosion in a huge steel vessel!

Nobody at Los Alamos was particularly enthusiastic about the idea, but since nothing better was suggested, plans were made to go ahead and build the container, which had already been dubbed Jumbo. In March 1944, Hans Bethe, in a memo about the numerous engineering problems of this undertaking, concluded that "the problem of a confining sphere is at present darker than ever." The same month Oppenheimer wrote to General Groves: "The probability that the reaction would not shatter the container is extremely small." In other words, Jumbo would be of value only if a nuclear explosion did not take place, or if it was a minor one.

All the steel companies approached by Oppenheimer expressed strong doubts of Jumbo's feasibility. Specifications for the gigantic steel bottle were extraordinary: 25 feet in length, 12 feet in diameter, with walls 14 inches thick, and a weight of 214 tons. The Project was beginning to lose hope of finding a manufacturer when the Babcock and Wilcox Corporation of Barberton, Ohio, finally accepted the job in August 1944. Jumbo was ready the following spring, and after a complicated trip from Ohio on a specially built flatcar, it arrived in May 1945 at a rail siding constructed by the Manhattan District at an abandoned railroad station in Pope, New Mexico. At Pope the huge container was loaded on a specially built, sixty-four-wheel trailer and pulled by three caterpillar tractors across the desert to the Trinity site.

But Jumbo was not used after all. By the time it arrived, plutonium production prospects had grown brighter, the scientists felt more confident in the success of the explosion, and the whole idea of containing the blast was abandoned. However, the huge contraption was kept on the site, "just in case." On June 11, 1945, Bainbridge was still mentioning it in a memo to Norris Bradbury: "Jumbo is a silent partner in all our plans and is not yet dead. . . . We must continue preparations for [its] use until Oppenheimer says to forget it for the first shot."

Since March 1945, the Trinity test had become a program of the highest priority, and a special division, Project TR, had been formed under Bainbridge's leadership. The first task was to prepare a trial in which one hundred tons of conventional high explosives would be detonated. No knowledge then existed concerning blast effects above the level of a few tons of TNT, and it was hoped that the huge explosion would provide data for the calibration of instruments that were to be used later for the atomic explosion.

With the "one-hundred-ton shot" set for May 7, hundreds of crates of high explosive, trucked from Fort Wingate, New Mexico, began to arrive at the site. The TNT was stacked on the platform of a twenty-foot-high tower, and all instruments for measuring the blast effects were placed at distances on a scale that would correspond to the forthcoming atomic blast, which was expected to be equivalent to five thousand tons of TNT. Fission products from a Hanford reactor were placed among the TNT crates in order to simulate the expected radioactivity.

Detonated before dawn, the one hundred-ton explosion lit the desert sky — a brilliant orange ball that was seen as far away as the Alamogordo base, sixty miles to the southeast. The test proved extremely valuable, providing much necessary data for calibrating instruments and redesigning shelters for greater efficiency. It also afforded an excellent opportunity for laboratory scientists to become accustomed to field work and for the correction of any mistakes and defects in Trinity's planning. Transportation methods between ground zero (the bomb site) and the various shelters, for example, proved inadequate. As a result, twenty miles of blacktop road were laid and a new communication system was installed.

Meanwhile, difficulties with implosion continued to upset early plans. Since March 1945 the overall direction of the implosion program had been turned over to a special "Cowpuncher Committee," composed of Allison, Bacher, Kistiakowsky, Charles C. Lauritsen, Captain Parsons and Hartley Rowe. By April it was clear that the previously set Fourth of July test date was not going to be met. Production of the explosive lenses had been considerably delayed. The timing devices were not ready either. Luis Alvarez' group was still experimenting with various models of electric detonators, which required an extraordinary degree of simultaneity in triggering the explosive charges, placed at different points of the bomb's surface. Time was measured in microseconds. The probability of a detonator's malfunction were reduced to one chance in ten thousand, but even this was not entirely satisfactory. In June the Cowpuncher Committee agreed that July 13 was the earliest possible date for the Trinity test.

Two hundred and fifty Los Alamos scientists were already assembled at the sizzling Trinity Camp when Fat Man's components began to arrive in the midst of frantic activity going on twenty-four hours a day. When Morrison and Aebersold's sedan with the plutonium core arrived at Trinity, Bainbridge instructed the convoy to drive to the McDonald ranch, a four-room frame house situated about a mile from ground zero. At the ranch, Brigadier General Thomas F. Farrell, deputy for General Groves, signed a receipt for the plutonium and handed the core to the physicist Louis Slotin. Thus the active material was formally transferred from the Los Alamos scientists to the Army.

Bacher, Morrison, Holloway and Slotin assembled the two hemispheres next morning in the ranch house in a vacuum-clean room with windows sealed by black tape. Because of the blisters on the hemisphere's surface, Cyril Smith was called in at the last minute. He carefully laid the gold foil on the flat surface of one hemisphere, then adjusted the second hemisphere on top of it. While the men in white surgical coats assembled the plutonium globe on a table, Oppenheimer nervously walked in and out like an expectant father, adding to the general tension.

Now the core of Fat Man was ready to be placed in its shell of ordinary explosives. These, assembled together with the rest of the non-nuclear parts of the bomb, had been brought from Los Alamos by Kistiakowsky the same day, Friday the thirteenth. Claiming that this superstition-shrouded date would bring luck, the chemist had waited until after midnight before leaving for Trinity. These parts, protected by a metal container placed in a wooden crate, were loaded on a truck with a convoy of six Army cars. Before leaving Los Alamos, Kisty had measured for the last time each non-nuclear part of Fat Man, then X-rayed it for structural defects, carefully photographing each step of the final checkup. On arrival at Trinity, the explosive components were taken to the base of the one hundred-foot tower, where final assembly took place under the supervision of Commander Bradbury in a canvas tent.

Early Friday afternoon, Kisty called the McDonald ranch to say he was ready. At the ranch Slotin slipped the small cylinder with the initiator between the plutonium hemispheres, and the eighty-pound core, now completely ready, was placed in a sedan and carefully driven to the tower. Two sergeants — Joe Zercinovic and Al Van Heusen — opened the top of the explosives shell, and then the plutonium globe, suspended by a chain from the tower hoist, was slowly lowered into the opening. It was the first time that a large quantity of active material had been placed within high explosives.

While Bacher followed the oscillations of the radioactive recorder, Holloway leaned over the bomb, his head inside it, directing the hoist by hand. Several scientists, including Oppenheimer, followed the operation in complete silence. They seemed outwardly calm, but everyone felt the tension in the air.

The core descended slowly into the hole, but just as it was about to click into place, it stuck, inexplicably. For a few agonizing moments the worst fears passed through everybody's mind. Bacher and Holloway were greatly disturbed — the parts had been checked several times and had been fitted to perfection.

Oppenheimer and Kistiakowsky joined them in emergency consultation. The four scientists came to the conclusion that, after leaving Los Alamos, the plutonium core must have expanded slightly from the heat of the desert as well as the heat generated by the active material. They waited five minutes so it could remain in contact with the colder parts of the bomb, to see if it would contract. They had guessed right: when Holloway signaled the second time for the hoist to be lowered, the core clicked neatly into place.

At eight o'clock the next morning the tent was removed, and the five-ton bomb started its slow ascent to the top of the tower, where a sheet-steel house had been specially constructed to shelter it. Several GI mattresses were stacked under the bomb in the hopes of softening the impact of an accidental drop. Powered by a motor, the hoist rose slowly, only a foot a minute. Sergeant Zercinovic and an engineer climbed just ahead of the bomb, guiding its passage from platform to platform until they could finally place it in the steel cage on top of the tower.

The fragile detonators were put into position only when the whole device was safely in position — it would have been far too risky to hoist up the bomb with the detonators already attached to it. The detonator crew climbed the tower for the final installation of the firing circuit. But the cables connecting Fat Man's detonators with the control post remained hooked into a dummy which had been used during the rehearsals. Every six hours the crew returned to the top of the tower to withdraw a manganese wire that was measuring the radioactivity.

Late at night on July 14, the work of assembly was practically finished, and Fat Man was left on the tower, under armed guard.

51

BEGINNING IN MARCH 1945, a Chevrolet with Tennessee license plates entered the Y–12 area at Oak Ridge once a week at 10:30 A.M. Though the occupants wore civilian clothes, somehow they looked too strong and physically fit to be scientists. Beneath their coats were pistols in shoulder holsters, while other weapons and ammunition were lying on the floor of the sedan. At Oak Ridge the men picked up specially made traveling cases, carefully loaded them in the car, and then drove off in the direction of Knoxville. The cargo these security officers were transporting was worth millions of dollars: the nickel containers inside the cases were filled with uranium–235, the bomb material that had taken three long years to produce. At Knoxville the couriers boarded the 12:50 P.M. Southland train for Chicago and locked themselves in a reserved compartment. The next morning, when the train pulled into the Chicago station, other security couriers were waiting for them. At 12:01 P.M. the Santa Fe Chief started its long journey west, carrying the new couriers as far as Lamy, a small station in the New Mexico desert. At 2:10 the next afternoon, a Los Alamos car met the train and transported the precious uranium–235 to the laboratory on the Hill.

For weeks and months, before the first shipment arrived, it had been awaited with impatience, anguish, hope and frustration by the scientists at Los Alamos. The building of the two different types of bombs – uranium and plutonium – each had the same priority and urgency. Yet during all the ups and downs of the plutonium program, and especially while the tough battle against implosion problems was being waged, the members of the Manhattan Project had been reassured by the feeling that it could ultimately rely on the uranium weapon. The uranium bomb's assembly by the gun method, difficult as it was, did not seem to present any insurmountable obstacles. The great question mark had always been the same: when – if ever – would Oak Ridge produce enough uranium–235?

The parts for the gun-type bombs were practically ready by the spring of 1945. The gun barrel had already been designed and manufactured at the Naval Gun Factory in Washington, D.C. But the development, and

the testing of the gun-target combination, had been long and complicated, necessitating a big expansion of Ordnance Division personnel and
facilities placed under the overall leadership of Navy Captain William S.
Parsons, who, since May 1943, had been stationed at Los Alamos.

Deak Parsons was probably the best qualified military man for the job.
An Annapolis graduate, he had worked on such important Navy projects
as radar and the proximity fuse. Since 1942 he had been a special assistant
to the OSRD director, Vannevar Bush. It was Bush who recommended
the energetic Navy captain to General Groves, with the hearty endorse-
ment of Admiral Purnell. A handsome, forty-one-year-old man with a
balding head, intelligent eyes and serious mouth, Parsons was obviously
a well-disciplined and dedicated officer with great experience in ordnance
and gunnery. He also showed a good understanding of modern science.
Groves liked him immediately. "I'm sure Parsons is the man we need," he
wrote to Oppenheimer after the interview. A few days later, the Los
Alamos director met Parsons in Washington and enthusiastically endorsed
the choice.

At Los Alamos, Parsons felt more or less at home. Although born in
Evanston, Illinois, he had spent most of his childhood in New Mexico, at
Fort Sumner, where his father was a prominent lawyer. As the only
military man among the laboratory leaders, Parsons nonetheless managed
to gain the scientists' respect and friendship. He was friendly though
never familiar, dynamic though quiet and dignified. At work he wore his
khaki uniform, but his Ordnance Division was run as a civilian outfit. Yet
his punctuality, reserve and exacting manner intimidated many of his
subordinates. Parsons, however, was much better liked by the Los Alamos
scientists than Groves. Also, because of his high rank, Parsons proved
extremely useful to the scientists: he could tell the general what the
laboratory needed and make much more of an impression than any
scientist. Groves often questioned civilian demands for added funds,
buildings or materials; but when such demands were endorsed by Parsons, he knew they must be entirely justified. This did not mean, however,
that in scientific matters Groves would necessarily side with Parsons
against the civilians. Once, for example, with a superb display of good
judgment, the general overruled Parsons's strong objections — perfectly
legitimate from a military point of view — to the implosion method, and
gave the green light to the questionable project. No matter what he
thought of various scientists, Groves had an uncanny knack for sensing
who was right in a technical discussion.

Except for uranium physics and metallurgy, the gun assembly of "Little
Boy," the uranium bomb, was mostly an ordnance problem entrusted to

Captain Parsons's division. The guns had to be very unusual — as light and short as possible in order to fit into an airborne weapon, and at the same time firing very fast in order to lessen the chances of pre-detonation.* Since standard guns, with a velocity of three thousand feet per second, were not sufficiently reliable, the new requirements presented quite a problem. There was only one consolation — the engineers did not have to worry about durability: each gun would be used only once.

Different models of cannons were studied and the first tubes were ordered from the Naval Gun Factory in September 1943. While waiting for their delivery, Parsons directed the extensive preparations for the first testings. Installations had to be built, more experts hired, new techniques perfected. Construction of the proving ground at Anchor Ranch was finished between June and September 1943. Besides the usual gun emplacements, sand butts, bombproof magazines and control room, new features which were required because of the tight security conditions had to be added to the Anchor Ranch testing ground.

From September 1943 until the following March, test firing was carried out with a 3"/50 naval antiaircraft gun. Thanks to these practice rounds, the instrumentation was greatly improved, and new photographic techniques, chronographs and gauges were developed. From March on, Edwin McMillan, deputy for Parsons on the gun, supervised the tests with the specially made barrels, and by July the soundness of the design was established. Meanwhile, after the physicists learned more about the properties of uranium, it fortunately became possible to make the gun specifications less complicated and rigid.

A reorganization of Los Alamos in August 1944 put Parsons in charge of turning both devices — the uranium and the plutonium — into combat weapons. Under him, Commander A. Francis Birch, a Harvard professor turned naval officer, directed the entire work on the uranium gun. Before the guns for the uranium bomb arrived in October 1944, Birch set to work developing satisfactory target units — the uranium parts into which the projectile was to be fired. Natural uranium was used as a stand-in for uranium–235 in the projectile, and reduced-scale targets were tested for months on the 3"/50 and on the 20 mm. Hispano guns.

Full-scale firing began in December. The cases enclosing the uranium target were made of high-alloy steel, so sturdily built that they could be

---

* In the gun-assembly method, a subcritical mass of uranium–235 (the projectile) is fired down a cannon barrel into another subcritical mass of U–235 (the target), which is placed in front of the muzzle. Both gun and target are encased in the bomb. When projectile and target contact, they form a critical mass which explodes.

If the firing is not fast enough, the neutrons emitted by the projectile will begin interacting with the target *before* the contact and *before* the mass has become critical. In this case, a pre-detonation occurs.

used again and again.* The new gun was very unconventional in appearance. Made of a special steel alloy, it weighed about half a ton, was six feet long and had a threaded muzzle. On January 1, 1943, Commander Birch had reported to the leaders of the laboratory on the progress of the gun, of which two models had been made. He insisted on a freezing of the final design — and without delay — if the weapon was to be ready by summer. But before the design could be frozen, it was necessary to have a precise determination of the critical mass.† Fortunately, the probable critical mass was determined within reasonable limits in February, thus making it possible to freeze the design of the gun and to select the lighter-weight model. For security reasons, construction of the gun was assigned to three independent plants: the Naval Gun Factory made the gun and the breech; the target case was produced at the Naval Ordnance Plant at Center Line, Michigan; and the Expert Tool and Die Company of Detroit made the bomb tail. One gun-and-target device was assembled at Los Alamos and tested successfully. After that, assembly was done at Wendover Field, Utah, which was the training base for the crews of the specially formed 509th Composite Group, whose B–29's would deliver the bomb. Thirty-two practice missions with dummy bombs were carried out there with complete success.

The components of Little Boy — gun, projectile and target — were ready. If the theories were correct, if the tests were conclusive, the bomb should now explode. But unlike the plutonium program, no test was planned for the complete uranium bomb — there simply was not enough material for two bombs. Production of uranium–235 was slow at Oak Ridge and the very first weapon that could be assembled was therefore earmarked for combat release. If Little Boy was to be used in August, no prior test or demonstration was possible.

A closed black truck escorted by seven carloads of heavily armed security agents left Los Alamos on July 14, 1945, for Albuquerque. The truck carried most of the bomb's components, packed in a fifteen-foot crate, and a lead cylinder, eighteen inches in diameter, containing the uranium projectile. Although the lead bucket was only two feet high, the men had difficulty in lifting it. Major Robert R. Furman, of General Groves's office, and Captain James F. Nolan, an Army radiologist at the

---

* Actually, the case that later went into the Hiroshima bomb was the very first one ever tried at Anchor Ranch range, and it had already been used four times.

† The fact that the entire program was moving ahead at full speed, even before anyone knew what would be the exact size of the uranium projectile, was a perfect illustration of the way the Manhattan Project operated — with a bold assault on all scientific fronts.

WESTFIELD MEMORIAL LIBRARY.
WESTFIELD, N. J.

Los Alamos hospital, had received orders to accompany the unique cargo all the way to the Pacific island of Tinian, where the B–29 bombers of the 509th Composite Group were waiting for the raid on Japan. The remaining part of the uranium–235 was to be sent separately later by air.

An Air Force plane flew Furman and Nolan with the major part of the uranium from Albuquerque to Hamilton Field in San Francisco. From there security agents escorted them to the Hunter's Point Navy Yard, where the lead cylinder was locked in the yard commandant's office, with a Marine sentry stationed outside the door. Before dawn on July 16, Furman and Nolan, dressed in the uniforms of Army artillery officers to avoid attracting attention, boarded the heavy cruiser USS *Indianapolis*, followed by two sailors carrying the heavy lead bucket on a crowbar. At the same time a crane hoisted the large crate onto the deck, as the sailors stared in amazement, their curiosity aroused by the extraordinary security measures. The lead cylinder was welded to the deck in a cabin shared by Nolan and Furman. One man was always left on guard whenever the other went out of the cabin.

The USS *Indianapolis* sailed immediately for Hawaii and Tinian. During the first days of the voyage, the crew asked many questions about the mysterious crate, but Furman and Nolan managed to parry them. The men most puzzled were the ship's gunnery officers — after exchanging a few words of shoptalk about cannons and ballistics, they were appalled by the ignorance of the two "artillery" officers. Even the captain of the USS *Indianapolis* did not know what the cargo was, except that it was tremendously important. His orders were clear: in case the ship sank, the lead cylinder had to be saved at all costs. It was to have absolute priority for a place in the first motor launch or raft, before any human passenger.

52

It had just started raining when Groves's car drew into Trinity Camp on Sunday afternoon, July 15, 1945. The sky had darkened and cast a gloom over the desert. Thunder rumbled in the distance. The general was traveling with Vannevar Bush and James Conant, who from the very outset were the two top civilians in atomic development in the United States.

During the days preceding the test, as the three men impatiently awaited a message from Oppenheimer, they visited Manhattan District installations on the West Coast. When word finally came from Oppenheimer that zero hour was fixed for early Monday morning, July 16, they flew from Berkeley on the way to Albuquerque, New Mexico, with a short stopover planned at Pasadena. As their plane approached the runway at Pasadena, they had a narrow escape when the pilot, barely missing some high-tension wires, hit the ground with a violent jolt. It was a close shave. At the Albuquerque airfield, a car was waiting for them. As they drove on toward Los Alamos, they shared the same thought: now at last, after three years of miraculous achievement by science, industry, engineering and the Army, the moment was at hand to see the results of an un-precedented combined effort. As the car pulled into the Trinity Camp, they could see the top of a steel tower on the test site. The bomb was ready.

At base camp, Oppenheimer briefed the three visitors. Everything seemed set to go. Fermi, Bethe and most of the other Los Alamos luminaries had already joined the scientists directly involved in the firing test. As the last busload of consultants arrived from the Hill, a car was sent to Albuquerque to bring Ernest Lawrence, Britain's Sir James Chadwick and William L. Laurence, the noted science reporter on the *New York Times*, who had been secretly assigned by the Manhattan Project to be the only newsman covering the atomic bomb tests.

The three nearest observation dugouts were ten thousand yards — over five miles — north, west and south of the bomb tower. Base camp itself, where observers were to be in the open, was nearly ten miles away. Because of the distances involved, all points were connected by radio to the control station, located at dugout S–10,000.

On arrival, Groves immediately sensed the tremendous excitement in the air. Everyone was overtired, and tension was mounting visibly as zero hour approached. Groves was particularly worried about Oppenheimer, who seemed to be reaching the limits of his endurance. Groves wanted the laboratory's director to be as calm as possible when making the final command decisions. There were altogether too many excited people around giving him advice on what he should do. Groves was annoyed, too, with Fermi, who was making bets with his colleagues on whether the bomb would ignite the atmosphere, and, if so, whether it would destroy only New Mexico — or the entire world. Fermi was also saying that, even if the bomb failed to go off, it would still be a worthwhile experience — it would prove, in that case, that an atomic explosion was probably impossible. But Groves sensed that Fermi was only trying to calm down some of the others; the Italian seemed confident and quite unaffected by his own words.

Weather was the greatest worry. This was important because it was feared that rain and wind could bring dangerous radioactive fallout over populated areas. By the end of the afternoon, several scientists were urging Oppenheimer to postpone the test for at least twenty-four hours. To get him away from all the excitement, Groves took Oppenheimer into an office at the base camp to discuss matters quietly. The meteorologist was consulted, but he proved of little help — long-range forecasts, perfectly accurate in past weeks, were far off at the moment; nothing, in his opinion, could be predicted with any certitude for the next twelve hours. Groves soon dismissed him from the meeting.

Any postponement would involve definite mechanical risks. The steel tower stood like a lightning rod in the middle of the desert, and the storm could come nearer any hour. Cables and wires, exposed to excessive moisture for too long, could have short circuits with a resulting misfire. The danger of sabotage had to be considered, too. Bainbridge, in charge of the test, reported that his men were already completely exhausted. If they had to run through all the numerous checks again because of a postponement, some of them would probably collapse of fatigue. Groves had a special reason to worry about any delay, a reason he could disclose to no one. That same day, at Potsdam, President Truman and Secretary Stimson were anxiously waiting to hear from Alamogordo before they, together with Churchill, saw Stalin again and before the Allies could issue the ultimatum to Japan.

Oppenheimer and Groves were forced to make their own weather prediction. At dusk they decided not to postpone the test more than a few hours at the most. They agreed to meet again at 1 A.M. to review the situation. The general urged Oppenheimer to get some sleep, but the scientist ignored his advice. As for Groves, he went straight to bed in the tent he shared with Bush and Conant. A few minutes later the man who carried the major burden of the entire Manhattan Project was sound asleep, undisturbed by the excitement around him. A heavy wind blew off the desert, causing the tent ropes to slap the canvas incessantly. For a couple of hours, Bush and Conant tossed sleeplessly on their cots, unable to understand how Groves could possibly sleep so unconcernedly before such a momentous occasion.

As rain continued to fall, the members of the seven-man arming party — Bainbridge, Kistiakowsky, Joseph L. McKibben, who was the scientist responsible for the circuits, Lieutenant Bush, two weathermen and a guard — left the base camp, shortly before 11 P.M., for the final trip to the tower. McKibbon, his face ashen with fatigue, again went over the forty-seven-point checklist of what had to be done before zero hour; then he was left to sleep for a while under the tower — Bainbridge wanted him alert and ready at test time.

Donald Hornig also came to the tower and climbed to the top to switch the detonating circuit from the practice dummy to the real bomb. Then he rushed back to the S–10,000 post — the control dugout — to man the stop switch, which could prevent the explosion, only seconds before the detonation, if anything suddenly went wrong with the automatic system.

Kistiakowsky climbed thirty feet up the tower to make a last adjustment on a light, then returned to his car to sleep for a few hours. Lieutenant Bush and an MP turned their flashlights on the tower to make sure no one came near it. It was a wet, dark night without a star in the sky, and only the voice of Bainbridge, as he conferred with John Williams at the control dugout on the land telephone, broke the silence.

Shortly after 1 A.M. Groves and Oppenheimer again left the base camp to go to the control dugout, four miles away. No observer would be allowed there, only the men on duty, who were now busily checking their equipment for the last time. Every five or ten minutes, Groves and Oppenheimer went outside to look at the weather, which had not improved since early evening. A first postponement of one hour had to be ordered, followed by a second one of thirty minutes. The general made an effort to keep Oppenheimer away from the mounting tension in the dugout so that the scientist could consider the situation as calmly as possible. Each time he seemed on the point of exploding Groves would take him out and walk with him in the drizzle, reassuring him all the while that everything would be all right.

Then a message was received from Captain Parsons, who was supposed to fly in one of the two observation planes. Because of poor flying conditions, the commander of the Albuquerque airfield had forbidden the planes to take off. Groves was disappointed, but he decided that the test should proceed without aerial observation.*

By 2 A.M. the weather began to improve. The rain stopped at four o'clock, and at 4:45 the weather report came: "Winds aloft very light, variable to 40,000 surface calm. Inversion about 17,000 feet. Humidity 12,000 to 18,000 above 80 percent. Conditions holding for next two hours. Sky now broken, becoming scattered." Groves made his decision. The explosion was set for go at 5:30.

The final phase of the arming began. At the tower, connections were checked, switches were thrown and all leads were connected. Each step was reported on the phone by Bainbridge to Williams. The arming party switched on the floodlights that would direct the B–29's and also make the tower visible by field glasses from the dugout. Thirty minutes before zero hour, the five remaining men of the arming party left the tower in jeeps and headed for the S–10,000 dugout.

Some concern had been expressed for the safety of the men in case the jeeps developed engine trouble en route. But Groves himself was unworried. "Knowing Kistiakowsky, I'm sure they'll find a safe position even in the event of a breakdown. After all, in thirty minutes they could walk several miles from the point of detonation, and I'm sure that they won't walk slowly."

Leaving Oppenheimer at the control dugout, Groves returned to the base camp, where all the high-ranking observers were assembled. It was the nearest point where people were permitted to stay outdoors during the blast. They were told to lie face down on the ground, with feet toward the blast, then to close their eyes and cover them with their hands as the countdown approached zero. Smoked glasses were distributed for observation after the flash.

At 5:10 the countdown began. The intercoms, the FM radios and the public-address system carried Sam Allison's voice, counting first at five-minute intervals, then in minutes, then in seconds. At the control point, the tension became almost unbearable. Many seemed to be praying. Oppenheimer grew paler as the seconds ticked off; scarcely breathing, he held onto a post to steady himself.

At minus 45 seconds, Joe McKibben threw the switch that started the precise automatic timer. Now only Hornig's stop switch could exercise any control over the test. At minus 30 seconds, Bainbridge and Williams

---

* At the last minute, Parsons did manage to take off, but he was unable to use his measuring instruments that were supposed to be dropped from the plane.

joined the others in the control dugout. At the outside observation point Groves was lying on the ground between Bush and Conant.

"Ten seconds." Allison's voice pierced the complete silence. "Nine, eight, seven . . ." Everyone closed his eyes and shielded his face with his hands. At 5:29 A.M., Allison shouted, "Now!"

The fierce light that followed, almost blinding in spite of their closed eyes, was impossible to describe. There was no frame of reference from anything the observers had experienced before. In a brief moment, the light within twenty miles was equal to several suns at midday. It was seen in Albuquerque, Santa Fe, El Paso and other points as far as one hundred eighty miles away. As Brigadier General Farrell wrote later in the report for the Secretary of War, it was "unprecedented, magnificent, beautiful, stupendous and terrifying." Farrell's account, written in the wake of the test, had nothing of the style of a perfunctory military report:

"No man-made phenomenon of such tremendous power had ever occurred before. The lighting effects beggared description. The whole country was lighted by a searing light with the intensity many times that of the midday sun. It was golden, purple, violet, gray and blue. It lighted every peak, crevasse and ridge of the nearby mountain range with a clarity and beauty that cannot be described but must be seen to be imagined. It was that beauty the great poets dream about but describe most poorly and inadequately. Thirty seconds after the explosion came, first, the air blast pressing hard against people and things, to be followed almost immediately by the strong, sustained, awesome roar which warned of doomsday and made us feel that we puny things were blasphemous to dare tamper with the forces heretofore reserved to the Almighty. Words are inadequate tools for the job of acquainting those not present with the physical, mental and psychological effects. It had to be witnessed to be realized."

William L. Laurence, the *New York Times* reporter, was to write: "It was like the grand finale of a mighty symphony of the elements; fascinating and terrifying, uplifting and crushing, ominous, devastating, full of great promise and great foreboding. . . . On that moment hung eternity. Time stood still. Space contracted to a pinpoint. It was as though the earth had opened and the skies split. One felt as though he had been privileged to witness the birth of the world — to be present at the moment of Creation when the Lord said: 'Let there be light.' "

Next to Laurence at the twenty-mile observation post was Feynman, who, typically, was the only man to disobey the instructions. Ignoring his thick dark glasses, he sat behind the windshield of a car as the whole group nervously tried to establish radio contact with the control post. But central control was so busy that it had forgotten the observers. As the tension mounted, people started adjusting their welder's glasses. "The heck with it!" Feynman muttered. "At twenty miles distance no light could be *that* bright."

But he was wrong. The tremendous white flash that illuminated the desert blinded him for a moment and forced him to turn his head away in pain. Though closed, his eyes saw, as an afterimage, the picture of the explosion in purple. When he opened his eyes a few seconds later, the blinding white light was turning yellow, and a wave of furiously boiling clouds was mounting in the sky. A bright ball of orange flames formed in the air, lighting the clouds with a strange violet glow. There was not a single sound. The spectacle was unfolding in eerie, absolute silence.

It lasted for about a minute and a half, an incredibly long time during which no one moved, no one said a word. Then, suddenly, there was a sharp, loud blast that tore the desert sky like an immense artillery barrage, followed by thunder rolling back and forth.

It came so late that Laurence, surprised, turned to Feynman. "What was that?" he asked, then mumbled, "Oh, that was the bomb we've just been watching . . ." Feynman himself was shaken by the realization that the blast could reach them with such strength after traveling for an entire minute and a half.

The sound came as a release for taut nerves. "That's it!" the men yelled, jumping with joy. Only Bob Wilson remained silently morose. "What a thing we've made!" he whispered as Feynman rushed to congratulate him.

"You're crazy, what's the matter with you?" Feynman shouted in disbelief. "You — of all people! Don't you remember that you're the guy that got me into it?"*

After seeing the blast from the observation post at base camp, Enrico Fermi wrote: "My first impression of the explosion was the very intense flash of light, and a sensation of heat on the parts of my body that were exposed. Although I did not look directly towards the object, I had the impression that suddenly the countryside became brighter than in full daylight. I subsequently looked in the direction of the explosion through the dark glasses and could see something that looked like a conglomeration of flames that promptly started rising. After a few seconds the rising flames lost their brightness and appeared as a huge pillar of smoke with an expanded head like a gigantic mushroom that rose rapidly beyond the clouds, probably to a height of the order of 30,000 feet. After reaching its

---

* In times to come, Feynman, as well as a number of his jubilant colleagues that day, was to have second thoughts about what he had created. But as the dawn rose for the second time that day, they could only feel proud and tremendously relieved that their three-year-long effort had finally been crowned with success.

full height, the smoke stayed stationary for a while before the wind started dispersing it."

Even during this historic moment, the scientist in Fermi did not miss the opportunity for an experiment. As the air blast was about to reach him, forty seconds after the explosion, he dropped a handful of torn paper scraps from about a six-foot height. Since there was no wind, he could measure their displacement as the blast was passing. The pieces of paper were blown about two and a half yards away. After making a swift mental calculation, he announced calmly, "That corresponds to the blast produced by ten thousand tons of TNT."

Sitting on the ground and watching the tremendous fireball in the sky, Groves, Bush and Conant shook hands in silence. At the control dugout, Oppenheimer's tense face relaxed with relief as Kistiakowsky gave him an exuberant embrace. "Oppie, you owe me ten dollars!" he shouted happily; he had bet his month's salary against ten dollars that the bomb would work. At all Trinity observation points, scientists, officers and technicians were congratulating each other enthusiastically. Fat Man had worked: the Manhattan Project was a success.

The world still did not know it. A press release, prepared in advance, was issued at the Alamogordo Air Base.* The released text read:

"Alamogordo, July 16 — The Commanding Officer of the Alamogordo Army Air Base made the following statement today:

"'Several inquiries have been received concerning a heavy explosion which occurred on the Alamogordo Air Base reservation this morning.

"'A remotely located ammunition magazine containing a considerable amount of high explosives and pyrotechnics exploded.

"'There was no loss of life or injury to anyone, and the property damage outside of the explosives magazine itself was negligible.

"'Weather conditions affecting the content of gas shells exploded by the blast may make it desirable for the Army to evacuate temporarily a few civilians from their homes.'"

In Washington, Jean O'Leary received General Groves's telephone call at 7:30 A.M. He was using the special code he had left with her before leaving. As soon as she decoded the message, she rushed to the Pentagon and handed it to George L. Harrison, one of Secretary Stimson's special assistants, whom he had assigned to Groves before leaving for Potsdam. Then, shortly afterwards, they prepared together a message to Stimson in Potsdam: "Operated on this morning. Diagnosis not yet complete but

---

* Other communiqués had been prepared to cover any eventuality — including one that spoke of the "strange deaths of many famous scientists, victims of an accidental explosion in New Mexico."

results seem satisfactory and already exceed expectations. Local press release necessary as interest extends a great distance. Dr. Groves pleased. He returns tomorrow. I will keep you posted."

A second message to Potsdam followed the next day after Groves returned to Washington: "Doctor has just returned most enthusiastic and confident that the little boy is as husky as his big brother. The light in his eyes discernible from here to Highhold* and I could hear his screams from here to my farm."

Then General Groves and Brigadier General Farrell sat down and wrote a detailed report to Secretary Stimson. It was kept so secret that only Mrs. O'Leary and one other secretary were allowed to type it. It was two o'clock in the morning when they finished. "At 0530, 16 July 1945," the report began, "in a remote section of the Alamogordo Air Base, New Mexico, the first full-scale test was made of the implosion-type, atomic-fission bomb. For the first time in history there was a nuclear explosion. And what an explosion! . . ."

---

* Highhold was Stimson's house on Long Island.

53

AUGUST 5, 1945, was a Sunday, but Leslie Groves had been in his office since early morning. The day before, he had received the message for which he had been waiting for five days. It was from his deputy in Tinian, Brigadier General Farrell. It informed him that weather conditions were finally expected to be good; the uranium bomb was being readied and the B–29 carrying it was scheduled to take off the next day.

The USS *Indianapolis*, carrying most of Little Boy's components, had arrived at Tinian on July 26.* The remaining small quantities of uranium–235, guarded by Los Alamos security officers, arrived from Albuquerque aboard a C–54 transport plane a few days later. Captain Parsons, who had been selected by Groves as the weaponeer for the first bombing mission to Japan, was waiting on Tinian with the pilot, Colonel Paul W. Tibbets, and crew of the bomber *Enola Gay*. Also waiting on the Pacific island were the detachment of scientists from Los Alamos who would assemble the bombs, the 509th Composite Group and the supervising Manhattan Project personnel. Little Boy had been ready for nearly a week, waiting only for the first favorable weather to be dropped over Japan.

Groves had expected to hear that the plane had taken off by 1 P.M. and results of the air raid before 7 P.M. that Sunday, but the day dragged on with not a word from Tinian. In Groves's outer office, a handful of officers anxiously waited as tension mounted steadily. Groves did not query Farrell, as most commanders would have done. He believed that subordinates should not be bothered unnecessarily while they are engaged in crucial operations. Finding it too much of a strain to sit idly at his desk, he decided to leave and play tennis. Though the duty officer was told how to contact him immediately if any messages came in, the general took an officer with him and asked him to sit next to the telephone at the tennis courts. Every few minutes the impatient officer would call in to find out if

---

* Four days after finishing her cargo mission, the cruiser, en route from Guam to the Philippines, was sunk by a Japanese submarine: 886 men were drowned or lost; 316 survived, all of them injured. This was one of the most tragic naval disasters in American history.

the message had come from Tinian. But there was still no word; the tennis game continued without interruption.

Shortly after returning to his office, Groves was told that General Marshall had just called. The Army Chief of Staff had returned from a weekend at his home in Leesburg, Virginia, and wanted to know if Groves had gotten any news about the bombing. When the duty officer replied, "I will call General Groves right away," General Marshall answered, "General Groves has enough on his mind without being bothered by me. I hope he will have news soon."

After another hour of waiting, Groves left his office again, this time to have an early dinner at the nearby Army-Navy Club with his wife and daughter and George Harrison, Secretary Stimson's special assistant. Mrs. Groves and Gwen did not notice anything unusual in the general's behavior that evening. "Still no news," he whispered to Harrison.

At Groves's office, the people who knew that the first atomic bomb was on its way to Japan began to be intensely concerned. Would it work? And if it did explode, would the blast destroy the plane too? The successful Trinity test three weeks earlier was no guarantee. It had involved an entirely different device — a plutonium bomb, not a uranium one, and an implosion-type mechanism instead of a gun assembly. The Fat Man that had exploded in the Alamogordo desert was detonated atop a tower; dropping a real, airborne weapon presented hundreds of new and different problems: would the proximity fuse explode at the proper height, would the uranium projectile seat itself properly in the target, would the initiator send its neutrons into the assembly at the exact fraction of a second? And there was another consideration: Little Boy would be using *all* the uranium–235 so far produced; no material for another uranium bomb existed. Though the gigantic plants at Oak Ridge were processing material for the second uranium bomb, it was still not ready, and it would be weeks, if not months, before there would be enough for another bomb.

The *Enola Gay* should be landing at Tinian at the very moment when Leslie Groves was ordering his favorite dessert. For the man who had directed for three years the titanic efforts to produce the bomb, these were tense hours of suspense; it was as if he were in a courtroom waiting for a jury to come in with a fateful verdict. A quick termination of the war might well result from the success of the mission. Indeed, the fate of hundreds of thousands of human lives, both American and Japanese, was being decided at that instant somewhere in the skies above Japan. For Groves, the awaited cable had an additional significance: it would be the final verdict, the only one that counted, on the entire Manhattan Project and on his leadership of that undertaking, representing almost two billions of dollars, spent without the American taxpayers' knowledge. The

day's news would bring the final judgment on the wisdom of his unorthodox methods and bold decisions, the fantastic risks that he had taken and
for which he would be held responsible. The news from Tinian could
give, in a matter of minutes, a different meaning to his whole life. It was
almost as if the key to some code held the power to change the significance of certain words; if the bomb failed, Groves's "courage" would be
changed to "recklessness," his "dedication" would become "stubbornness,"
and his "wisdom" — only "folly." In a few hours Leslie Groves was going
to be a national hero — or the defendant in what would certainly be the
greatest Congressional investigation in history.

General Thomas T. Handy, the Deputy Chief of Staff under General
Marshall, who was dining at another table, stopped by and, leaning over
Groves, asked for news. "Nothing," sighed Groves. At 6:45 he was called
to the telephone. Major J. H. Derry, the duty officer, read the first
message. Yes, *Enola Gay* had left as scheduled; but still no further news
from Captain Parsons or Colonel Tibbets. Groves felt a little better and
he whispered the news to Handy and Harrison as he returned to the
table. They both stopped eating, but Mrs. Groves and Gwen still were not
aware of any tension: Groves showed no signs of concern. After dinner,
his wife and daughter drove the general to his office in the old family car.
He would not come home that night, he told them. He had never done
that before, but Mrs. Groves as usual asked no questions and, in fact,
gave it little thought.

The people in the general's office remained in his outer room, waiting in
silence. Groves, true to form, showed no outward nervousness and began
working on some papers.* In order to relieve the tension among his
officers, he did something very unusual for him: he took off his tie, un-
buttoned his collar and rolled up his sleeves. But it was enough for the
other officers to realize how exceptional was the impending moment.

At 11:15 the telephone rang. It was the secretary of the general staff,
Colonel F. McCarthy, inquiring on behalf of General Marshall. "No, we
haven't received any news about the actual strike," answered Groves.
McCarthy then said that General Marshall had instructed him that if any
news came after that hour, he should not be called but should be told the
next morning when he reached his desk at 7 A.M.

Groves was beginning to feel greatly disturbed. The news should have
been received long before. Either there was some breakdown in communications — which seemed unlikely, for messages had never been delayed

---

* But several years later, recalling that night, he admitted that "the hours went by
more slowly than I had ever imagined hours could go by."

before — or the lines were in order, and in that case the continuing silence could only mean one thing: failure.

Ten thousand miles away, and several hours before, in the B-29 flying over Japan, Captain Parsons was taking a few moments between completing the assembly of Little Boy and fusing it to bring his log up to date:

6 August 1945	0245 take off
0300	started final loading of gun
0315	finished loading
0605	headed for Empire from Iwo
0730	red plugs in
0741	started climb. Weather report received that the weather over primary and tertiary targets was good but not over secondary target.*
0838	leveled off at 32,700 feet
0847	electronic fuses were tested and found to be OK
0904	course west
0909	target Hiroshima in sight

Then, at precisely 0915½ (Tinian time), the bomb was dropped on Hiroshima.

Only fifteen minutes after General Marshall's call, the long-awaited message from Captain Parsons came in. As decoded by Groves personally, it read: "Results clear-cut, successful in all respects. Visible effects greater than New Mexico tests. Conditions normal in airplane following delivery."

A wave of relief swept through the room. The Manhattan Project had succeeded. After calling Colonel McCarthy and advising him to call General Marshall — in spite of the instructions given only a few minutes before — Groves went straight to his desk and wrote the rough draft of his report to the Chief of Staff. Then he stretched out on the cot in his office for a short nap while waiting for Brigadier General Farrell's cable that would give fuller details of the Hiroshima bombing.

The uranium bomb had worked.

Three days later, on August 9, the plutonium bomb dropped for the first time from a plane destroyed the city of Nagasaki.

---

* Hiroshima was the primary, Kokura the secondary and Nagasaki the tertiary target.

Bibliography

ALLARDICE, CORBIN and TRAPNELL, EDWARD R. *The First Pile*. Atomic Energy Commission Report TID 292, March 1955. Washington, D.C.: Government Printing Office.

AMRINE, MICHAEL. *The Great Decision*. New York: G. P. Putnam's Sons, 1959.

BAXTER, JAMES PHINNEY, 3RD. *Scientists Against Time*. Boston: Little, Brown, 1946.

COMPTON, ARTHUR HOLLY. *Atomic Quest*. New York: Oxford University Press, 1956.

DEAN, GORDON. *Report on the Atom*. New York: Alfred A. Knopf, 1953.

Engineering News-Record, December 13, 1945. New York: McGraw-Hill.

FERMI, LAURA. *Atoms in the Family*. Chicago: University of Chicago Press, 1954.

GOLDSCHMIDT, BERTRAND. *Atomic Adventure*. New York: Pergamon, 1964.

GOWING, MARGARET. *Britain and Atomic Energy, 1939–1945*. United Kingdom Atomic Energy Commission. New York: St. Martin's, 1964.

GROVES, LIEUTENANT GENERAL LESLIE R. *Now It Can Be Told*. New York: Harper and Row, 1962.

HAWKINS, DAVID. *Manhattan District History; Project Y; The Los Alamos Project*, Vol. I. University of California and United States Atomic Energy Commission, 1945.

HEWLETT, RICHARD G. and ANDERSON, OSCAR E., JR. *The New World, 1939–1946*. Vol. I, *A History of the United States Atomic Energy Commission*. University Park, Pa.: Pennsylvania State University Press, 1962.

In the Matter of J. Robert Oppenheimer: Transcript of Hearings. Washington: Government Printing Office, 1954.

JUNGK, ROBERT. *Brighter Than a Thousand Suns*. New York: Harcourt, Brace and World, Inc., 1958.

KNEBEL, FLETCHER and BAILEY, CHARLES W. *No High Ground*. New York: Harper and Brothers, 1960.

LAMONT, LANSING. *Day of Trinity*. New York: Atheneum, 1965.

LAURENCE, WILLIAM L. *Men and Atoms*. New York: Simon and Schuster, 1959.

RIEDMAN, SARAH R. *Men and Women Behind the Atom*. New York: Abelard-Schuman, Limited, 1960.

BIBLIOGRAPHY

Robinson, George O., Jr. *The Oak Ridge Story*. Kingsport, Tennessee: Southern Publishers, Inc., 1950.

Smyth, Henry De Wolf. *Atomic Energy for Military Purposes*. Princeton, N.J.: Princeton University Press, 1945.

Storms, Barbara and Savage, John. *Reach to the Unknown*. Los Alamos Scientific Laboratory, special anniversary edition of the *Atom*, July 16, 1965.

Van Arsdol, Ted. *Hanford . . . the Big Secret*. Richland, Wash.: *Columbia Basin News*, 1958.

Index